TREES AND AFTERCARE

A PRACTICAL HANDBOOK

BARBARA KISER

BTCV

British Trust for Conservation Volunteers

The author would like to thank the following peple for their help and advice in writing this handbook.
Gordon Cale, Tony Chadwick, Penny Evans, Tony Hitchcott, Mike King, David Rossney, Neil Sinden, Dr Charles Watkins and Elaine Weir.

ISBN   0 946752 07 9

Compiled by Barbara Kiser

Illustrations new in this handbook by Linda Francis

BTCV acknowledges the financial support of The Peacock Trust in meeting the costs for the production of *Trees and Aftercare*.

This handbook incorporates material previously published by BTCV in *Tree Nurseries* (1978)

© BTCV MCMXCI

3 5 7 9 8 6 4

Typeset in Palatino 10/12pt by Rob Bowker
using PageMaker 4.0 on an Apple Macintosh IIcx 4/40 supplied to BTCV with the generous support of The Paul Hamlyn Foundation and the Nature Conservancy Council.
Printed by Bocardo Press, Didcot, Oxfordshire.
on 80 gm² Sylvan Bond recycled paper

Published by The British Trust for Conservation Volunteers, 36 St. Mary's Street, Wallingford, Oxfordshire OX10 0EU
Registered charity N°. 261009

Contents

Introduction

This is a practical handbook on the raising, planting and maintenance of trees. Conceived in response to the upsurge in tree planting which has resulted from concern about recent tree loss, this handbook covers tree care from the seedling stage through to maturity. Its emphasis is on caring for the individual tree, and in this and other respects (such as a more in-depth approach to urban tree planting) it differs from 'Woodlands' (Brooks, revised 1988), which focuses primarily on woodland management.

The planning and design of a planting scheme and the diverse conditions and requirements on potential sites are discussed in chapter 2. The chapter on raising trees covers all aspects of running a small tree nursery, from seed collection and storage through to growing the trees on in preparation for lifting and transport. Procedures for planting, aftercare and maintenance, including coppicing, pollarding and thinning, are included in the final two chapters. The felling of larger trees is not covered. While planting in established and new woodlands for conservation and amenity purposes is given most emphasis, other aims and types of planting scheme are also considered. This handbook is intended for use by conservation volunteers and others with an interest in any of these aspects of working with trees.

Trees in Britain are intimately connected with history and culture, a fact evident even in many place-names of old villages and towns. But while the names often survive, the trees and woodlands which inspired them have all but disappeared.

At the start of this century, Britain was one of the least wooded European countries, due to extensive clearances over the preceding 6000 years. Of the few ancient semi-natural woodlands which remained, a further 30-50% have been lost in the last 40 years. Natural disasters have also taken their toll, with Dutch elm disease and the storms of October 1987 and January/February 1990 together accounting for losses of over 35 million trees. Approximately 10% of the land in Britain is currently under tree cover, and two-thirds of this is comprised of coniferous plantations, mainly of non-native species.

This situation is critical for Britain's wildlife. Many species have adapted to native woodland habitats, while others are dependent on them for survival. Even the oldest existing woodlands in Britain have a history of management, but traditional techniques such as coppicing have created the range of habitats upon which many plants and animals depend. The coverts, hedgerows and shelterbelts of the traditional farming landscape also provide valuable wildlife havens. Any ancient woodlands lost are irretrievable, but sensitive tree planting schemes, whether aimed at aiding natural regeneration or creating new woodlands, can still help compensate for the loss already suffered. The task of producing enough planting stock to supply such schemes, and attracting enough workers to plant and care for the trees, presents a considerable challenge.

In the past few years, many positive responses to this challenge have developed. National and regional tree planting campaigns and local planting schemes have helped involve thousands of people in regenerating or improving the landscape. The Forestry Commission's Policy for Broadleaves, issued in 1985, has encouraged the planting and management of broadleaved woodlands. Ancient semi-natural woodlands have been given protection. The tax incentives that led to the mass plantings of conifers in upland Britain, which destroyed valuable moorland, have been withdrawn.

New uses for surplus agricultural land are being backed by grant aid. The Farm Woodland Scheme was introduced in 1988 to encourage planting - of broadleaves in particular - on 36,000 hectares of agricultural land by the end of 1991. The Set-Aside Scheme, introduced in 1987, aims to help farmers manage their surplus land in ways that will benefit the landscape, wildlife and local people.

That nature conservation can be combined with other aims, such as amenity, landscape and timber production, is being increasingly recognised. Creating new woodlands, which can benefit the economy by providing jobs and reducing timber imports, also opens up new possibilities for recreation. The particular combination of qualities inherent in trees makes such varied uses possible. The practical value of trees as sources of shelter and shade is enhanced by the aesthetic pleasure they give. Their biological capacity to absorb carbon dioxide and oxygenate the air is now viewed from a different perspective, as the world's rainforests swiftly decline and global warming becomes more of a threat.

As a recognition of how valuable trees are to the well-being of people, the 'greening' of many British cities in the past few decades has been dramatic, leading to the improvement of much formerly derelict land. Planting schemes along canals and railway cuts, forming 'greenways' connecting the surrounding countryside to inner cities, are proving equally beneficial for wildlife and people.

In an atmosphere of increasing interest in trees, it is not difficult to generate enthusiasm for tree growing and planting. To survive to healthy maturity, however, a tree depends in part on aftercare. Trees are long-term projects, and caring for them throughout their lifespans demands perseverance, knowledge and, preferably, the involvement of the local community.

Luckily, working with trees offers great scope and variety. The voluntary workers, landowners, and individuals in schools and organisations who engage in the practical work of tree establishment can all find something of lasting interest - whether in the experi-mentation of the tree nursery or the precise method for pruning a mature tree. On the way, valuable skills can be learnt and passed on. By helping to achieve the overall aim of creating and maintaining a varied, beautiful landscape for wildlife and people, those engaged in tree work can make a very personal and satisfying contribution to conservation in Britain.

In the text, tree species are generally referred to by their common names. Measurements are generally given first in metric units, followed in brackets by the imperial equivalent approximated to the accuracy required. Some dimensions and product specifica-tions are given in metric units only, according to suppliers' or manufacturers' listings.

A Look at Trees

Throughout history, trees have exerted a remarkable pull on human imagination and ingenuity. As the longest-living and largest of land organisms, and as sources of shelter, food and raw material for a multitude of uses, trees are unique, and have been valued as such. However, trees and woodlands have also often been perceived as obstacles to progress, particularly of agriculture, as the widespread clearances occurring over the past 6000 years attest. In Britain, these very different perceptions and treatments of trees have alternated and overlapped, so that the natural history of native trees in woodlands is closely linked to a long, complex history of management and exploitation.

As a result, none of the post-glacial forests that once covered Britain exist in unaltered form. 'Ancient' woodlands are now classified as any that were in existence before 1600, for two reasons: around this time, maps became available, which allow the history of woodland sites to be traced; and after this date, planting became common. Sadly, since the 17th century much ancient woodland has been lost to replanting schemes. Such plantations on ancient sites may still retain some links with the past at ground level; but even those remaining fragments of woods which are recognised as being older, and closer in character to the original forests, are referred to as 'ancient semi-natural' woodlands because of the extensive human activity that has altered them over the centuries. A look at how the landscapes and cityscapes of Britain have evolved will help begin to clarify not only how planting should proceed, but why.

Trees in the Landscape

The trees that successively colonised Britain after the last Ice Age formed, after several thousand years, the forests of prehistory. Beginning about 10,000 years ago, when land bridges still connected Britain to the Continent and Ireland to Great Britain, willow and dwarf birch, followed by silver and downy birch, Scots pine, hazel, oak and elm, spread slowly over the country. In the relatively warm and wet climatic conditions of 5500-3000 BC, common alder became widespread and lime entered the lowlands of England. The trees covering the land during this era can be seen as the last truly virgin forests (Peterken, 1981, p6), a mosaic of woodlands generally dominated by pine and birch in the north and oak, alder, elm and lime in regions further south.

The first widespread clearances and management of this original forest began in Neolithic times, from around 4000 BC. As successive settlers improved agricultural and clearance techniques over the millennia, they laid more and more land to crops or pasture. By the Iron Age (500 BC), the natural woodlands may have been halved. Gradually, the fields extended to the point where the woodlands formed isolated blocks within them. This process became so far advanced in England that it is estimated only 15% of ancient woodlands were still standing in 1086 (Rackham, 1986, p76). The lowland clearances prior to 1350 accelerated the decline of these woodlands, although some abandoned farmland reverted to secondary woodland after the medieval plague years, 1348-50.

COPPICE WOODS AND PASTURE-WOODLANDS

By the 13th century, coppicing and pasture-woodlands had become the two primary forms of woodland management in England; the Welsh woods followed some time later. Coppicing, the practice of harvesting broadleaved trees by periodic cutting and gathering of the resultant multiple stems, had actually begun as early as the Neolithic period. Coppice woodlands (also called copses) are traditionally cut on a rotation of 7 to 25 years, depending on the product required. Usually one coupe, or part of the wood, is harvested each year.

Coppicing would remain the most widespread method of woodland management until the 19th century. The immense span of their management history, as well as the likelihood that they were naturally occurring rather than planted, means that ancient coppice woodlands are likely to be biologically closest to the original forests. Coppice with standards, where some trees are grown as standards and the coppice forms an understorey, is also an ancient system, dating from at least 1200. Coppice species occurred in characteristic combinations on different soils and in different regions, with hazel and ash, for example, widespread on the clay soils of the Midlands.

The decline of coppicing, which began in the late 18th century, was due to a variety of social and economic factors. A need for larger timber, mainly for shipbuilding, led many landowners to turn to the plantation system (see below). Importations of timber were also becoming more common, with the access to virgin forests overseas which had begun in the 17th century. In the 19th century, a growing reliance on coal and coke for fuel diminished the need for charcoal and firewood, and the general decline of agriculture meant that the hazel used for hurdles and other farm products was no longer in such demand. The change in the 20th century from farm tenancies to owner-occupation also encouraged the severance of the coppice management link.

Pasture-woodlands are woods in which grazing or browsing is an important part of land use. In their earliest form, they were probably wooded commons, used since prehistoric times for the grazing of live-stock (Rackham, 1986, p120). The parks which developed around the time of the Normans were, in marked contrast, deer preserves owned by the higher echelons of society. The Normans also designated many Forests, defined in the legal medieval sense as tracts of land where certain rules applied, regardless of whether the land was arable or afforested. About half of these were owned by the crown, but many retained woodcutting and grazing rights even after deer had been introduced.

In pasture-woodlands used by farming communities, the trees were traditionally pollarded at 2-3m (6-10') above the ground to prevent browsing damage from livestock. Like coppicing, this provided a re-newable resource of wood and timber, and a much prolonged lifespan for the tree itself. The few pasture-woodlands that survive today are distinguished by ancient pollards, some of them nearly 1000 years old.

The subsequent history of pasture-woodlands is gen-erally one of decline, although a number of the larger parks were remodelled by the great landscape de-signers of the 17th and 18th centuries (p12). Com-mons and Forests have not fared so well. Many were destroyed during the 18th and 19th centuries, and converted to plantations or, in the case of some wooded Forests, to arable land. The New Forest still contains large tracts of pasture-woodland, and the Commons Registration Act of 1965 has given protection to some ancient wooded commons.

PLANTING AND PLANTATIONS

In Britain, planting trees on cleared land, as a practice distinct from hedge planting, probably began with the Romano-Britons. The Romans may have intro-duced several species (e.g. horse chestnut, walnut), and a Roman farm discovered in Yorkshire contains the apparent remains of a windbreak with ash, alder, willow, oak, elder, sweet chestnut and walnut among the species, some of which were probably planted (Peterken, 1981, p84). Although some scattered notes on planting survive from the Anglo-Saxon era, records of tree planting really start from the middle ages.

At that time there was a saying that a man was not complete until he had begotten a child, written a book, built a house and planted a tree. Planting on any scale, however, was mostly the preserve of the mon-asteries and manorial estates, where orchards were cultivated within walled enclosures. The deliberate establishment of plantations was rare. In the early 1300s two Abbots, Godfrey of Peterborough and John de Rutherwyk at Chertsey in Surrey, are recorded as having planted woods, but these are remarkable examples (Rackham, 1986, p153, 184). Widespread planting did not begin in earnest until after 1600, when the traditional methods of woodland man-agement were seen as inadequate for providing Britain's timber requirements.

The 'plantation movement', which continued well into the 19th century, was characterised by experi-mentation with species choice, primarily for practical ends. Oak, ash, beech, elm, sweet chestnut and syca-more were raised for the purpose of producing items ranging from ships' keels to coffins. Oak was usually the dominant species planted, partly because John Evelyn's influential book 'Sylva' (1664) emphasized the need to supply oak for shipping. In 1731 Alexan-der Pope expressed this national preoccupation in a poem to his friend the Earl of Burlington, an enthusi-astic planter, 'whose rising forests, not for pride and show,/But future buildings, future navies, grow'.

Most of the new planting took place in Scotland, where by the beginning of the 18th century it had become a fashionable hobby. Here, Scots pine - much of it from English seed-trees - was the favoured species, although European larch gained widely in popularity towards the end of the century. In England and Wales, landowners produced timber by supple-mentary planting in coppice woodlands or by ex-tending existing parks and woods, as new sites for afforestation were fewer. Oak and beech, with Scots pine as a 'nurse' (see p30), were very widely used.

Many of the privately owned English and Welsh plantations were abandoned when the Industrial Revolution gained force in the 19th century. Economic upheaval and huge imports of cheap timber from other countries then under British rule made private domestic planting for timber production practically obsolete. Stands of oak planted during the heyday of the plantation movement were rendered virtually unsaleable before they reached a marketable size. The derelict remains of these plantations comprise many thousands of today's 'traditional woodlands'.

Towards the end of the 19th century private planting had nearly come to a standstill, and with a few isolated exceptions would not revive again until the 1950s. The start of the 20th century saw Britain almost completely reliant on imported timber and forestry products. As a result, the heavy demands of the First World War on timber availability led to fellings on almost 180,000 hectares (450,000 acres) of privately owned land (Edlin, 1970, p133).

The Forestry Commission, established in 1919 to preclude further such disasters, began a massive planting campaign. Using primarily conifers and other fast-growing species, the Commission established 230 new forests on about 265,000 hectares (655,000 acres) of land, with 145,000 hectares (359,000 acres) actually planted up (Edlin, 1970, p135). Single species or simple mixtures in straight lines were planted close together in large, even-age blocks, and laid out with little consideration for landscape variations. Like many 19th century oak plantations, these new forests were too uniform in structure and species to benefit most wildlife appreciably.

When the Second World War began, the Commission plantations were too young to harvest, thus necessitating a second major clearance in which 212,000 hectares (524,000 acres) of private woodland were clear-felled or depleted. The Commission thereafter continued to plant conifers, often in environmentally sensitive areas such as moorland. In some cases, old disused coppice was also suppressed and replanted, although private planters were responsible for much more of this. Pressure from conservation and amenity groups and a more advanced awareness of the multiple value of woodlands eventually led the Commission to adopt new approaches to the land under its control. After the Countryside Act of 1968 in particular, the Commission began to devote more attention to landscape and wildlife considerations.

The 'Guidelines for the Management of Broadleaved Woodlands', issued in 1985, outline the commitment of the Forestry Commission to broadleaved woods. Most recently, the Forestry Commission is supporting the Countryside Commission in a major new project for a 'national forest' in the Midlands. Planned to cover at least 38,850 hectares (96,000 acres), the forest will combine farmland with mixed-use woodland and entail the planting of some 30 million trees, most of them broadleaves.

COVERTS AND OTHER SMALL WOODS

The small woodlands common to the farming landscape, called coverts or copses (a shortened form of 'coppices'), were often adapted from existing coppice, some of it very old. These small woods were - and often still are - managed for game, with or without the traditional coppice rotation. Other existing small woods, such as the landscape 'follies' and hilltop beech groves of the 18th and 19th centuries, were generally planted for amenity interest.

In contrast to the more ancient coverts, which usually have irregular boundaries, those which were purposely planted are often rigidly geometrical in outline. Other coverts evolved from areas of 'scrub' in pasture-woodland, which were enclosed in the 19th century and left to regenerate. Planted coverts are generally 0.4-2 hectares (1-5 acres) in extent, but many smaller woods such as shelterbelts were also useful as habitats for game.

During the 19th century and to some extent since, gamekeepers were responsible for the retention of much coppice on sporting grounds. Where coppice was absent, exotic understorey shrubs such as rhododendron and cherry laurel were planted. The value of these shrubs is questionable, as they are very invasive and tend to choke out the more desirable woodland flora. In general, however, the mixture of species and high proportion of woodland edge which are maintained in coverts for the benefit of game makes them very valuable for many species of birds and mammals.

SCRUB

Scrub was recognised as a category of woodland by the Forestry Commission Census of Woodlands and Trees 1979-82, although it had been recognised by ecologists much earlier. It is also defined as 'poor quality woodland' which is poorly stocked with marketable species and higher quality timber trees (Evans, 1984, p90). Such woods may, however, be very valuable for wildlife, landscape or amenity.

Existing scrub may have grown up on land previously cleared for agriculture or industrial purposes, or it may be the result of discontinued management in a previously managed wood. Since clearance has been going on throughout history, scrub has probably been developing somewhere at all times, but the most recent wave of development occurred after the changes in farming practice of the 19th century. Scrub of this type can be termed secondary succession, and if left, it usually reverts to woodland. Other sites may have characteristics of soil or climate which limit the succession to woodland, and scrub may remain as the natural climax vegetation (Peterken, 1981, p82). Planting to improve scrub for timber production is discussed on p30.

THE 20TH CENTURY LANDSCAPE

It is perhaps odd to think that the British landscape had about the same amount of tree cover (10%) in 1350 that it has today. This figure, of course, reflects nothing of the huge difference in composition between the woodlands of that time and this, brought about by the many changes in land use noted above. From 1350 to the early Victorian era, however, the prevalence of traditional management practice meant that old woodlands retained their character, figuring as a small but vital part of the countryside. In the 19th century, significant damage to ancient woodlands occurred with the expansion of modern forestry, but it was not until after the Second World War that the destruction of old woods accelerated alarmingly (Rackham, 1986, p93).

Since 1945, the loss of trees has been the single most important change in the landscape. The demands of intensive farming and modern forestry have led to the destruction of 30-50% of the ancient semi-natural lowland woodlands - more than were cleared in the last 1000 years - although many ancient replanted sites remain. In some arable counties of eastern England, over 80% of the trees have disappeared. The decline of hedgerows and hedgerow trees is well documented: between 1945 and 1970, for example, more than 200,000 km (140,000 miles) are estimated to have been lost. In addition, eighteen million elms in southern England have died or been felled as a result of Dutch elm disease. About two-thirds of British trees are now non-native conifers in upland plantations.

The 1987 storm

The most dramatic recent loss was that of the estimated 15 million trees uprooted during the storm of mid-October 1987. The gale devastated many of the mature woodland trees of South East England, causing the worst recorded damage to trees in this country. 'The 1987 Storm: Impacts and Responses' (Forestry Commission Bulletin 87, 1989) has been used for the following information.

The loss was serious primarily because the South East was so rich in woodlands. Woodland trees constituted 95% by volume of total blown trees, and most were broadleaves. Privately owned woodlands and trees, many of which were managed for purposes other than forestry, sustained 72% of the damage. Of rural 'non-woodland' trees, which include those in hedgerows and shelterbelts, 200,000 were uprooted and half a million more damaged. Old and sometimes individually famous trees in many parks and gardens were blown, changing familiar landscapes literally overnight, and in London alone an estimated 55,000 street trees were lost. The storm also may have loosened the roots of many trees that were not blown down, making them more vulnerable to future windthrow. It is not yet known if this factor contributed significantly to the destruction of 4 million trees in the gales of early 1990.

However devastating in effect the storm has been in terms of tree loss, it has also had several positive impacts. A very important one is the identification of weaknesses in trees which could have contributed to their uprooting. In urban areas, for example, it was found that many street trees planted too close to kerbs had few or no roots on one side, making them unstable and particularly liable to windthrow. Decay in the roots and branches of some trees also contributed to storm damage, and indicates the need for better aftercare.

In some areas with severe storm damage, greater amounts of available light have encouraged natural regeneration. Where owners have chosen to replant, there is now the opportunity of increasing the diversity of species and ages, and introducing better woodland or urban forest design. The advantages to wildlife of leaving a proportion of blown trees lying has also been widely recognised. The trunk bases of damaged trees felled after a storm can coppice if the root system has been left relatively undamaged, and blown trees with some roots still anchored in the ground may continue to grow from a prone position. Any uprooted trees that were left to decay in woodlands or parks have provided a valuable habitat for invertebrates, small mammals and woodland flora.

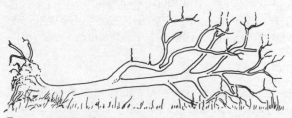

Tree continuing to grow from prone position

Perhaps the most important positive outcome of the storm, however, is that it has highlighted the overall serious record of tree loss this century. While ancient semi-natural woodlands, once gone, are irreplaceable, tree planting to create new 'woodland' or to aid natural regeneration is now recognised as being of major concern.

Global warming: an eye to the future

The possible impacts of global warming on the biosphere and human life are currently the subject of huge speculation. Not least among the topics of concern are the implications for existing woodlands and plantations, and future planting operations, in temperate climates such as Britain's.

Global warming, the result of the 'greenhouse effect', was recognised a century ago as the probable outcome of industrial activity. The greenhouse effect occurs when incident energy which enters the atmosphere is reflected from the earth's surface at a different frequency. Instead of then being transmitted out from the atmosphere, this energy is absorbed by water vapour, carbon dioxide (CO_2), methane and other greenhouse gases, and the temperature consequently rises. The naturally occurring greenhouse effect has been very important for the survival and stability of terrestrial life, as without it the earth's surface temperature would be about 33°C lower. But if emissions of greenhouse gases increase too much, as is happening now, global warming accelerates and the stability of the biosphere is threatened. This discussion centres on CO_2, as trees are directly involved in its cycling and production.

Industrial emissions from the burning of fossil fuels and the felling and burning of the world's rainforests are currently the main sources of CO_2 increases in the atmosphere, as is well known. The attention focused on the demise of tropical forests, however, may be overshadowing the fact that deforestation anywhere contributes to global warming. Retaining or planting woodlands is the most efficient biological method of 'locking up' carbon.

The argument for woodland conservation and tree planting in temperate countries such as Britain is thus given a new, and immeasurably important, dimension. If current trends continue, tree planting itself may be in for a period of adjustment, however. There are two reasons for this: the direct impact of CO_2 on tree growth, and the indirect impact of any changes in rainfall and seasonal weather patterns which arise from climatic shifts. The native British species may acclimatise to an increasing concentration of CO_2, but it is less sure that they can adjust if the climate alters radically, causing severe gales, droughts or other disturbances. As during prehistoric climatic changes such as the Atlantic period, the distribution of some native species may become much wider, while others may not survive in particular areas. In the context of amenity planting and forestry, new species may need to be introduced. For further information, see 'Carbon Dioxide, Global Warming and Forestry' (Forestry Commission Research Information Note 146, 1989).

Trees in Towns and Cities

The following information is in part from 'Trees in Towns' (Clouston and Stansfield, 1981, pp2-7, 129) and 'The Greening of the Cities' (Nicholson-Lord, 1987, pp28-29, 90, 182).

Most British towns and cities at the start of the 18th century were minuscule by today's standards, both in population and size. They were still intimately linked to the surrounding countryside, with commons and fields within easy reach and any existing trees or woodlands simply left to grow within or around them. During the next two centuries, the Industrial Revolution and an increasing population swelled the cities, while the Enclosure Acts (1760-1840) forced some farm labourers out of the countryside through the loss of common land. Although some existing trees and commons were incorporated into the rapidly growing cities, tree planting would not become an urban practice until the start of the 19th century.

THE ORIGINS OF URBAN PARKS

Amenity planting in the 18th century was, like the commercial plantations of the time, largely the preserve of wealthy landowners aiming to enhance their rural estates. The styles they or their designers evolved were to become the main influences on later urban park design. At the beginning of the century, and in Scotland until much later, many estates still had extensive gardens modelled on the French Baroque pattern made famous at Versailles. This was rigidly formal and geometric in layout, with clipped trees planted in rows, statuary and ornamental hedging (Reed, 1983, pp93-4). Long avenues of trees, a major feature of these gardens, were later to be copied in the tree-lined streets of towns and cities. In the first few decades of the 18th century, however, a new, naturalistic style began to emerge.

The landscaped parks designed by Lancelot 'Capability' Brown, William Kent and others were in many cases remodelled from land under pasture-woodland management, although some formal gardens were destroyed to make them. Petworth in West Sussex, which has been managed to retain Brown's original design, is one of the finer examples of landscape parks. From 1751 to his death in 1783, Brown dominated landscape design, perfecting a style in which vistas of rolling green hills and single speci

mens or clumps of trees predominated. Although he uprooted many existing trees in the course of his work, he also planted thousands of oak, beech, elm, ash, lime and chestnut, using Scots pine, larch and cedar less frequently (Reed, 1983, p99).

By the first decades of the 19th century, many cities were in the first stages of urban sprawl, and sectors for the privileged and the poor were clearly defined. Amenity trees became common in the wealthier areas, where first evergreens such as yew, and later the pollution-resistant plane and sycamore, were planted along streets and in private squares. Most city dwellers, however, lived in overcrowded conditions with no access to green space, and by the 1840s public outcry had forced the government to recognise that public health and morale were being endangered. A Select Committee subsequently recommended the establishment of public parks, and these slowly became a feature of the larger cities. From the start they were overwhelmingly popular. Nearly 118,000 people, for example, visited Victoria Park in London on one day shortly after it opened in 1841. Completely free public access was still some way off, however, as the parks were fenced and locked at night, games were banned and park police forces established.

In general form the parks were scaled-down imitations of the great 18th century landscape parks, but with a difference. Whereas the innovative landscape style of Brown had emphasised the natural shape of trees within the context of sweeping lines and broad views, the 'gardenesque' style created by park designers such as John Loudon reintroduced formal elements of the Baroque. Flower beds in geometric shapes were brought back, along with ornamental trees and avenues. The trees, in keeping with the 19th century craze for botany and horticulture, were often exotics or hybrid native varieties.

THE 'GREENING' OF CITIES

Ebenezer Howard's 'Garden Cities of Tomorrow' (1898) inspired a new approach to solving the urban crisis. Howard advocated the building of planned towns incorporating low-density housing with trees and green spaces, and separated from each other by open country. Letchworth and Welwyn Garden City, now richly endowed with trees, were built to his design. Howard's ideas also gave impetus to the New Towns Committee, set up in 1945, and the 28 New Towns designated since 1946 have had a high success rate, in both commercial and amenity terms, with their urban forestry schemes (Hibberd, 1989, pp19-20). In the older cities, however, runaway development persisted, but no overall landscaping plan developed to balance it. While some trees and woodlands survived to form part of the urban expansion, many were felled to make way for road-widening and building schemes. The Greater London Plan of 1945, which provided for the green belt, did not address the issue of green space within the city.

The ideas behind Howard's 'garden cities' became increasingly attractive to many people living in conurbations over the next few decades, and by the 1970s urban ecology had become a distinct discipline. The 'greening movement' compelled a fresh look at the open spaces of the cities. On average, open space comprises nearly a fifth of cities and towns in Britain, and a significantly larger proportion is made up of green space of all types. Over the last two decades, the potential for tree planting on many of these 'empty' sites has been explored, with promising results.

Many schemes have been tiny, involving local communities or schools in creating nature parks on sites that were formerly covered with Tarmac, grass or rubble. Larger-scale projects, such as the 40-hectare Hanley Forest Park in Stoke-on-Trent, have transformed reclaimed colliery tips and disused industrial sites. An ambitious recent proposal for urban improvement, put forward by the Forestry and Countryside Commissions, is for 'community forests' to be planted on the outskirts of 17 - and possibly more - major cities, beginning in 1990. As with the proposed national forest (see p9), most trees planted will be native broadleaves, and farmlands will be integral to the design. With 12 forests alone, over 180 million trees would be planted, adding about 10% to the present woodland cover of England and Wales.

Finding ways to maximise the wildlife value of urban woodlands can be challenging. Continuity of cover, for example, must be present if wildlife are to be able to migrate with relative ease. In rural areas, shelterbelts and hedges provide this continuity by serving as wooded 'corridors' which connect small woodlands and so save them from isolation within a relatively inhospitable environment. In urban areas, a similar solution has been worked out with the creation of 'green networks'. These are achieved by linking wooded 'islands' within the city (nature parks, churchyards, hospital grounds, etc.) with existing linear thoroughfares such as canal banks, motorway verges and abandoned railway cuts. As these thoroughfares were originally designed to lead out of the city, they very naturally merge with the open countryside beyond. In some cities, green networks have developed in a piecemeal fashion, but in others they have been part of an overall strategy for improvement. During the 1970s, miles of derelict river valleys in Manchester were replanted and linked to nature parks as part of such an overall plan.

While it has been relatively common on the Continent and in the United States for some decades now, urban forestry is a recent development in Britain. Included are not only the wooded areas discussed above, but also trees in parks and gardens, street trees, and trees grouped around buildings or in open spaces. The move to more widespread urban forestry has gained momentum from studies revealing its cost-effectiveness.

A Joint Forestry Survey undertaken in 1988 by the Forestry and Countryside Commissions found that, in the experience of the New Town Corporations, urban woodlands are financially beneficial not only in terms of returns for timber. Mature trees in landscaped areas were also found to attract home buyers and business investors. Moreover, well-managed urban woodlands have proven cheaper to maintain than other types of open space (Hibberd, 1989, p21). In this context, David Nicholson-Lord notes that native semi-natural plantings 'can cost less than a tenth of orthodox grass with trees and...a fifth, in both laying and maintenance costs, of concrete on hardcore' (1987,p182).

Urban woodlands on the Continent are often owned and managed by local communities. In Britain the situation is usually more complex, with local authorities, business and industrial interests, landowners, local residents and voluntary organisations all involved. Co-operation is obviously vital, and an important step towards this is attention to the interests and needs of the local community. If these concerns are integrated into the planning process, trees and woodlands are more likely to be perceived as desirable additions to the environment, and patterns of neglect or vandalism may be avoided (Hibberd, 1989, pp12-14).

Why Plant Trees?

This question has been answered in some sense by the history of trees in rural and urban areas, as discussed above. One of the main reasons for planting trees in the rural landscape is to replace those lost through clearance, particularly in the last five decades, as well as through disease, natural disasters or old age. In urban areas, a major reason for planting amenity trees may simply be to improve areas that have been treeless within living memory. Other reasons for planting trees will vary from site to site, and are related to their specific uses. Although only one or two uses may be priorities in a given scheme, a look at trees in the context of their specific functions and attributes will help in clarifying the objectives of a planting scheme. General objectives for planting are further discussed in chapter 2.

The following information is mainly from Rushforth (1987, pp9-22) and McCullen and Webb (1982, pp3-4,9-14,17-18).

AIR QUALITY

The capability of woodlands to affect indirectly climate through the cycling of CO_2 is inevitably much publicised now because of the connection with global warming. When grouped together, trees can directly affect climate and air quality in the following ways: by oxygenating, humidifying, modifying temperature and wind patterns, and metabolizing pollution. Benefits from these functions of trees will be more tangible in cities, where atmospheric pollution and 'trapped', devitalised air are common problems. Air pollution can also be serious, however, in rural areas with extensive road systems or industrial activity.

Even smaller groupings of some species can be useful as oxygenators. The foliage of a single mature beech, for example, can extract more than 2.5kg (5.5lb) of CO_2 from the atmosphere, and produce 1.7kg (3.7lb) of oxygen, in one hour: in theory, enough for the needs of ten people in a year. Depending partly on leaf size, trees can also transpire impressive amounts of water, a process which cools as well as humidifies the surrounding air. A mature beech, for example, can transpire up to 440l (100gal) of water a day. Trees only function effectively as 'air conditioners', however, where they are thickly planted over large areas. Planted in a green network around and within built-up areas, trees will work in several ways: by cooling the air through transpiration, controlling the heat which radiates from roads and buildings, and dispersing the warm, polluted air that tends to hover over inner cities.

In general, trees reduce air pollutants such as industrial or automobile emissions through creating air turbulence. Woodland edge plantings, with shrubby understoreys and ground flora, create more turbulence and so are particularly suited to this purpose.

Species such as birch or conifers are useful, as the smaller the leaf of the tree, the greater its capability for creating air movement. Pollutants can also be filtered and to some extent absorbed by the foliage of trees. Dust is easily filtered out from the atmosphere, becoming trapped on the leaves of the tree and then washed down by rain. Sulphur dioxide, which is present in emissions from coal and petroleum burning plants, is filtered somewhat less efficiently but can be measurably reduced by a belt of trees only 30m (about 100ft) wide. A study in 1979 further found that a shelterbelt of trees reduced airborne lead by 85%. Some pollution-tolerant native species are listed in the table on pp22-23.

Belts of trees filtering dust and pollution

NOISE REDUCTION

Excessive noise from traffic, farm machinery or other sources is now recognised as a form of environmental pollution, and trees can be useful in lessening it to some degree. The leaves of a tree tend to scatter sound, and its trunk to reflect it. Trees with dense foliage and larger leaves, such as plane or large-leaved lime, are the best choice, although some conifers may need to be interplanted to provide a measure of protection during the winter months. Woodland plantings are even more effective, as the soft surface created by leaf fall, deadwood and ground cover tends to absorb sound. Where there is only room for a smaller planting, the trees will need to be planted in a belt 8-12m (27-39 ft) in width, with a substantial understorey on either side. The belt should reach a height of 5m (16ft) in the middle. Significant noise reduction will also depend on a number of other factors, such as the type and level of noise, the planting density, and the weather at any one time.

SOIL STABILISATION

Trees can prevent soil from drying out and eroding in several ways. Although trees planted on shrinkable clay can reduce soil moisture during droughts, under normal circumstances trees help keep the water table nearer the surface of the soil. By shading the ground during hot weather, trees prevent it from drying out too rapidly. Fallen leaves and other organic debris from trees, once incorporated into the soil, also help it

to retain moisture, and at the same time improve its structure. In the context of soil moisture, it should be noted that wooded areas have greater rates of transpiration and interception of rainfall than do areas of herbaceous vegetation and grass, and for this reason trees are best not planted on reservoir catchments.

Damage to soil structure can be prevented by the tree canopy, which lessens the force of hard rainfall, while the tree's roots prevent soil from washing away, particularly on steep slopes. On wet sites, willows and alders are particularly useful in binding the softer soils together.

SHELTER

Clumps or belts of trees and tall hedges have been planted as windbreaks on farmland for many centuries to shield crops, buildings and livestock from exposure. Open spaces such as playing fields, traditional parks, and large urban squares, as well as industrial sites, can also be improved by the planting of strategic shelterbelts.

Trees reduce the force of wind and modify its movements around buildings. Factors influencing the effectiveness of windbreaks and shelterbelts include the dimensions of the group of trees and the planting density. Very dense barriers are actually counter-productive, so some permeability will be necessary. Belts of trees can also have great value for lowering energy consumption when planted around buildings. Studies in the United States indicate that shelterbelts surrounding buildings can reduce fuel consumption in winter by 10-25%. Broadleaves in particular are useful for this purpose, as they provide shade in summer and do not obstruct the sun's warmth or light in winter. Shelterbelts are further discussed on p37.

WILDLIFE VALUE

The complex nature of native semi-natural woodlands in Britain is the result of long evolution and human interference, as discussed above. Broadly speaking, a new 'woodland' planting will take decades, at least, to attract the colonisation of a wide range of woodland flora and fauna. To best encourage both immediate benefits for wildlife, and the gradual natural colonisation of species, many factors will need to be taken into account. These include the species of tree chosen, soils, location, proximity to other wooded areas (especially established semi-natural woodland), planting layout and maintenance procedures, and many others.

Smaller woods such as coverts or woodland edge plantings can be very useful on a range of sites, such as farms, school or hospital grounds, plots set aside in city parks, and even large gardens. Usually only sites with very cramped space, or toxic soils which support little existing vegetation, will be completely unsuitable. Even two or three native trees planted with shrubs and, later, appropriate herbaceous ground cover, can support a number of insects and offer temporary shelter and food to passing birds. Planting schemes primarily intended for other purposes, such as timber production, also have great potential for attracting wildlife if a 'multi-use' approach is taken to planting and maintenance. Some non-native species used in amenity plantings also have wildlife value, either by providing safe nesting sites or winter food sources.

Planting woods for purposes of wildlife conservation will be aimed at increasing the range of habitats, the variety of associated species, and the diversity of structure. Generally speaking, woodlands have a four-tier structure composed of ground, field and shrub layers and the tree canopy. Trees of varying size, shape and stages of maturity will greatly increase the structural diversity of a wood, and attract a greater range of species. It has, for example, been proven that the number of bird species in a woodland is related much less to the variety of tree species than to a varied structure, which offers more opportunities for breeding, nesting and feeding.

Improving the wildlife value of existing woods will be feasible if the woods have a limited structural variety. Single-species plantations and scrub, for example, may need supplementary planting to introduce diversity in the number and types of layers as well as the species. Such planting may also be suitable in pasture-woodlands, as long as it does not lead to too much competition for old pollards. Introducing rides, glades and wildlife margins in new or established woodlands is also very valuable for wildlife, especially those species which thrive in lighter conditions but still need shelter and humidity. These include epiphytes, ie non-parasitic plants which grow on other plants; and invertebrate animals.

Different tree species create microclimates which influence what grows beneath them. They do this by controlling the amount of moisture and wind reaching the lower layers, the light intensity at ground level, the organic composition of the soil (through leaf fall), and the uptake of soil moisture and nutrients. The trees you plant will therefore determine, to a large degree, which species will colonise in the layers below. Some species, such as beech and most conifers, cast a heavy shade which effectively prevents the development of most species in the understorey. Further information on appropriate species for planting in new or established woodlands will be found in chapter 2.

RECREATION AND AMENITY

Most tree planting schemes will have as one of their aims the enjoyment of the area in future years. Woodlands are especially attractive for recreational purposes, with their combination of open space (glades, rides, etc.) and deep or partial shelter and shade, and species which vary in colour, height and shape. Even a small patch of woodland can accommodate a fair number of people and still offer a feeling of solitude. The introduction of nature walks and rides can serve to direct visitors' progress through the wood and at the same time prevent the trampling of vegetation and small, naturally regenerated saplings. In an urban site under heavy use, replanting schemes might be planned, or areas useful for natural regeneration might be fenced off.

Groupings of amenity trees are very important for providing visual relief in urban areas, where the angularity of buildings and the sometimes bleak appearance of open squares can be alleviated by the structural beauty of trees. Trees are also well suited for screening, whether to separate areas or actually hide unattractive buildings. Screens need not be dense to be effective. The important factor is that they draw attention away from the unsightly object behind, so broadleaves are as useful for this purpose as are the more commonly planted conifers. If a building is to be screened by trees, it is best to extend the trees beyond the edge of the building, to 'break up' its hard outline satisfactorily .

Trees can soften hard lines of architecture

Linked groups of trees can give aesthetic unity to streets, squares and parks in particular areas of a city. Trees in the traditional lowland farming landscapes of Britain can also unify the view, when planted to renew depleted hedges, or to form new coverts or other small woodlands in conjunction with them. The local topography will play an important part in determining placement of trees. Planting to improve landscape value is further discussed on pp17 & 35.

The seasonal changes of broadleaved species are equally effective in rural woodlands and urban settings. The greens of emergent and mature leaves usually vary in shade, and the foliage of many species, such as birch, beech and several of the maples, turn brilliant colours in autumn. The shape of the same tree in summer and winter can be attractive in entirely different ways. If aesthetics are a major objective of a planting scheme, a tree's trunk shape, texture and colour, as well as its flowers, fruit seed, and overall appearance in different weather conditions, can be important factors in species choice. In urban areas, exotics, varieties and cultivators may be added to the range of suitable species, widening choice considerably.

Most people familiar with woodlands have experienced the sense of relief afforded by walking among or even just looking at trees. Studies in the United States have shown that hospital patients are often discharged sooner if the view from their windows includes trees. Trees surrounding a hospital can provide not only views, but also 'therapeutic' walks for patients, visitors and staff (Sinden, 1989, p70).

EDUCATION

Perhaps one of the most valuable aspects of trees is their usefulness in education. Trees can be used as objects of study in many disciplines, biology and ecology being only the most obvious. For children living in the inner cities, visits to a woodland or a well-planted park can provide a basis of interest that will naturally lead on to such studies.

School ground nature areas have even more educational value. If small-scale seed collection and tree nursery work are taught in conjunction with tree planting and aftercare, students can learn the complexities of the tree's biological cycle, as well as aspects of woodland ecology, at first hand. It has also been found that students often develop a sense of responsibility for trees and woodlands through such practical experience, particularly because the site itself is personally significant to them. Children taught in this way are usually much more likely to show a positive interest in trees growing in their own neighbourhoods, making vandalism less of a possibility. (See chapter 5 for information on running small tree nurseries.)

TIMBER PRODUCTION

Currently, the figure for British timber imports stands at around 90%. This figure alone argues the need for allotting space to timber production. The conflict between timber production and nature conservation is by no means insoluble. It has been shown that careful design and management planning can result in woodlands which successfully fulfil conservation, amenity and other aims as well as those related to timber production.

Changes in forestry practice can go a long way towards increasing the overlap between timber production and conservation, without any great loss to either. With selection management, for example, individual trees are felled when they reach the required size. In this way, felling and replacement (often by natural regeneration) are distributed widely throughout the wood, giving a more natural appearance and varied structure, some wildlife value, and potentially high financial returns.

Timber production from small woodlands can range from producing firewood and other small-diameter timber for local use, to hardwood such as cherry or walnut for veneers or joinery. It should also be noted that, in small woodlands, a better financial return will result from quality rather than quantity. A few individual trees, particularly broadleaves, which are of very high quality will bring in more revenue than a greater number of poorer quality trees. This last point is particularly important in multi-use small woodlands because small-scale harvesting allows gradual regeneration, more continuous cover for wildlife and game, and a more attractive woodland; it also prevents the sudden and drastic changes in the landscape which can occur with clear-felling (Hibberd, 1988, p7,38).

Coppice management is particularly valuable for small multi-use woodlands. For a discussion of how to establish a coppice, see p28.; coppicing techniques are dealt with on p123.

Planting for Conservation and Amenity

This chapter looks at the considerations which are important at the planning stage, such as assessing the site, formulating objectives, choosing species to plant and drawing up planting plans. The specific situations in which planting might take place will also be covered in this chapter, including both a brief overview of management systems and a more detailed discussion of rural and urban locations. With any such division, there is the inevitability of some overlap in the discussion (for instance, many farm woods are under coppice management), but the aim here is to help the volunteer deal with most eventualities. A detailed treatment of woodlands, including information on woodland ecology and woodland types, can be found in 'Woodlands' (Brooks, revised 1988).

Planning and Design

Planning considerations are at least as important as good tree maintenance. Careful attention to the preliminary steps of a tree planting scheme often has the added benefit of reducing the aftercare needed. A plan which takes into account the appropriate species for the site's soil and micro-climate, matches objectives to both site and species, and safeguards the trees by considering any contingent laws and present or future land plans, will help prevent serious and possibly expensive mistakes afterwards. Working with trees is a long-term project which demands patience, perseverance and knowledge of the requirements of trees, and plans will need to be made accordingly.

GENERAL OBJECTIVES FOR PLANTING SCHEMES

When planning any new planting scheme, or a replanting scheme within an existing wooded area, it is important to think carefully through the objectives of the scheme, and state them clearly at the outset. The nature of the site often determines objectives, but there can be multiple complementary objectives for most sites. Planting in high forest is, for example, often for the purpose of timber production, but nature conservation, landscape and recreation considerations are equally important and feasible as objectives.

Nature conservation

Nature conservation will be the primary objective if the existing woodland is a nature reserve, Site of Special Scientific Interest (SSSI) or ancient woodland.

For other woodlands, including new urban sites intended to be used as nature areas, the objective of nature conservation in the context of planting and future maintenance may include creating and maintaining the following:

a An age range of trees and shrubs, with old trees and deadwood

b A structural diversity of trees, shrubs and ground flora

c A range of habitats within or near the wood, including open glades, rides and woodland edges, streams, ponds, bogs, rocky outcrops, etc.

The success of other objectives will often be directly related to sound management for nature conservation. For example, woods planted and maintained in this way are likely to be a valuable landscape feature whether in the city or countryside, and will also be attractive for recreation. Choice of species which suit the natural conditions of the site is also an important criterion for successful timber production.

Landscape

Landscape enhancement as an objective for woodlands is mainly relevant in areas which are patchily rather than continuously wooded, simply because the trees can then be seen to form a pattern in the landscape. Smaller woodlands, such as urban nature areas or farm coverts, will therefore usually have landscape considerations as one of the primary objectives.

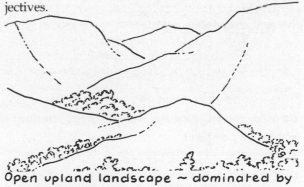

Open upland landscape ~ dominated by strong landform

The local topography is very important too. The more extensive woodlands in Britain tend to be in the hillier regions. Woodlands on hillsides and in undulating country are often visible from a great distance and thus may have visual importance over a wide area. Any planting to supplement natural regeneration in these woods must be done with sensitivity to these factors. Extending the edges of a wood or planting a new wood so that it appears square or rectangular should be avoided. Natural landscape boundaries, such as streams and rocky outcrops, should be followed whenever possible.

The visual importance of a wood in flat country is related less to the shape and area of the woodland than to its edge. Avenues and lines of trees, and woodland edges along roads and residential areas, are of great landscape value. Clusters of trees around buildings in rural areas provide not only shelter, but also scale and interest in a flat landscape. In urban areas, the patterns created by linked groups of trees along streets, in parks and gardens, and in new or existing woodland areas, are both aesthetically appealing and very valuable as urban wildlife 'stepping stones'.

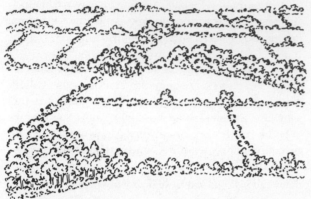

Lowland landscape ~ dominated by strong pattern of hedgerows and small woods

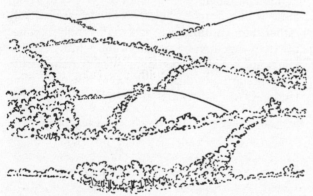

Hilly landscape ~ hedgerow pattern less dominant higher up, landforms becoming more important

If landscape objectives are among the most important, proposals for woodland management should consider immediate, short and long term effects of any work. For example, thinning, felling or replanting should, as far as possible, be phased over space and time to minimise the visual effects of any change. Attention must also be given to the appearance of the individual species chosen, and their ability to thrive on the site. When planting mixtures, groupings of trees and woods, design for visual effect as well as silvicultural success is important. The need to choose the most economical fencing lines, ie straight lines, may conflict with the desire to produce a natural-looking planting, so some compromise may be called for.

Recreation

Recreation, like many other objectives of tree planting schemes, cannot be considered in isolation. Surrounding influences and outside factors may be important. You may decide to discourage recreation in the area you are planting, but you should consider whether it will be easy or even feasible to do so. Will recreation conflict with other objectives, particularly nature conservation or timber production?

You will need to consider over- or under-use of existing rights of way, as well as unofficial access to the planting area. Unofficial access may include evidence of parking at the edge of the wood or along roadsides, litter, paths, dens and tree-houses. Woods near densely populated areas often have this sort of use, and control may be difficult and even counter-productive when there is repeated vandalism of fencing.

If you wish to encourage the recreational use of your planting site by opening up new walks and nature trails or upgrading existing rights of way, consider beforehand the likely effects on surrounding areas. For example, placing a car-park near a habitat which is best left undisturbed may well be undesirable.

Remember that fencing, gates, stiles, signposts and other recreational facilities will need maintenance. If in your plan you are unable to provide for their upkeep, it may not be worth putting them in. This is, on the other hand, an ideal job for a community organisation or nearby school, and if your planting area is taken on as a long-term project the maintenance of trees and facilities both can be planned for. The planting of natural barriers such as hedges or thorny shrubs can provide an alternative form of 'invisible crowd control' to guide visitors where you want them to go, without the use of signposts and other facilities.

Timber production

Timber production, as indicated in chapter 1, is a very important concern in Britain, where most of the timber is imported. In addition, there is a great potential for increased production of hardwoods from British woodland (Evans, 1984, p9). While both the need and the potential for some increase in timber production are great, however, many new and existing woods have importance for other objectives. Many woods are also too small, or the access is too difficult, to make timber production economically viable.

Timber production can be incorporated with many other management objectives, particularly where clear-felling is avoided. Planning for timber production can be difficult, as markets many decades hence cannot be predicted. Changes in grants and tax regulations may also alter the economic viability of a scheme. With the exception of a few high value timbers, however (details in Evans, 1984, p111), the best rule to adopt when planning any planting is to choose those species which will grow best on that particular site. The successful marketing of timber may depend on choosing the year when prices are right, or in seeking out particular markets or craftsmen for the product you have to offer.

Shelter

On farms, the planting of trees to provide shelter for livestock can provide returns on timber as well as on meat and milk. Livestock can, however, create conditions detrimental to the survival of the trees (see p39). Combining recreation with sheltered grazing may also be difficult because of the need for fencing, the possibility of dogs worrying stock, and the likelihood of stock churning up the ground so that walking becomes unpleasant.

SITE ASSESSMENT

After you have begun to think about objectives for your site, you will need to make a site assessment. This can be in the nature of a simple survey to determine the exact conditions of the site - soil, climate and topography - so that you will be better equipped to finalise your objectives and choose appropriate species. More detailed site surveys, appropriate as part of overall management plans, are described fully in 'Woodlands' (Brooks, chapter 2). The following checklist covers the points which should be considered when planning your scheme. It is taken from the leaflet, 'Assessing a Site for Tree and Shrub Planting', by Jerry Langford (BTCV, South Glamorgan, 1985, photocopied) and from Clouston and Stansfield (1981).

Should trees be planted at all?

a Who owns the site? Will the owner give permission for planting?

b What is the site used for? Will planting affect this use?

c Why plant trees on this site? Will they increase the wildlife interest? Will they provide or improve an attractive amenity? Will they provide useful timber?

d Will tree planting damage interesting habitats already present? New planting may shade out old grassland, streams or ponds. Thickets and old orchards are valuable habitats which should be considered for retention, and any bogs or very damp ground should be left unplanted.

e Will tree planting damage any archaeological remains present? Tree planting operations can destroy earthworks and disturb bones. Check any available maps and consult the appropriate archaeological bodies for information about the site, as archaeological remains are not always easily visible.

f Are young trees already growing of their own accord? If so, is extra planting really justified? Natural regeneration may be preferable for wildlife interest, and is cheaper.

g Will the trees you plant have a secure future? May the site be developed in the future, resulting in loss of the trees? This will be a particularly important point with urban sites. Seek assurance from the owner about the site's future.

h There may be a good reason for the site being treeless. The soil may be thin or polluted; the site may be too exposed, waterlogged, or overgrazed. Perhaps only certain parts of the site are suitable for planting.

How the site may affect choice of species

a Look at any existing trees on the site. These may indicate a remnant of semi-natural cover or, in the case of obviously planted trees, will indicate which species are likely to be successful on the site.

b Consider the location. In a rural site you should choose species in keeping with any existing woodland. In an urban site consider whether you want to create an attractive ornamental planting, or a 'natural' area. Will the use of introduced species be acceptable?

c Consider the eventual height of the trees. Is there enough space for forest trees such as oak, ash or beech? Will the trees shade gardens or windows, interfere with overhead lines or overhang roads? Will they grow to block attractive views?

d Consider the vigour of the tree's root system. Are the roots likely to interfere with underground services such as cables and pipes?

e Is the soil natural or has it been disturbed? Soil on building sites or derelict land may be badly churned up, mixed with rubble and rubbish, or completely removed. It may be polluted with chemicals or be very low in nutrients. If there are no trees or other vegetation already growing, you may have problems. Consult the local planning authority.

f Bring along a soil testing kit (available from garden centres) to determine the pH of the soil; is it alkaline or acid? Further check to determine whether the soil type is sandy or clayey, well drained or subject to getting waterlogged. Plant only species which suit the soil type. On shrinkable clay soils near buildings, choice of species is particularly important.

g Is any part of the site very exposed to the wind, or are there hollows where frost will be severe?

h Is air pollution a problem, or is the site on the coast and exposed to salt winds? Either of these will limit the choice of species.

Planting

a What size of young trees should you plant? Which planting methods should you use? Will you be planting standards, and if so, are stakes absolutely necessary?

b Will the trees need protection against browsing by farm stock, or against rabbits or deer? Either fence the site or use individual tree guards, whichever is the cheaper.

c Is vandalism likely? If so use small trees and thorny shrubs, and plant brambles to protect the trees. Avoid using stakes or guards which draw attention to the planted trees unless absolutely necessary. Will the trees need any additional protection from hazards of the urban environment?

Aftercare

a Watering, weeding, removal of ties and stakes, and replacement of dead trees may be needed. Who will do this?

b Most sites will need weeding for the first three or four years. Mulches or herbicides are the best methods for encouraging good growth of the young trees. What mulching materials can you obtain? If you decide to use herbicide, is there someone properly trained who will be able to do the work?

c Will the trees be easily visible amongst the weed growth, by the time the herbicide is applied?

d Any guards or tree shelters remaining after five years or so should be removed. Can you ensure this will be done?

e If trees die will you be able to replace them? This may be a condition of grant aid.

f Do you have proper records of the scheme, so that anyone taking over can continue with the mainte-nance?

CHOICE OF SPECIES

Indications of some species appropriate to types of locality are given in the latter part of this chapter. The table on pp22-23 summarises the site requirements and characteristics of 28 native species of trees. This table is an outline guide only, and should be used in conjunction with a careful survey of the site and locality. Further information on these species, and on many native shrubs, is given in Tables 1 and 2 in Appendix B. The choice and planting of native trees and shrubs is fully covered in Beckett (1979), a par-ticularly useful book for conservation purposes as it gives details on characteristics, requirements, wild-life value, propagation and natural distribution in Britain. Evans (1984) gives silvicultural details on many broadleaved species.

The range of species can be greatly increased by including introduced species, which although of less value for nature conservation, may be more suitable than any of the native species for certain sites and situations. Some of these are discussed below.

Urban areas and amenity planting

Most areas available for tree planting in towns and residential areas are fairly small, often with limited space both for top growth and root growth. Aside from the special nature of soils on derelict sites (p42), urban soils may have very variable pH, texture and presence of nutrients and, in areas where de-icing salt is used, a high soluble salt content (McCullen and Webb, 1982, p77). Other limitations include polluted air and the need to choose species which do not inconvenience or endanger the public by heavy leaf-fall, honeydew or brittle branches. Urban areas do, however, offer at least one advantage in that average temperatures are slightly higher than in surrounding rural areas, which can give a longer period of growth and increase the range of species that can be grown.

These limitations may restrict the use of the large native trees (see Table 2A), leaving only a few natives which are suitable. In such small clumps of trees, isolated from other semi-natural habitats, the use of natives is usually less important than elsewhere, as the opportunity for recreating a 'woodland' habitat, with its assemblage of dependent insects, birds, fungi and so on, is greatly limited. It is therefore reasonable to use cultivars of native species, plus naturalised and long-introduced species, particularly if these make tree-planting acceptable and appreciated on a site which might otherwise not be planted at all.

A 'cultivar' of a species is one which has either been bred for horticultural purposes, or has arisen natu-rally, either in the wild or in cultivation, and then has been selected, named and propagated. These forms are selected because of desirable qualities of height, shape, colour of foliage or blossom, autumn colouring and so on. By using a cultivar of a native species, you are perpetuating some of the ecological value, whilst growing it in a form which is more suitable for an urban area. Examples include weeping or `fastigiate' (upright) forms of the large native trees such as ash and beech, holly and yew in various shapes and colours, and the many forms of hawthorn, wild cherry, myrobalan, rowan and whitebeam which have been selected mainly for their blossoms and berries. The best source of information on these trees is `Hillier's Manual of Trees and Shrubs' (1977), but note that only the more commonly planted cultivars will be easily obtainable. Table 3 in Appendix B shows examples of cultivars and varieties suitable for different urban situations.

The most obvious effect of using non-native trees is their appearance, which, with a few possible exceptions such as sweet chestnut, is immediately associated with gardens or parks. In recent years there has been a strong movement away from the 'green desert' type of urban park, with its ranks of 'lollipop trees', towards more natural plantings of trees and shrubs with areas of long grass, damp ground and so on. In large areas such as parks, derelict building plots, and sites adjoining 'waste' land or railway embankments there is considerable value in using natives, both for their own appearance and in their potential for supporting wildlife, thus effectively recreating a piece of native habitat. Smaller areas, in school grounds and even private gardens, can also benefit from less ambitious versions of such schemes.

Coastal or exposed conditions

Sites which are exposed to cold or salt winds are very restricted in the tree species they can support, and under natural conditions, would probably be wooded sparsely, if at all. Tree planting may be desirable, however, to provide screening of car parks or buildings, or shelter for livestock, and the use of introduced species such as holm oak or Leyland cypress, which will succeed on such sites, is therefore justified.

Timber production

Most timber production in this country is of introduced species, because of their fast growth and tolerance of cold or exposed sites. Conservation plantings will normally avoid these species, but there may be instances where it is important to gain some fairly quick financial return from a woodland, in order to make it viable. There are also a few species which may be worth planting because their timber is of a high value, although these do take many decades to mature. A mixture which includes some non-natives may therefore be used. Hibberd (1988) gives useful infor-

mation on natives and non-natives suitable for planting in mixtures, for timber production.

DRAWING UP A PLAN

Once suitable species for the site have been determined, a closer look at the locality to choose the best planting plot will be needed, in preparation for drawing up a final planting plan.

Site selection

If possible, the site should butt up against an existing copse, hedgerow or remnant of woodland, or should incorporate any mature trees within the new area. This will not only provide a pleasing visual continuity, but will also greatly increase the wildlife value of the new planting. The woodland remnant will contain plant and animal species, many of them hidden or inconspicuous invertebrates, fungi and lichens as well as seed, which can then spread into the new planting. If instead, the new planting is isolated by perhaps 100 metres of arable land, many of these species will never make it to the new planting area.

Avoid planting up areas of boggy ground or old grassland, which are better maintained as they are. Ponds and boggy ground can, however, be incorporated within tree planting areas, although in most cases they should be left open to the sunlight and not planted on their southern sides. An exception is farm ponds which are used for irrigation. These may actually benefit from tree shade, which reduces the build-up in summer of pump-clogging algae. Some tree species also drop substantial amounts of pollen , which if dropped into a pond will attract ducks and other wildlife. In boggy areas, avoid trees which rapidly seed and colonise new areas, such as birch, or a thicket will soon spring up. Also be aware that any areas incorporating both bogs and trees will need long-term management due to natural succession, which in this case means that trees would colonise the ground anyway.

Field corners that are unproductive for arable farming provide possible sites for tree planting, and are usually of limited existing wildlife interest due to the use of herbicides. Note the following:

a Modern cultivators and harvesters require a turning radius of approximately 15m (50'), leaving a corner about the size shown below. If the field is not going to be grazed for at least 10 years, it is cheaper to protect the trees with individual tree shelters. Where grazing is possible, the trees should be protected by fencing, as sheep and cattle will rub against and damage the young trees, even if they do not browse them.

TABLE 2A SITE REQUIREMENTS AND CHARACTERISTICS OF NATIVE TREE SPECIES

SPECIES	WET GROUND	LIGHT SANDY SOIL	HEAVY SOILS	ACID	ALKALINE	WITHSTANDS SHADE
Alder	✓[1]				✓	✓
Ash	✓	✓	✓		✓	
Aspen			✓	✓	✓	
Beech		✓			✓	✓
Birch, Downy	✓			✓		
Birch, Silver		✓		✓		
Cherry, Wild		✓			✓	
Crab Apple		✓	✓	✓	✓	
Elm, Wych			✓		✓	✓
Hawthorn		✓	✓	✓	✓	
Hawthorn, Midland			✓		✓	✓
Hazel			✓		✓	✓
Holly		✓	✓	✓	✓	✓
Hornbeam	✓[2]		✓		✓	✓
Juniper		✓		✓	✓	
Lime, Small-leaved			✓		✓	✓
Lime, Large-leaved			✓		✓	
Maple, Field			✓		✓	✓
Oak, Pedunculate	✓[2]		✓		✓	
Oak, Sessile	✓	✓	✓	✓		✓
Pine, Scots		✓		✓		
Poplar, Black	✓[3]	✓	✓		✓	
Rowan		✓		✓		
Whitebeam, Comm.		✓	✓		✓	
Wild Service Tree			✓		✓	✓
Willow, Crack	✓[1]				✓	
Willow, White	✓[1]				✓	
Yew		✓			✓	✓

1 Only species to survive on sites with anaerobic soil conditions.

2 Will do well on sites that are seasonally wet.

3 Will only tolerate wet ground if there is some seasonality, or 'flushing' (water movement) within the soil and subsoil.

| AVE. ULTIMATE HEIGHT | | | GROWTH RATE | | | TOLERANT OF SITES THAT ARE | | | BIRD VALUE | INSECT VALUE |
0.5-5m	6-15m	16m+	FAST	MEDIUM	SLOW	POLLUTED	COASTAL	EXPOSED		
	✓		✓					✓		✓
		✓		✓		✓	✓	✓		
		✓	✓			✓	✓	✓		✓
		✓		✓						✓
		✓	✓			✓		✓		✓
		✓	✓			✓		✓		✓
	✓			✓		✓				
	✓				✓	✓			✓	✓
		✓		✓		✓	✓	✓		✓
✓					✓	✓	✓	✓	✓	✓
✓					✓				✓	✓
	✓		✓							✓
	✓				✓	✓	✓	✓	✓	
		✓		✓		✓		✓		
	✓							✓		
		✓		✓						✓
		✓		✓				✓		✓
	✓			✓		✓				
		✓		✓				✓	✓	✓
		✓		✓				✓	✓	✓
		✓		✓				✓		✓
		✓	✓							✓
	✓		✓			✓	✓	✓	✓	
	✓			✓						✓
	✓			✓				✓	✓	
	✓		✓			✓	✓	✓	✓	✓
	✓		✓			✓	✓	✓	✓	✓
	✓				✓	✓		✓	✓	

b If possible, amalgamate the corner plantings to give one large plot, rather than several separate plots. A single plot will be about 80 square metres (1/50 acre), with two adjoining plots about 135 square metres (1/30 acre). At least 400 square metres (1/10 acre) is needed to create a reasonable area of habitat, and fencing costs become cheaper as the area increases (see below).

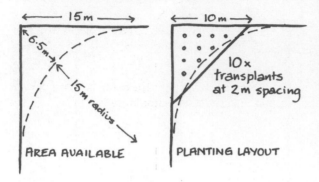

Layout

You will need to balance the various advantages and disadvantages of larger blocks of planting against those of more varied outlines.

Concentrating planting into one block with a regular outline is the cheapest solution where a fence has to be constructed all the way around. A circle gives the greatest area for the shortest perimeter, but is not usually the cheapest because a strained wire fence cannot easily be constructed in a curve, and more expensive forms of wooden fencing need to be used. Circular woods can be very effective as hilltop clumps, but otherwise look rather out of place in semi-natural landscapes, and do not fit in easily with other land uses. Squares and oblongs are the next most efficient shapes for fencing. For further details on tree protection see page 94.

Blocks of woodland have advantages for wildlife, as they are of sufficient size to provide the shaded and sheltered micro-climate which many woodland plants and animals need, and large enough for viable populations. On the other hand, blocks of single age trees, particularly when past the thicket stage, may be poor in wildlife because of the lack of habitat variety. Often the most valuable part for wildlife is the woodland edge, where the varied structure of herbs, shrubs and small trees can flourish in the space and sunlight. Therefore a varied outline, which increases the length of the woodland edge, is beneficial to wildlife. Too much emphasis on creating 'edge' can, however, result in patchy and sinuous plantings, which never develop the sheltered conditions of woodland. Taken to extremes, small isolated clumps of trees support only a meagre wildlife.

Where space permits, the optimum to aim for is a basic block of woodland which is cheap to fence, and within that create sheltered glades, rides and areas of thicket and scrub to provide a variety of habitat. This in effect provides 'edge' within as well as outside the wood, and is of course closer to the natural conditions in which the plants and animals of the woodland edge developed. Such a layout is extravagant of space where timber production is an objective, and also has the disadvantage that any trees growing along an internal or external edge will have a spreading and branching form, which is less productive in timber.

Planting plans

Any team of people who will be planting on the designated site will need a planting plan. The purposes of planting plans are:

a to record, on paper, all the details concerning the planting scheme. These details are needed for your own information, for the owner or client, and for anyone responsible for future management. They are also necessary for grant applications.

b to communicate your instructions for the design and implementation of the scheme to your work team supervisor and work team.

The plan should be concise and easily understood to prevent misunderstandings about the objectives of the planting scheme.

The plan should be worked out on a map at 1:1250 or 1:2500. If the site is in an urban area, the local council can supply a scaled map which can be enlarged or reduced as you need, to be used as a base map for your design.

Information required

The information presented on the plan should include:

a Location of planting areas

b The mixtures of species to be used in each area

c The type of nursery stock to be used in each area, for example whips, standards and so on

d The number of trees and the planting spacing for each

e The method of planting, for example pit, notch and so on

f The use of planting aids such as rabbit guards, mulching, stakes

g Any requirement for soil treatments, pre-planting weed control, drainage

h Any further information on the grouping of species within each mixture, for example, 'plant in groups of 3-5 individuals of each species', and whether in grid or randomly distributed

i Scale and north point.

Urban designs

For an urban site, especially one where trees are to be planted in a confined space, in clumps or groups, or in a formal pattern, a more detailed plan (bottom, below may be called for, showing crown spread of any existing trees and exact placement of the trees to be planted. Other information on the plan should be the same as for a basic planting plan. For planting schemes in confined spaces, an elevated sketch (see p41) may be necessary.

Presentation

The presentation should be simple and concise, preferably on one side of A4, with supplementary species lists as necessary. The information must be detailed enough for work to proceed without the designer being present, but not cluttered with unnecessary information which makes the plan difficult to understand. Note the following:

a For field use, it is advisable to keep the plans in re-sealable plastic envelopes (available from stationers), or attach a copy of the plan to a stout piece of card, possibly with any further information on the reverse, and then encase the whole thing in a clear polythene bag, sellotaped to fit neatly. Flimsy pieces of paper will not last long in the field. Always use a waterproof pen!

b Provide several copies, as the team may be working in different areas at the same time.

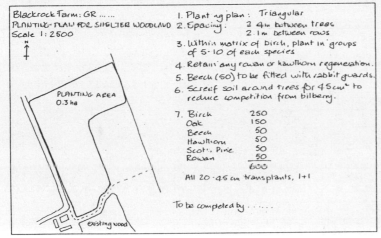

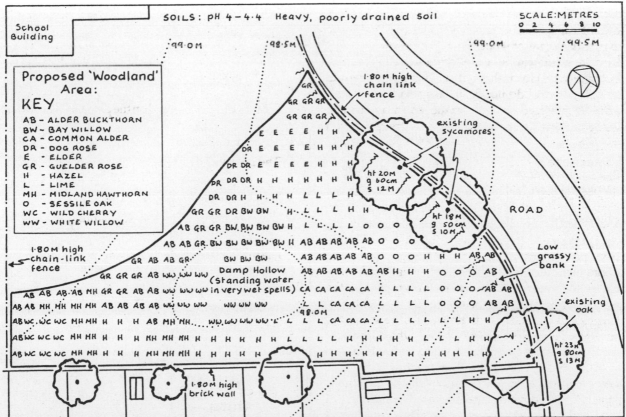

Planting plan: Greengrove School nature area

ESTIMATES

Having gathered the information for the planting plan, an estimate can be made of the cost of planting. This is best done on a standard form, an example of which is given below. You will probably need to design your own standard form, to suit the working practices and conditions in your particular area. **NB**: As there is an average failure rate of 5-10% for trees planted, you will need to reserve some money for replacement plantings.

PLANTING ESTIMATE FORM

General

Site	Grid Ref	
Area to be planted (ha)		
Site preparation		
Planting pattern	Spacing	
No./ha	No .trees required	

Details of trees

Species	Quantity	Type/size	Cost
1			
2			
3			
4			
5 etc.			
		Subtotal	

Accessories

Type	Quantity		Cost
Tree shelters			
Mulching mats			
Rabbit guards			
Tree stakes			
Tree ties			
Mulch			
Herbicide			
		Subtotal	
		VAT	
		TOTAL	

FENCING ESTIMATE FORM		
Type of fencing		
Total length		
Length of stock netting		
Length of plain wire		
Length of barbed wire		
Number of: straining/turning posts	struts	stakes
Gates (no. and width)	gateposts	
Stiles		
Rails and other extras		

Systems of Management

Whether planting a new wood, or extending or re-stocking an established one, a system of management will need to be chosen. For a multi-use wood, coppicing is perhaps the most effective system, as it combines maximum benefit for wildlife with wood production. High forest management also lends itself well to a variety of objectives, however, and may be seen as complementary to coppicing. Woodland management is discussed comprehensively in 'Woodlands' (Brooks, revised 1988).

COPPICE WOODS

The following information is in part from Crowther and Evans (1986), which should be consulted for details.

As stated in chapter 1, coppicing is probably the oldest form of woodland management in Britain, stretching in a largely unbroken line from Neolithic times until the present day. Commercial demand for coppice produce was the most important reason for the survival of coppice woods from the 17th to the 19th centuries. Today, only sweet chestnut coppice is

managed to any great extent because of the demand for fence palings and pulp, although ash, hazel, hornbeam and sycamore are also coppiced to some degree in the south and east of Britain.

One-year regrowth of hazel coppice

Aside from its commercial importance, coppicing is extremely valuable for wildlife. A broadleaved coppice woodland which has been maintained regularly over a long period of time provides rich habitats for

27

wildlife, especially birds, invertebrates and flowering plants. The continuity of cover over time is very important for species which have difficulty in colonising new habitats. The relatively short traditional coppice rotations of 15-20 years also provides a range of conditions from dense shade to open ground, allowing a variety of species to persist indefinitely through their own cycles of growth and dormancy. Coppice derived from natural woodland also allows native tree and shrub species to persist for very long periods.

The discontinuation of coppice management in a wood will result in a decline in structural variety and, with it, the conservation value of the wood. Species dependent on the habitats created by regular coppicing decline or disappear. Because accumulated leaf litter and dead wood enrich the soil in derelict coppice woods, resuming the coppice cycle there may encourage the growth of brambles and result in a loss of interesting flora which thrive on nutrient-poor soil.

Where coppice woodlands are converted to high forest (see below), floristic and structural diversity decreases and the amount of woodland edge habitat declines. Clearance and replanting, especially with beech or evergreen conifers, causes drastic changes in ground flora, although planting with oak, larch or ash is less damaging. A possible exception to these situations is with the pure oak coppice woods in Devon and Cornwall, among other locations. Some ecologists feel that these are of 'industrial archaeology' value only, being species-poor and similar in some ways to farmed crops. With such woods, it may actually be better to convert to coppice with standards or high forest.

For all these reasons, it is vital to consider carefully before establishing a new coppice wood. The coppice cycle will need to be sustained regularly if the conservation value of the wood is not to decline. It should also be noted that working coppice woods are in themselves not always ideal for nature conservation purposes, as the absence of old-wood and dead-wood habitats limits the proliferation of lichens, mosses, fungi, invertebrates and hole-nesting birds.

Types of coppice

The following types of coppice are recognised by Evans (1984, p69).

1 Simple coppice. This is worked on one cycle, so forming an even-aged stand. Nearly all sweet chestnut is worked in this way.

2 Coppice with standards. This forms a two-storey woodland, with coppice beneath and a scattering of trees being grown as standards, usually oak. The coppice component is known as 'underwood'.

3 Stored coppice. This has been left to grow on beyond its normal rotation, usually through neglect. Many woods of this nature, which now resemble high forest, exist due to the decline in coppice working early this century. Deliberately storing coppice can, however, be a valuable alternative to restoring coppice, as much lower inputs are required.

4 Short rotation coppice. This is worked on a rotation of less than 10 years, to provide material for coppice crafts such as the making of hurdles.

Establishing a coppice

This is similar to establishing any other type of woodland, in principle (see chapter 6). The spacing of new plants is related to the length of rotation envisaged. For example, hazel worked on a 7-10 year rotation is planted at 1500-2000 stools per hectare (600-800 per acre), whereas sweet chestnut on a 15-year rotation is more thinly planted, at 800-1000 stools per hectare (320-400 per acre). Oak and ash on 23-25 year rotations usually have 200-500 stools per hectare (80-200 per acre).

Species should be chosen first to suit the available site and soil (see p20), as with any wood, and then according to demand. For care in the early years after planting, see chapters 6 and 7. Coppicing can begin as soon as the trees are established, ie at 5-8 years, or when the crop reaches marketable size. An early cut will encourage a better yield in the first crop, but will delay it by a few years. The first coppicing of young trees should be done in March or April, so that the new shoots emerge in June, after any risk of frost.

As indicated above, even coppicing primarily for the objective of wood production will have much conservation value. Productive coppicing embraces a wide range of species and uses, one example being hazel coppice, used for hurdles and thatching spars. Species appropriate to both conservation and productive coppicing, with general ranges of coppice rotations, are listed below. (A = up to 12 years; B = 12-15 years; C = 15-30+ years.)

Species	Rotation
Alder	A, B
Ash	B, C
Birch	A, B
Chestnut, sweet	A, B, C
Hazel	A, B
Hornbeam	C
Oak	B, C
Willow, osier	A
Willow, white	A

The longer rotations will, of course, give crops of a larger diameter suitable, for instance, for firewood and turnery.

Where wood production is a secondary consideration, and the wood is to be coppiced to enhance wildlife potential, conservation coppicing can be introduced. This is often used as a way of improving derelict woodlands, but the system can also be applied to a newly established coppice wood.

In conservation coppicing, the traditional rotations of 7-15 years are very useful for maintaining necessary habitats for many species. Ten-year-old coppice is usually the optimum age for providing opportunities for nesting birds, for example, while after 20 years it begins to decline for this purpose.

After the coppice has become established, restocking may become necessary if any stools have died or become damaged during extraction operations. The easiest way to do this is by layering, or by propagating new plants by layering or stooling (p124) and then transplanting them in the gaps. If you are restocking an existing ancient semi-natural coppice, you must use plants raised from seed gathered in that wood to prevent the loss of local genotypes. Note that re-planting around large existing coppice stools can present some problems, as the stools can reduce growth in young trees from some distance away (Davies, 1987, p18).

'Gapping up', the term for restocking in a coppice wood, should be done at the same time the coupe is felled, as layering and stooling fit in with the felling operation, and the young plants will benefit from a few years of higher light levels. The sites of any layering, stooling or transplanting should be marked to allow the plants to be easily found again. The young plants should be protected as for newly planted trees (chapter 6), until they are coppiced at about 5 years old. After coppicing, the regrowth may need protection from browsing damage by deer, either via permanent (p95) or temporary fencing.

For further information on uses of coppice wood, and productive and conservation coppicing, see Brooks (revised 1988, pp33-37). Further information about conservation coppicing is available in Peterken (1972), Mummery and Tabor (1976) and Ranson (1979). Coppice techniques are discussed in chapter 7.

HIGH FOREST

High forest is described variously as woodland in which the main purpose is to grow timber, and in which at least half the species are marketable (Evans, 1984, p12); and as stands grown mainly from seed-lings, rather than coppice shoots (Peterken, 1981,

p66). In Britain, most high forest stands are plantations, making them neither natural nor semi-natural woods; many were, however, established on ancient sites. High forest can also be the result of neglected coppice, or coppice converted by 'singling' (removing all but the most vigorous shoot) or storing, in which cases it is called 'false' high forest.

Oak is the principle species of about 30% of all broad-leaved high forest in Britain, with beech, ash, birch and sycamore making up a further 47%. Most of this woodland is in the southern half of England (Evans, 1984).

The effects of forestry practices

Afforested upland areas which have grown up into high forest are usually less valuable for a range of wildlife than coppice woods or semi-natural woodlands, especially if the stands are made up of trees with dense canopies like conifers. If some stands mature and are felled and replanted, a more diverse overall structure, and thus more wildlife value, results.

The replacement of broadleaved woods by conifers occasions a loss of semi-natural habitat and a decline, in number and interest, of plant and animal species. To a somewhat lesser extent this also occurs when mixed broadleaved woodlands are converted to single-species broadleaved plantations. If planting is to follow either of these courses, the establishment of new roads and rides and more intense maintenance of existing ones (p33) should be considered.

The churning up of soil during forestry work such as clear-felling can cause soil compaction and a possibility of impaired drainage, although some disturbance of soil during clear-felling can aid natural regeneration, particularly of smaller-seeded species. The water table may rise for a time after felling, due to compaction and the reduction in transpiration which accompanies the loss of trees. This can limit the success of trees which do not respond well to poorly drained sites.

Planting for conservation

Choose locally occurring native species. If natural regeneration is not feasible, try to collect seed locally and propagate the plants in a nursery prior to planting out (see chapter 5). Naturalised species can also have a place in high forests. Recent research indicates that some species, such as sycamore, are not as poor in the wildlife they support as had been previously thought. Mixed broadleaved and conifer woodland supports the most numbers and species of birds; this is followed by broadleaved only, and lastly pure conifer plantations.

Operations such as clearance and drainage should be kept to a minimum before and during the establishment phase of the new crop. Climbing plants such as ivy and honeysuckle can be detrimental to good stem growth initially, but some should be allowed to grow later for the benefit of butterflies. Avoid forestry operations of any major kind during the breeding season or on breeding sites to prevent the disturbance of birds and animals during that time.

Planting for timber production

If planting hardwoods, choosing a species suitable for the site is more important than other considerations, as there are no market reasons for planting particular species. The site should be reasonably sheltered to produce quality timber, and stands must be carefully managed to minimise defects in the wood. The trees are usually planted at 1.8-3m (6-10') spacing. If conservation is an important objective, closer spacing, and thinning for firewood or other marketing purposes, should be considered.

Mixtures of broadleaves and conifers are commonly planted in woods aimed at hardwood production. Conifers act as a nurse crop, providing site shelter for broadleaves; they can then be thinned and sold before they grow tall enough to dominate the slower-growing broadleaves, thus providing an early return. A nurse crop of larch planted with a main crop of oak results in a much higher growth rate - up to 25% faster - in the oak. Disease can also be lessened. Beech grown with pine, for instance, is less disease-prone (Sinden, 1989, p47).

In practice, however, planting mixtures can present problems. It is very difficult to plant so that the final effect appears 'natural'. Planting in interspersed blocks is preferable to planting in rows. It is also difficult to ensure that the crop is not swamped by the nurse. Broadleaved only mixtures may be a better choice. Growth rate differences between main and nurse crop will then be less, and the visual effect of the planting pattern is also less obtrusive. The following mixtures of broadleaves are recommended by Evans (1984, p29), provided that the site and soil conditions are suitable:

ASH with common alder or sycamore

BEECH with cherry

OAK with common alder, ash, cherry or sweet chestnut.

Nurse species which require no thinning include understorey shrubs such as hazel, or fast-growing, light-demanding species such as rowan, which become suppressed as the canopy closes. For details of management for timber production, consult Evans (1984).

SCRUB

Scrub, defined in forestry terminology as 'poor quality woodland', can be very valuable in terms of conservation and amenity. The common presence in scrub of species such as elder, field maple, hazel, sallow, thorns and whitebeam, and a number of old or damaged trees, make scrubland poor quality in terms of marketable species and timber, but rich in habitats for wildlife, particularly birds and invertebrates. The often sparse growth in scrubland also provides numerous glades in which flowering plants can flourish.

If a scrubland is the climax community, due to poor soils or other conditions, or if natural succession is simply very slow, planting and other management for conservation and amenity should be kept to the minimum. Scrub on relatively fertile soil, which is in the process of naturally succeeding to high forest and has reached the thicket stage (below 10m, or 33', in height), can be left to grow for 10 or 15 years before thinning is needed. For scrublands (and woodlands) which are important in terms of conservation, recreation and amenity, non-intervention may also be indicated.

The coppicing, improvement or enrichment of scrub for timber production may be feasible. Coppicing is a possibility in scrub consisting mainly of tree rather than shrub species, although some woods such as thorn and sallow do not provide useful timber, and beech tends to respond poorly. The improvement of scrub consists in favouring individual trees which are suitable in forestry terms (ie species, form and quality) during the cleaning and thinning processes. Scrub enrichment entails the planting of trees which will produce a marketable crop, either in existing gaps or in swathes cut through the scrub. The width of these swathes should be at least equal to the height of adjacent trees, with 4m (13') the minimum practical width. Weeding, and the thinning of competing trees, will be necessary for the production of a good crop. As transplants are recommended for planting, at spacing of 3-4m (10-13'), tree shelters should be used to promote good growth. For further information, see Evans (1984, p93).

Planting in Rural Locations

Planting in rural areas embraces a wide range of sites, from lowland farms to landscaped parks. In established woodlands, the management systems already in use will affect planting plans in that any planting within these woodlands for purposes of conservation and amenity will tend either to maintain or improve the desirable conditions which have developed. Planting within ancient semi-natural woodlands, for example, will be largely dictated by the delicate balance between communities of flora and fauna which have developed over centuries of careful management.

When considering tree planting in woodlands, several of the general management principles for nature conservation, as devised by Peterken (1977), are relevant. These are as follows:

a Distinguish between individual woods of high conservation value, woodland areas of high conservation value and other woodlands.

b Give special treatment to special sites and special areas.

c When considering afforestation, develop large blocks of connected woodland while maintaining a scatter of small woods between the large blocks.

d Minimise rate of change within woods, for example in the amount and distribution of tree species, in order to give wildlife time to adjust.

e If felling will be part of your management plans, encourage maturity by maintaining long rotations between fellings. If this is not possible, retain a scatter of old trees after restocking.

f Encourage native tree species and use non-native species only where necessary.

g Encourage diversity of woodland structure, habitats and species of trees and shrubs, insofar as this is compatible with other principles.

h Encourage restocking by natural regeneration or coppice regrowth.

i Retain records of any operations done on the site.

NATIVE UPLAND WOODLANDS

These include native pine woods in Scotland and broadleaved woods in the uplands of England, Scotland and Wales. Some of these woods are remnants of the ancient natural and semi-natural forest, while others derive from the ornamental plantings of the 18th and 19th centuries. The value of these woods lies in their beauty in the landscape, the wildlife they support and their importance as ecological links to the past - not in commercial potential. Lack of natural regeneration is the main problem with these woods.

As most planting by volunteers in upland woodlands takes place in broadleaved woods, only those will be considered here. Evans (1984, p104) identifies the following types of upland broadleaved woodland. Soil type usually determines the dominant species.

a Oak woods. These occur on acid soils in high rainfall areas. In southwest England they are found as high as 400m (1320') but in the Scottish highlands they rarely occur above 200m (660'). Though dominated by sessile oak, other species of trees and shrubs occur, and at higher altitudes the woods merge into areas of rowan and birch.

b Ash woods. These are much less extensive than oak woods, and occur only on base-rich and calcareous soils in the Mendips, Derbyshire Dales and northern Pennines.

c Birch woods. Although often a successional stage between pine and oak woods, there are extensive semi-natural stands of birch in Wales and Scotland. Natural regeneration may be profuse at woodland edges or where the soil has been disturbed.

d Alder woods. These are widespread throughout Britain, but confined to wet soils beside streams or areas of impeded drainage.

Other upland woods are mainly planted, and include beech, Scots pine and sycamore.

Many surveys have shown that the area of upland woods is declining, and all attribute the primary cause to uncontrolled grazing and browsing by wildlife and livestock, which prevents natural regeneration. Among other factors preventing natural regeneration are irregularity of seed years; uncontrolled burning of adjacent moorland, which can affect the woodland edge; and lack of light resulting from the trees growing in thick stands.

Planting should take place in these woods only if natural regeneration does not occur. The young trees should, if possible, be grown from seeds of local provenance (p58). If a new wood is to be planted, keep in mind that exposure and generally poor soil on these sites will make establishment of new broadleaved planting difficult. Rowan, alder and birch are the most successful species, but planting mixtures of broadleaves and conifers will aid establishment (see p30). Sites with good drainage and some shelter should be chosen, and either fencing or individual protection (such as tree shelters) must be used to prevent damage from browsing.

PASTURE-WOODLANDS, PARKS AND AVENUES

The following is in part from Rushforth (1987, pp50-57).

With a few exceptions, the trees in parks and pasture-woodlands are the oldest in the country, making these sites of special value for wildlife. Planting within such areas will be dictated to some degree by the existing designs, which are often of great historical significance as well as aesthetic value. Planting will therefore usually consist of replacing old trees that have died, to preserve the continuity of landscape, although surveys should still be carried out to determine whether those species were the best ones for the site. It is important to study the original designs, where available (or information about them, where not) in order to preserve the character of the park. It is equally important to keep not only good records but also the original planting plan. The desired parkland 'look' can take decades to achieve, and this necessitates either continuity of managers or a good plan to which reference can be made.

In semi-natural pasture-woodland, natural regeneration or the planting of trees derived from stock of local provenance is preferable, but exotics may have a place in landscape parks. The individual trees will need to be fenced against deer or livestock, and protection from spray drift of agricultural chemicals and vandalism may also be necessary.

Parkland planting

Parkland landscapes are generally on the grand scale, so the trees themselves will need to be large, or boldly grouped, to avoid appearing insignificant. When planting in parks on this large a scale, it may be best to plan with the advice of a landscape architect. As the trees will be so obvious in the open landscape, their heights and crown patterns will be particularly important in the overall design. Other aesthetic considerations, such as autumn colour, should also be taken into account when choosing species. 'Hilliers' Manual of Trees and Shrubs' (1977), Miles (1967, pp140-5) and Mitchell and Jobling (1984) list ornamental trees for a variety of situations.

Usually, trees in a parkland are arranged to highlight topographic elements of the landscape, such as knolls, or to frame a view. The trees are most often planted singly or in widely spaced groups, belts, clumps or groves, depending in most cases on whether the land is in agricultural use. Generally speaking, groups of trees look more natural if planted in groups of odd numbers.

The following points should be noted:

a If you will be planting single trees, choose young specimens which are well-formed and symmetrical. These may need careful formative pruning as the tree grows (p113). In the overall design, single trees should not be too numerous.

b Groups of three to five trees produce a more substantial effect than single trees. They should be planted to allow each tree room for healthy growth (usually at spacing of 3-5m), but after the crowns have grown together, they should be pruned and otherwise managed as a single tree. Generally, each group should be composed of one species.

c Clumps can be used to break up a background, obscure or break up the skyline, and lend depth and variety to the scene. In informal settings, a mixture of species and an irregular outline are usually best.

d Groves can be used to break up an area into smaller sections, e.g. to separate formal parts of a park from the more naturalistic landscape beyond. Groves can be planted along ridges, on high or broken ground, or as short rides or avenues on level ground. Irregular areas of varying widths and broken margins appear more 'natural'. The species of trees should be planted according to their function, such as shelter, screening or shooting.

Avenues

Formal avenues in rural areas, which are often part of or adjacent to a park, may need restoration if they have fallen into decay, or complete replanting.

Avenues are usually of a single species, as the formality of the design demands some degree of uniformity. Some avenues are very broad and long, forming a framework for a feature such as a house or monument. These can be 'patched' by interplanting young trees, or by planting new rows within or without the general lines when the existing trees start to age and die off. The avenues called 'malls' were originally planted primarily to create an attractive pattern of tracery and dappled shade when seen from beneath, but as these require absolute symmetry, they must be replanted afresh.

In almost every case it is best to resist felling existing avenue trees until they die completely. Replacement planting should if possible use naturally regenerated saplings of the original stock, or seedlings grown from the seeds of original stock. Avenue 'purists' will often insist on planting clones of the original trees. Thinning may be necessary as trees in an avenue mature. Planting an excess number of trees in an avenue with the intention of thinning some out later is not necessarily recommended, however, unless you can guarantee that the work will be carried out at the appropriate time.

The length of an avenue, the species planted and the number of rows will determine the width. Normally, an avenue 100m (100 yd) long is about 10m (10 yd) wide. An avenue 1km (1/2 mile) long may be 60m (60 yd) wide. Trees in rows may be planted relatively close, at 5-10m (5-10 yd) intervals, to eventually almost merge into a tall hedge. They can, alternatively, be planted further apart, at 10-20m (10-20yd) intervals, to form broader, individuated crowns. Very large-scale avenues should be planted in widely spaced clumps so that replacement is easier; the effect will also be less artificial, and if one tree dies, the avenue will not be ruined.

If you are planting a new avenue as a rural landscape feature, the choice of species is wide, including the native limes, beech and oak as well as sweet chestnut and a variety of exotics. If the avenue is very long or wide and can take two rows of trees on either side, a 'two-term' avenue can be planted. This will have quick-growing trees on the inner rows and the permanent species on the outer, to create an earlier effect. The inner row of trees can be thinned out in 20-30 years (Rushforth, 1987, p55).

ASSOCIATED WOODLAND HABITATS

Rides, roads, glades and wood margins

Rides, glades and wood margins provide open, sunny conditions which are at the same time sheltered and humid: a suitable habitat for plants and animals unable to thrive in dense woodland. They also provide the woodland edge habitat so valuable for a rich variety of species. New rides, roads and paths will be required in newly planted areas, and occasionally in existing woodlands. Retention of the rides, glades and margins of ancient woodlands which have evolved over many centuries of management is very important.

Rides are generally straight arteries through a wood, traditionally 6m (20') wide, ditched and often drained, compacted and able to carry vehicles at almost any season. Their flora is predominately of the grassland variety. Roads are about 2.5m (8') wide, often winding, not ditched or permanently compacted, and used for periodically extracting material from the wood when the going is firm. They have a woodland flora (Mummery and Tabor, 1978, p7). The verges of Tarmac roads which run through wooded areas have similar flora present.

Details of the design of rides to standards suitable for vehicular access and timber extraction are given in Blatchford (1978). Footpath and bridleway construction and management is discussed in 'Footpaths' (Agate, 1983). Access requirements will largely determine ride and road orientation, although the need to provide sunlight in different seasons will also affect choice of orientation (see below). In order to prevent a 'wind-tunnel' effect, rides should have occasional distinct curves and should be angled just before emerging from the woodland, especially on the side of the prevailing wind. 'Bays' or 'scallops' (see below) are also useful for diverting wind and providing shelter.

In coppice woodlands, glades of a temporary nature are provided by the coppice plots. In high forest, a glade mosaic can be achieved by clear felling and then replanting blocks of an appropriate size. Wood margins can, in general, be maintained in the same way as ride or glade edges, to provide a variety of sheltered edges. The banks or ditches which define margins of ancient woodlands should be left untouched, but trees growing on them should be pollarded or coppiced on rotation. To ensure that the interior of the wood is not exposed too much, this management should be planned in conjunction with the felling of coppice coupes.

Enhancing rides, roadsides and wood margins

The information following is in part from Warren and Fuller (1990b).

Any plans to improve a ride- or roadside for wildlife will need to take into account the level of shade in the ride, its width, and the type of cutting or mowing regime envisaged.

The level of shade in a ride is affected by the width and orientation of the ride, as well as the height of the surrounding trees. Wider rides or shorter trees will create sunnier conditions. East/west orientations will allow more sun during the summer (except in the far north), whereas a north/south orientation will let in more sun in the winter. Generally, open rides will need to be 1.5 times as wide as the height of the surrounding trees. A ride running through mature woodland, where the trees are 20 to 30m tall, will thus need to be at least 30-45m wide to benefit those species (such as the majority of British butterflies) which need the most sunlight. The width of the bands cut on either side of the ride will need to be at least 5m but preferably 10m to provide adequate 'edge' habitat.

There are several cutting regimes for ride or road margins, but if the aim is to create maximum diversity of structure and species in the edge vegetation, a three-zone system is best. The shrub layer is coppiced, while the tall herbaceous layer and the grassy verge are mown, at the varied frequencies shown.

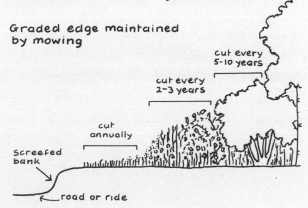

Graded edge maintained by mowing

cut every 5-10 years

cut every 2-3 years

cut annually

screefed bank

road or ride

Diversity can be increased even more if alternate edges are mown in different years, as shown below.

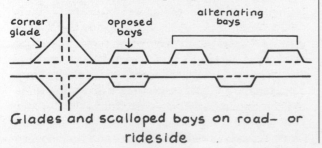

3 = year of mowing

In semi-natural woods, most enhancement of ride or road verges and woodland edges will consist of creating graded edges, as above, or coppicing, and protecting naturally regenerated saplings with tree shelters and identification tags.

Where the site is a road running through a single-species plantation of heavy-shading trees such as beech or conifers, the crop trees will need to be completely cleared in a 5-10m band on either side, after which replanting will need to take place to create the graded edge. Species with light crowns, such as birch or aspen, should be planted as the canopy layer. The shrub layer may regenerate naturally if the ad-jacent ground is left bare, or native shrubs can be planted. The field layer in front of the shrub belt should form by itself. A method for encouraging native wildflowers such as wild strawberry is to screef the ditch bank next to the ride or road, leaving it as a seedbed for naturally regenerating plants.

Bays incorporated into the design of road or ride verges will provide a more natural, undulating line, prevent 'wind-tunnel' effects and, if placed in opposing positions across a road or ride, create more light across it. The smallest bay length which is useful is 7m (23'), but if the trees in the wood or plantation are taller than 20m (66'), bays will need to be a minimum of 25m (83') long to admit enough light.

At intersections, large glades which allow in light from varying angles can be made by 'cutting off' all four corners of the wooded areas to create a 'box-junction' glade. Diversity can be created in such glades by indenting its margins; retaining a few trees within one sector; and cutting each sector of the glade every 2-15 years on rotation, depending on the habitats desired. To benefit wildlife appreciably, such glades should be at least .25 ha (1/2 acre) in size, but prefer-ably 0.5-2 ha (1-5 acres), if space permits.

Glades and scalloped bays on road- or rideside

Ponds and streams

Open-water habitats are often very valuable in them-selves, and their presence in a woodland greatly increases the site's diversity as well as improving its amenity value. Heavily shaded ponds or streams are, however, almost barren of wildlife, although par-tially shaded streams are ideal for bryophytes.

Planting around bodies or streams of water should be done with great care. The Forestry Commission Envi-ronmental Leaflet, 'Forests and Water' (1989), is useful as a general guide. Note the following points:

a Protective strips should be established along all watercourses. Conifers or heavy-foliaged broadleaved trees should not be planted within 5m of headwater streams. Trees should not be planted along the banks of larger streams and rivers in strips two to three times the width of the stream bed. The strips should vary in width to create habitat diversity and also to appear more natural.

b You should aim to have at least half of the stream open to sunlight, with the remaining portion under intermittent shade from light-canopy broadleaved trees and shrubs. These include birch, willow, rowan, ash, hazel or aspen, but they must be suitable for both site and locality. Periodic thinning of invasive trees or shrubs may be needed.

c In the course of thinning or other felling operations, fell trees away from streams and keep branches and tops out of the water.

d Chemicals such as herbicides should never be applied to trees within 10m (33') of streams, or 20m (66') of reservoirs.

FARM WOODS AND COVERTS

It is estimated (Forestry Commission Census of Woodlands and Trees, 1979-80) that small farm woods of less than 10 ha (25 acres) total 295,000 ha (728,975 acres) in Britain - 39% of the total of broadleaved woodland. Many clumps and rows of trees are not included in this estimate. Farm woodlands therefore constitute a vital part of woodland in Britain.

Many farm woodlands have been traditionally man-aged as coverts for game. A great number of them have, however, suffered neglect in the last few dec-ades, resulting in spindly growth or lack of natural regeneration.

Timber production on farm woodlands can be problematic. Their generally small size makes woodland operations more expensive, and they often have little or no access for management and timber extraction.

The conservation and sporting value of farm woods is usually high, however, and as they can often be enhanced by managing for timber production, maintaining them can be worthwhile. Along with hedgerows and shelterbelts, these woodlands are very important as wildlife havens, especially when located in the midst of intensively farmed land.

Landscape considerations

Landscape design considerations are particularly important with farm woodlands because they so often form a distinctive pattern, with hedges and shelterbelts, in the traditional farming landscape. The following information is from Hibberd (1988, pp75-80), which should be consulted for details. Also useful are the 'Forest Landscape Design Guidelines' (1989), available as a booklet from the Forestry Commission.

Initially, an appraisal of the area to be planted or replanted will have to be made. You will need to observe the topography, to determine whether it is flat or with rounded or rugged hills; the patterns of existing vegetation; land use patterns, which will reveal an open or hedgerow aspect; and the scale of the landscape generally, which will range from the large and open to the small and enclosed. Next, a look at the site from a variety of likely viewpoints, such as roads and footpaths, will be useful. Finally, after noting major landscape features on a scaled map (OSI:10 000 is recommended), sketches on overlays should be made of the various possible planting designs, in addition to planting plans (p24).

Keep in mind that either the landform or the hedgerow pattern will dominate the landscape. If landform is dominant, as on most upland sites, irregularly shaped woods reflecting the landform and creating an impression of large scale should be designed. If hedgerow patterns dominate, smaller scale layouts which follow a slightly more geometric form can be considered. This will be a benefit if fencing is required to keep livestock out of the wood, as fencing in straight lines is cheaper; but avoid planting square or rectangular woods if at all possible.

Woods in hilly landscapes should generally fall slightly on features like spurs or hilltops, and rise in ravines and hollows. In all situations, try to concentrate on creating a 'natural' looking shape.

Planting for timber production

This section is derived from Hibberd (1988) and Insley (1988), which should be consulted for details.

On farms, planting for timber production will usually involve either high forest or coppice crop systems. Widely spaced tree systems such as the growing of poplar or cricket bat willow, or 'agroforestry' - which is still in the experimental stage in Britain - are beyond the scope of this book; reference should be made to Insley (1988). It will usually be possible to combine sporting and conservation value with the objective of wood production, especially if coppicing is the system used.

When a combination of such objectives is feasible, it is important to keep in mind that production of smaller amounts of high quality timber allows greater flexibility of management; harvesting will be small-scale, and will allow gradual regeneration, visual amenity, continuity of landscape, and the maintenance of cover for wildlife and game.

High forest crop systems are discussed on p29 Coppice systems generally are discussed on p28. Coppice systems useable on farms include coppice with standards, short rotation coppice, and stored coppice, although the latter may cause problems arising from 'singling' (see below), and is also less valuable for conservation purposes because it makes for decreased structural diversity.

Coppice with standards, to work best for conservation, should be planned so that there are no more than 25 standards per hectare (10 per acre) when small, and 12 per hectare (5 per acre) when large. For greater production value, 30-100 standards per hectare (12-40 per acre) may be planted, but this will result in decreased underwood and ground flora. Where there are too few standards, you may want to plant new seedlings or protect existing ones, or promote standards from selected coppice poles, a procedure called 'singling'. Singling is also employed in stored coppice systems.

It entails cutting all but one to three stems, usually when the coppice stool is still young, ie less than 20 years. This procedure may produce inferior timber, however, as a pronounced curve (known as 'basal sweep') may develop at the stem base. Singling may also result in a higher percentage of decay and staining entering from the stools. In addition, the stem(s) may tend to bend over in the wind or, if cut when older, actually unbalance the stool and pull it over.

Oak, the most common standard species, is usually grown for 5-6 coppice cycles (100-130 years). Ash is grown for 3-5 cycles (60-100 years). Further species suitable for productive coppicing are listed on p28.

Sporting value

Although shooting may seem at odds with nature conservation interests, many woods have avoided clearance in the last few decades because of their sporting value. Many farmers value their woods for rough shooting, pheasant shooting, or as fox coverts. Broadleaved woods are especially valuable, as their varied structure and species provide good sources of food, cover and shelter. The woodland edge habitat is also maximised by the long and irregular boundaries of most small farm woods.

Planting a wood primarily for pheasant shooting should concentrate on providing a fairly open woodland structure, so that sunlight and warmth reach the woodland floor. Some ground cover, or a boundary hedge, should be provided for shelter from the wind. Wide, sunny rides are valuable for feeding sites. Ideal tree species include sweet chestnut, oak, whitebeam and ash, with an understorey of hawthorn and rowan. The Game Conservancy Booklet 15, 'Woodlands for Pheasants', should be consulted for further information.

In farm woods on upland sites where conifers may predominate, broadleaves should be planted and the structure of the wood diversified. 'Game strips' can be created by planting irregular strips of broadleaves or pines and larches through spruce plantations. In lowland woods the priority is usually to let more sunlight into the wood, and to open up rides or glades. These measures will all improve the conservation value of the wood, and can be integrated with wood production activities. 'Woodland Management' (Gray), available from the Game Conservancy, gives details on woodland design and management for game.

Hedgerows and farm trees

Hedgerows and isolated farm trees provide much landscape value in lowland sites, as they often form part of an overall distinctive design, in conjunction with coverts and other small woods. They are also very important in areas where woodlands are scarce, offering shelter and some wildlife habitat where these are at a premium. In addition, hedgerow trees, with small woods of less than 2 hectares (5 acres), provide 20% of Britain's total hardwood output.

It is probable, however, that the hedgerow trees proividing part of this output are not being replaced by new plantings. Together with the alarming loss of hedgerows from the landscape in the last few decades, this lack of replacement planting makes the need for new hedgerows and farm trees urgent. Although hedgerow trees are often unpopular with farmers because they cost money to maintain, shade land adjacent to them and get in the way of machinery, careful siting of new trees should solve most such problems. Field corners and boundaries where shade will not be detrimental are examples of such sites.

If you will be replacing hedgerow trees or planting new ones, keep the following points in mind:

a The promotion of saplings already growing in the hedge, which are called 'tillers', is usually the simplest way to ensure the replacement of unsafe or dying hedgerow trees. But if a hedge is beyond recovery or contains unsuitable tree species, new trees can be planted in or beside the hedge.

b Planting in an existing hedge is a laborious process, however. Individual beds are prepared for each tree by cutting away part of the hedge and digging a hole in the bottom. Great care must be taken to ensure that the roots of the hedge are not damaged. Also, competition for water, light and nutrients from the existing hedge will make the survival of new trees difficult. The use of tree shelters will enhance the growth of the new trees, as will regular trimming of the hedge around them. If a new hedge is being layed, plant hedgerow trees in it at the same time.

c Planting beside the hedge is easier, but the trees will need to be fenced off or provided with individual guards to protect them from livestock. Trees planted beside a hedge take up more room than those planted in one, and make mechanical trimming difficult. If mechanical trimming only is used on the farm, ensure that newly planted trees are marked with brightly coloured pieces of cloth or plastic tied around the stems. Stout stakes with easily seen painted tops, placed on either side of the saplings, will further protect them. Alternatively, consult county councils and the Tree Council about the availability of special tree tags. These are usually only distributed to groups which have an agreement from a farmer or landowner to carry out the work of tagging.

d The most promising location for new hedgerow trees is along roadsides, especially newly built or internal roads which lack adequate screening and shelter. Hedgerows lining roads which have a 'waste' verge on one side are also appropriate, although planting may not be suitable if the verge constitutes the only good grassland habitat in the area. Legal considerations are discussed in point e on p42.

e Plant hedgerow trees at irregular intervals, but at

least 10-12m (30-40') apart to allow each tree to develop fully.

Suitable species for hedgerow trees

Suitable native and naturalised species for hedgerow trees, depending on soil and climate requirements, include the following (from Beddall, 1950, p53). Many of these species will have landscape and conservation value as well. It is a good idea to consult local experts before making the final choice.

For timber and/or replacing elms

Alder, Ash, Beech, Birch, Black poplar, Lime, Oak, Sweet chestnut, Willow (black and white).

For more information on suitable species for hedgerows, see Brooks, 'Hedging' (1988, pp56-58).

Shelterbelts

Narrow woodlands and rough hedges are very useful for providing shelter on farms. Such shelterbelts as exist are often ancient features of the farming landscape, and any replacement planting should take into account their historic, landscape and wildlife value. Those which have been planned and planted are usually found in upland or very exposed areas, where they can protect forestry plantings and provide windbreaks for buildings and shelter for crops and livestock.

Planning and planting a shelterbelt requires careful siting, design and maintenance to ensure its survival and usefulness. For details on siting and design, consult Caborn (1965), Ministry of Agriculture, Fisheries and Food (1977) and chapter 5 of Blyth, Evan, *et al.* (1987). A brief overview is given in Leaflet 3 of the Countryside Commission Handbook, on the planting and aftercare of trees and shrubs (1979).

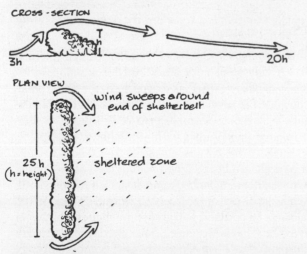

The design of shelterbelts must allow for wind permeability in order to avoid the formation of eddies; for optimum efficiency, about 40% permeability is needed. The desired effect is to create shelter for about 20 times the height of the belt on the downwind side,

and about three times the height of the upwind side. The wind will sweep around the ends of the belt, leaving a triangular sheltered zone, as shown. To allow for variations in wind direction, the length of a belt designed for crop protection should be about 25 times its expected height (Blyth *et al.*, 1987).

The base is the most important part of a shelterbelt, as if it becomes sparse, wind speeds are increased through the wood as well as the area beyond. Remedying this situation is difficult because new plants cannot be established in such draughty conditions unless given artificial shelter. The correct choice of species and management will ensure that the base is kept thick.

Wider belts are no more efficient than narrower belts of the same permeability, so where crop protection is the main objective and cropping space is valuable, a shelter of three, five or seven rows, up to about 20m (66') width, is sufficient. Narrow belts are, however, difficult to regenerate without clear-felling and replanting, and are less attractive as landscape and wildlife features than wider strips.

The trees are usually planted using triangular or staggered spacing, so that they stand 2.4 m (8') apart along rows that are 2.1 m (7') apart. Each tree will then stand 2.4 m (8') apart from adjacent trees. Altogether there will be about 1916 trees per hectare with this spacing. Keep in mind that, generally, the trees should not be planted closer than 1.8 m (6') centres (Countryside Commission, 1979). For most purposes an A-shaped profile is suitable, with the middle third planted with tall trees and the outer third planted with smaller trees and shrubs.

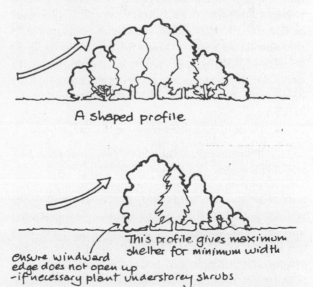

A shaped profile

Avoid gaps, openings and re-entrants on the windward side of shelterbelts. If an opening is needed, make it oblique to the wind and plant the edges with wind-firm species.

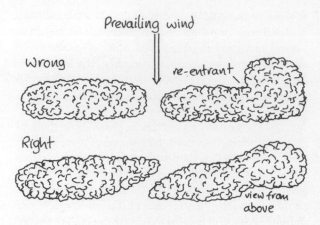

Where the aim is maximum shelter for minimum width, plant tall, wind-firm species up to the windward edge, with smaller trees and shrubs along the leeward edge. In all cases, conifers should be interplanted with broadleaves to give winter shelter and act as a nurse crop (see below).

Suitable species for shelterbelts

Given the appropriate soil and climate, suitable species include the following:

TALL   Lime, oak, sycamore, Scots pine

MEDIUM   Whitebeam, cherry, rowan

SMALL   Hawthorn, holly, hazel.

Note that with tall-growing species, 50 to 80 years may elapse before the trees reach their final height. In harsh upland situations, birch, alder and willow may be suitable on more fertile sites, with Scots pine and the non-native Shore pine and Noble fir best on infertile soil. Shrub species which may be suitable for edge planting, depending on site conditions, include blackthorn, box, broom, privet and osier willow.

Establishment and maintenance of shelterbelts

Establishment and maintenance can be approached in several ways, as follows:

a Nurse species can be planted. They will grow quickly and shelter the slower-growing, longer-lived species. Suitable conifers include Scots pine, and introduced species such as Sitka spruce, European larch and hybrid larch. In areas where rainfall reaches 750mm (30") annually, willow and poplar can also be used as a nurse. The nurse trees can either be planted in a strip along the windward edge with an outer strip of understorey shrubs, or can be mixed throughout the planting. Both methods present problems, however. When a windward strip is felled or deteriorates,

the increased exposure may damage the remaining trees. Nurse crops which are mixed throughout need careful thinning and removal to make sure the slower-growing species are not swamped.

b The belt can be established in two stages, planting half the width initially, and the other half as the planting begins to mature and become sparse at the base.

c Plant the full belt initially and thin it heavily at about 15 years, and more lightly thereafter at about 5 year intervals, at the same time under-planting with shade-bearing shrubs, small trees or successor species such as beech.

In extreme conditions, especially near the coast where salt air can burn foliage for several miles inland, it may be necessary to plant behind a fairly permeable screen (e.g. wattle hurdles, brashings, chestnut paling or slatted timber fences). Take a close look at site conditions and seek local advice on species which do well in the locality, since plants which are generally tolerant of salt winds may not be so in every situation.

Old, sparse, ineffective shelterbelts can be revitalised in several ways. Where a belt casts a heavy shade, plant a new margin one to three rows deep along its windward edge. Then thin and underplant the old belt. Alternatively, replant existing gaps in the belt and then gradually extend the replanted areas by further fellings. A third method is to cut a series of V-shaped wedges through the width of the belt, starting at a point on the leeward edge. These should be replanted and progressively widened out by further fellings until the whole belt is eventually replanted.

Shelter for stock

In upland and exposed sites, woodland may be planted to provide shelter for stock. Shelter is valuable for stock in bad weather, as this reduces the food intake they need to keep warm. It can also be helpful to the farmer, as the stock are easier to locate in bad weather, when they will gather within the shelter.

a Woods can be designed so that they offer shelter, whilst still being fenced against stock. On open land, where stock can move freely all around the perimeter, blocks of woodland will give some shelter whichever way the wind is blowing. Some woods are planted in the plan of an 'L' or 'X', to increase the amount of edge and shelter. Unlike shelterbelts, the permeability of the woodland is not significant, and any species that suit the site can be used. It may be possible to combine the shelter function with management for wildlife, landscape or timber value.

b Other woods intended for shelter are partly or completely unfenced, allowing access for stock. This gives better shelter, but management of the woodland is more difficult than for fenced woods. The ground can become badly trampled or 'poached', which not only destroys the ground flora but damages the root systems of trees. Browsing and bark damage will occur, and natural regeneration will be halted. A better method is to divide the woodland into three or four fenced compartments, using one per season in rotation. Any natural regeneration may need extra protection, such as tree shelters, until large enough to withstand browsing.

Planting in Urban Locations

As indicated in chapter 1, from the 18th until well into the 19th century, trees in cities were usually planted as components of squares and parks. Currently, the growing interest in land reclamation and the beautification of cities means that trees are being planted on a large range of sites, in most categories from the very formal to the very informal. Urban forestry encompasses existing woodland which has been incorporated into a city, or planted in the past few decades, parks, plots along streets and in squares, urban nature areas such as those on school grounds, and other wooded sites in the inner cities, suburbs and urban fringe.

On urban sites planning and design are particularly important, primarily because in many cases trees will be 'in competition' with buildings, but also because of the often difficult nature of the site itself, and the need to encourage the co-operation of the local community, private owners, the local authority and volunteer organisations. The aims and interests of these groups regarding tree planting may well differ, and if compromises are not reached, tree planting schemes can fail.

COMMUNITY INVOLVEMENT

How, then, can people become involved in all the stages of tree planting, from discussion through to aftercare? The following information is taken from Hibberd (1989, pp26-36).

a Generate interest. This can be done by notifying residents in the area where trees are to be planted, and providing technical information on tree planting and aftercare, and displays in local public buildings.

b Consult local residents. Approaches to this include public meetings, discussions among community groups, and the establishment of 'tree committees' with representatives from local volunteer organisations and larger community groups.

c Encourage practical participation. Good methods include tree appeals, tree sponsoring schemes and community tree planting days which also encourage residents to take up aftercare tasks. The election of tree wardens and the establishment of tree nurseries (Chapter 5) in the locality are also likely to encourage ongoing interest and participation.

d Encourage long-term projects. This will require attention to resources, a regular commitment to providing tree-related events, continuing interest in the site itself, and the development of relevant skills within the community. Planting on derelict ground, for instance, must be a project which involves residents at an early stage, if they are to become involved in the work of the site. Residents will need to feel that such a resource, which will not mature for some years, will be in their best interests.

Management planning

Management planning is important for urban sites, for the following reasons (Hibberd, 1989, p17):

a Tree growing is a long-term project in itself, and trees may be under many ownerships during their lifespan. Management planning can provide continuity of care. In the artificial conditions of many urban sites, such planning will be especially important for trees during difficult weather conditions such as drought, or in areas where development or vandalism are likely.

b Planning can make allowance for the growth of trees on a particular site. Trees are still often treated as static 'objects' in a landscape or architectural design. They are, for example, often planted as standards to match an architect's drawing. These trees are not only more costly to buy and maintain; they will also usually end up conforming to the original plan for the space of perhaps only 10-15 years, after which they may become too large. Planning so that the trees are part of the design, from the whip stage to maturity and through seasonal changes, is a cheaper and more flexible solution. The eventual replacement of trees should also be a provision of the plan. For further information on the development of a planting programme within an overall landscape design policy, see Fairbrother (1974) and Clouston (1977).

A management plan as described above need only consist of a statement of objectives, an original design, a plan showing operations, and a copy of any proposals for action in the future. The aftercare and maintenance required should be included, along with an ongoing record of any relevant actions taken. Existing trees on the site should also be accounted for. For example, fast-growing trees may need to be thinned at some point so as not to shade out the newly planted trees (Hibberd, 1989, p65).

FORMAL AND INFORMAL PLANTINGS

Before planting, you will need to decide whether your design will be formal or informal, classifications which to some extent are dictated by the surroundings.

Formal plantings are appropriate in small squares, courtyards and around city centre buildings. The site should, however, be important enough in itself to warrant such a design. Formal plantings should consist of an arrangement of species designed to produce a balanced blend of foliage and flowers. Groups of trees are generally more effective visually than single specimens, and they also form their own micro-climate, which tends to improve growth (McCullen and Webb, 1982, p74).

Avoid planting too many species, as this can produce an unattractive 'ragbag' effect. As indicated in the section on management planning, (p39), it is important to consider the size of plants at maturity and, if they are deciduous, the effects of seasonal changes in their appearance. Strict geometric designs such as straight lines and square blocks should be avoided unless the planting is along a broad avenue or street. Instead, aim for layouts which suit the landscape. Around tall buildings, for example, plant trees which will be tall at maturity closest to the building. Trees and shrubs of successively lower heights can be planted in front of these to give a formal effect that also has some of the visual and wildlife value of a woodland edge.

When planting around buildings it is very important to be aware of any persistent patterns of wind which may harm young trees. Very high buildings can sometimes cause the formation of eddies and turbulence, and narrow corridors between tall buildings can create a 'wind-tunnel' effect.

Whenever possible, plant whips rather than standards. Larger specimens are popular as they are instantly effective, but they are also more costly and less likely to thrive. Mixing fast- and slow-growing trees can, over time, serve to break up the monotony of a single-height planting (McCullen and Webb, 1982, p74).

Sites suitable for informal plantings can include public open spaces, school grounds, derelict land, railway cuts or canal sides, private gardens, and large areas around buildings such as hospitals. On these sites, whips and shrubs can be planted at fairly close spacing, provided that later thinning takes place so that the plants can grow to maturity. Denser plantings such as barriers, clumps and thickets produce a more natural woodland effect and are less prone to vandalism than irregular or scattered planting.

Where space allows, plan woodland blocks or corner plantings with graded 'edges' for structural diversity. As with formal plantings, use pioneer species or nurse trees to give diversity early on and to provide suitable conditions for the 'climax' species.

SUITABLE SPECIES

Whenever possible, use native species; but recognise that some exotics also have great amenity and wildlife value, and may be better suited to areas with poor soil or limited space. Fastigiate (columnar) forms of trees such as oak, lime or beech, or slow-growing varieties, can be used where native species might grow too large or require lopping. Consider problems of public safety and the effect of trees on soils and building foundations (see below).

Native species which tolerate poor soils and air pollution are listed in the table on pp22-23. Street trees must be especially resistant to a number of pollutants and hazards. Note that the de-icing salts used on roads in winter can harm certain species (e.g. London plane, beech, maples, chestnuts and limes), so choose tolerant species such as hawthorn or grey willow. Street trees must also be able to withstand a certain amount of bark damage from vehicles and pedestrians, so avoid planting those with very thin or tender bark whenever possible. On exposed or very windy sites, choose wind-firm species and, where necessary, use some form of artificial shelter.

For further information on native and exotic species suitable for urban plantings, see Bean (1970), Hibberd (1989), Hillier (1977), or McCullen and Webb (1982). Table 1 in Appendix B contains useful information on native varieties and their tolerance for certain urban conditions (e.g. pollution). Table 3 in the same appendix outlines a method for choosing native species and related varieties and cultivars for various urban sites.

TREES IN CONFINED SPACES

With trees in confined spaces, such as areas around buildings, next to roads and in gardens, the effect of plantings and the eventual size of the trees must be carefully considered in advance. The following is based on Clouston and Stansfield (1981, pp17-25).

Trees and buildings

Problems associated with trees around buildings can be divided into above- and below-ground considerations. The above-ground problems are, of course, more easily observable and also usually form the basis of complaints from homeowners. They include the following:

a Blocking of gutters with leaves or needles. Species with large leaves, such as sycamore and large-leaved lime, can cause blockage if they overhang gutters.

b Obstruction of light. Trees planted near enough to buildings so that their branches grow in front of or above a window can prevent sunlight from falling on that window.

c Physical impact of branches on a building.

d Interference with overhead services. Overhead cables, and television reception, can sometimes be obstructed by trees.

Underground problems from trees can include the following:

a Drain blockage. Usually, tree roots will only begin to penetrate a drain if it is already cracked; the tree roots then tend to grow toward the resulting supply of water. A single root entering the crack can branch enough times to create a blockage; the crack may even become enlarged when the root grows radially, allowing more roots to enter and increasing the amount of leakage. Trees planted on shrinkable clay soils near drains may dry the soil and cause it to move slightly, cracking the drain. On the whole, however, such problems have been found to be rare, but careful site surveys (see below) are still necessary to guarantee that any damage to drains will not occur.

b Damage by physical root growth. Generally, the major roots of a tree grow in a radial fashion from the stem base, within the top 300-500 mm (12-20") of the soil. Although roots can laterally extend as much as 1.5 times the tree's height, most problems arising from the growth of roots will be located around the trunk of the tree (Hibberd, 1989, p108). If, for example, a vigorously rooting species is planted in too small a space, it may crack or lift paving slabs, low walls or driveways. House walls can be damaged only if the tree is planted very close to the building. In any case, sufficient space for root expansion is vital for urban trees, as not only the above mentioned damage but also wind-throw can occur if tree roots are cramped and consequently unable to provide a stable base for the tree.

c Damage from shrinkage of clay soils. Trees planted on shrinkable clay soils can dry the soil by removing water through their root systems. If any buildings are located nearby, subsidence of their foundations can occur. Such subsidence depends on a number of factors, among them the tree's rooting pattern, climate, the distance between tree and building, and the exact nature of the clay soil (not all clay soils shrink);

but the general pattern of clay soil shrinkage due to a tree's moisture needs is as follows.

A localised moisture deficit can develop, in heavy clay, around a tree's roots. If the roots are using water from soil underlying the foundations of a building, the soil can become very dry. On permeable soils the deficit is usually made up during winter, when a tree's loss of leaves means it does not transpire as much and thus use as much moisture. In clay soils, however, the deficit may increase year by year. The soil may then crack and undergo dimensional shifts. If sections of the building's foundations, such as those under a bay window, then move, subsidence can occur.

Planning for confined spaces

Solutions to the above problems are best dealt with at the planning stage. The following points are based mainly on Edlin (1975, pp32-46).

a Map out trees near buildings or roads before planting, using a simple plan at a scale of 1:50 for small gardens and 1:100 for larger areas. Where trees are to be sited near buildings or overhead obstructions such as telephone wires, make an elevated sketch at 1:50 showing the outline of the trees at the time of planting and when mature. This provides a check against planting too close. As a rule of thumb, most open-grown conifers achieve a total crown spread of about 33% of their height at maturity. Broadleaved trees are more variable, but a spread of 40% of height is realistic.

b On your maps, indicate constraints on planting such as crowns and stems of neighbouring trees which are to be retained, buildings, fences, hedges and walls, posts and poles which carry wires, signs or lights, drains and sewers, water and gas mains, electric and telephone cables and building foundations. On shrinkable clay soils, the depth of the building foundations is an especially important point. Further constraints include sight lines at road junctions, supply of light to windows, patterns of light cast by street lamps, clear margins at roadsides and the attitudes of adjacent landowners who may be affected.

c Site trees no closer than 5m (16'6") to drains and sewage pipes. Keep the larger species of willows further away, as they are very prone to send roots into drains for water (see above).

d Never plant poplars within 18m (60') of any building. Their roots are very aggressive and can damage foundations. They also cause shrinkage of clay soils, especially in areas subject to summer drought, such as London and East Anglia. Alder and oak can also deprive shrinkable clay soils of moisture. Species which are suitable on such soils include holly, birch, mulberry and pines, which can survive with little water.

e Legally, no tree may be planted within 4.57m (15') of the centre of any made-up carriageway. For safety's sake, it is usually best to plant roadside trees at least 9m (30') apart in any direction. Keep trees at least 6m (20') from road junctions to leave sight lines clear.

TREES ON DERELICT LAND

Derelict land presents special problems for planting schemes because the soil is often contaminated with toxins, full of rubble or badly compacted. Surveying the site before deciding what sorts of planting and aftercare are feasible is necessary to determine not only such problems, but also whether a planting scheme is actually needed. Industrial wasteland and derelict urban sites often support very interesting plant communities which may be destroyed by too-hasty 'improvement' plantings. Given time, they may develop into secondary woodland without any help or expense. Sometimes, all that you need to do is to tidy up around the edges to show that the site is cared for. Provide paths, benches or fencing according to the nature of the site and the type of access which is planned for it.

Soils

Sites vary greatly in their soils and suitability for various species. Spoil tips and slag heaps may contain heavy metals such as copper or zinc, which limit reclamation to top-soiling and grassing over. They may be unstable and require landscaping with heavy machinery before planting can be considered. Other soils may contain materials so toxic to plant life they are unreclaimable. Such materials can include cadmium, lead, nickel, mercury and cyanide (Hibberd, 1989, p44).

Normal drainage channels may be blocked, soil is likely to have poor structure, if any, and surfaces are often compacted and eroded while lower levels may be porous and tend to dry out. At the opposite extreme, quarry working such as chalk, sand and gravel pits can have a dry porous soil which is liable to seasonal flooding or getting waterlogged. Clay soils or those which have been worked in wet weather are liable to be compacted, and need drainage before planting can take place. Coarse-structured soils can be treated by the addition of organic material and very acid soils can be limed. Gemmell (1977) and Hibberd (1989) give details. Some points on reducing compaction are discussed on p81.

City sites often consist of rubble, which may vary from a fine dust of ground-up bricks to boulders and lumps of concrete. Once dug over and 'rototilled' to reduce compaction, these sites can often support a surprising range of plants since they are often rich in calcium, and sometimes phosphate, from the mortar in the brick. Where trees and shrubs are planted, it is usually necessary to add topsoil to the planting pit, to supply the phosphorus and nitrogen necessary for tree growth. Broadcast topsoil is expensive and may be unnecessary.

Refuse tips often contain much decaying organic material and make good sites for plants, but it may be necessary to first remove or bury the larger lumps or non-degradable debris. Tips are sometimes set alight or catch fire spontaneously and obviously must be put out before planting begins, since otherwise they may continue to burn below the soil surface.

Suitable species

Species which are useful on a variety of derelict sites include grey alder (a non-native), birch and Scots pine on light soils, larch and oak on intermediate soils, and poplars, willows and the native common alder on wet soils. Beech, and the non-native species of sycamore, Austrian pine and western red cedar are suitable for calcareous soils.

Railway cuts and canal sides

Abandoned railway cuts and canal sides have often evolved into scrub or secondary woodland through decades of benign neglect. These narrow strips of land are usually extremely valuable as wildlife 'corridors' (see p12), particularly if linked to other wooded areas, e.g. in parks or churchyards. In addition, those stretches of canal or track which run through heavily built-up areas provide a much-needed resource, supplying recreation, visual relief and micro-climatic control.

Treatment of such areas will depend on their condition. It may be considered better to leave them regenerating naturally, protecting some saplings with tree shelters and engaging in supplementary planting if necessary. Sections of bare ground which are near residential areas or are used for recreational purposes can be improved with either informal or landscaped plantings, to form 'strip parks'. Suitable species will include those listed above, under 'Soils', as well as appropriate selections from Table 1 in Appendix B.

Trees and the Law

This chapter covers legal considerations which are likely to affect tree planting and aftercare intended primarily for conservation and amenity purposes, both in urban and rural areas. Although felling is described only briefly in this handbook (chapter 7), the legislation surrounding it is included because the control of felling licences serves as one of the main existing methods of tree protection. The information in this chapter is mainly from the Department of the Environment Circular 36/78 (Welsh Office Circular 64/78), 'Trees and Forestry' (available from the Forestry Commission), 'Trees in Towns' (Clouston and Stansfield, 1981, chapter 5), and Griffin and Watkins (1988), all of which should be consulted for details. The discussion of trees as legal nuisance is by no means exhaustive, so it may be best to receive professional advice in individual cases.

Protection of Trees

TREE PRESERVATION ORDERS

Tree Preservation Orders (TPOs) are the principal means of planning control over the felling or maltreatment of amenity trees. Further information on TPOs in England and Wales is given in the leaflet 'Protected Trees - A Guide to Tree Preservation Procedures', available from the Department of the Environment and the Welsh Office. In Northern Ireland, the protection of individual trees lies with the Department of Environment Planning Service, and TPOs as such do not exist.

TPOs can be made by a local planning authority (county or district council, or London borough) to protect individual trees of exceptional amenity value, groups of trees and woodlands in the interests of good forestry or because of special amenity value, or all trees within a specified area, whether urban or rural. TPOs do not, however, normally include blanket protection over large areas. TPOs are designed to protect amenity trees which might be at risk, but not to hinder careful silvicultural management, so they are not usually made over areas where for many years a high standard of woodland husbandry has been maintained and where no change of practice or ownership is likely.

Tree Preservation Orders may:

a Prohibit the damage or destruction, felling, lopping, topping or uprooting of trees except with the consent of the local planning authority.

b Ensure the replanting according to specified conditions of any part of a woodland area which is felled as part of permitted forestry operations.

c Require the replacement as soon as reasonably possible of any tree (other than one which is part of a woodland) which is removed or destroyed in contravention of the order, or which dies. The replacement tree is protected by the original order.

A landowner whose trees are made subject to a TPO must be informed by the Council making the order, and the trees identified on a map. A seller of land is bound to inform a buyer about any TPOs that apply to the property. Anyone can check whether TPOs are in force on any trees by contacting the relevant District Council.

Street trees are not usually protected by TPOs. Those living in areas where street trees are regularly vandalised can contact the Council tree officer to discuss the possibility of issuing TPOs for them.

PROTECTION BY GENERAL LAW

Trees, under the definition of private property, are protected by the law of tort. Anyone trespassing on an owner's land who injures a tree may have to pay damages to the owner as compensation. Factories which harm trees through the emission of toxic fumes may be prevented from further emission by a court injunction, and may also be liable for damages. Trees in a tended area (ie not growing wild) are protected from vandalism by the Criminal Damage Act 1971. Trees growing wild are also protected by this Act, except in respect to their foliage and fruit.

CONSERVATION AREAS

In Conservation Areas, of which there are 5,000 in Britain, trees are given additional protection. With certain exceptions, anyone proposing to cut down, top, lop or uproot a tree in one of these areas must give six weeks' notice of their intention to the district council concerned. If the work is not completed within two years of giving notice, a further notice is needed. A felling licence is required for the felling of trees in a Conservation Area, unless any of the exceptions listed under 'Felling', below, apply. The trees may also be subject to a TPO, in which case the details given above apply.

FELLING LICENCES

The regulations are set out in the booklet 'Control of Tree Felling' (Forestry Commission, revised 1987), from which this information is taken. These regulations do not apply to Northern Ireland or the inner London boroughs.

A licence from the Forestry Commission is normally required to fell growing trees (though not for lopping and topping), but in any calendar quarter up to 5 cubic metres may be felled by an occupier or his/her agent, provided not more than 2 cubic metres are sold.

Licences are not, however, required to fell trees if any of the following conditions apply:

a The felling is in accordance with an approved plan of operations under one of the Forestry Commission's grant schemes.

b The trees are in a garden, orchard, churchyard or public open space.

c The trees are all below 8cm (3") in diameter, measured 1.3m (4'3") from the ground; or in the case of thinnings, below 10cm (4") in diameter; or in the case of coppice or underwood, below 15cm (6") in diameter.

d The trees are interfering with permitted development or statutory works by public bodies.

e The trees are dead, dangerous, causing a nuisance or are badly affected by Dutch elm disease.

f The felling is in compliance with an Act of Parliament.

Application

The application for a felling licence should be made by the landowner, tenant, or an agent acting on behalf of owner or tenant. Applications should be submitted along with a map of the area at least three months before felling is due to commence, to the relevant regional office of the Forestry Commission (addresses on page 145), on forms obtainable from them. Felling must not commence until a licence has been issued.

Usually the Forestry Commission will arrange for the trees to be inspected. Consultations may be made with the local authority and any other statutory authority concerned, in order to ensure that relevant environmental or land-use aspects of the proposal are taken into account.

Where forestry or amenity considerations are important, a licence may only be issued on condition that replanting is carried out. A licence for the felling of broadleaves will normally be conditional on their being replaced with broadleaves. Any such conditions will be discussed with the applicant before the licence is issued. Planting grants will normally be available where a replanting condition has been imposed. Information on grants is given on page 137.

Provision is made for appeal against refusal of a licence, and for appeal against replanting conditions.

The licence is valid for a set period of years, and if it expires before felling is completed, a replacement licence must be applied for and issued before felling can continue. Any felling without a licence (except in cases a through f, above) is an offence and carries a liability to a fine not exceeding £1000 or twice the value of the trees, whichever is higher.

In certain circumstances, whether or not a felling licence is needed, permission is required for any proposed felling. This may include SSSIs (see below), Conservation Areas, or where a Tree Preservation Order applies.

If an owner wishes to fell trees covered by a TPO, he or she should first determine whether the proposed felling comes within one of the exceptions from felling licences listed above, or requires a licence. If the former, the owner makes an application for consent to fell to the planning authority. If the latter, the owner applies to the Forestry Commission, who then forward it, with their comments, to the planning authority. It will then be dealt with as an application for consent to fell under the TPO.

The exception to this procedure is for applications requiring a licence where the intention is to clear fell a woodland under a TPO without replanting. In such a case the Forestry Commission will decide the application. This new procedure is the result of a case in Canterbury which caused concern about the effectiveness of TPOs on woodlands and led, in 1988, to modified regulations surrounding them. In effect, these regulations permitted the protection of trees in a woodland because of their amenity value (not previously stated in law) and reduced the possibility of large compensation claims against local authorities if they refused consent to fell trees within a woodland protected by a TPO (Charles Watkins, pers. comm.).

The Wildlife and Countryside Act

SITES OF SPECIAL SCIENTIFIC INTEREST

Under the Wildlife and Countryside Act 1981, English Nature (formerly the Nature Conservancy Council may designate Sites of Special Scientific Interest (SSSIs) for their geological or ecological value. (In Northern Ireland, such sites are known as Areas of Special Scientific Interest (ASSIs), with designation controlled by the Department of Environment Countryside and Wildlife Branch.) The intention is that the occupier of the land should not operate in any way which would destroy or damage the special features noted in the designation.

English Nature has to notify the landowner of the boundary of an SSSI, and of any operations or management practices which would affect the site. The landowner must notify English Nature of intention to carry out any of the operations given in the SSSI notification, in time for discussions to take place.

As far as tree planting and aftercare are concerned, this not only affects woodland SSSIs, but proposed planting on non-wooded SSSIs. Examples might include downland or wetland, whose value would be reduced if planted with trees. These habitats are not just affected by the shading and other changes brought about by tree cover, but also by operations such as drainage, fertilising or herbicide application which may be part of the tree planting programme.

Information on felling operations on an SSSI can be found in the leaflet 'Control of Tree Felling' (Forestry Commission, 1987).

SPECIES PROTECTION

The Wildlife and Countryside Act 1981 also controls the disturbance, killing and removal of various plants and animals. Protected plants are listed in Schedule 8, and include trees in the wild which have not been planted, but which are naturally occurring. Any up rooting of such trees during tree planting or aftercare operations must therefore be avoided. Copies of the Act and Schedules are available at public libraries.

Trees as Obstruction or Nuisance

RIGHTS OF WAY AND PUBLIC SERVICES

Some local and national authorities are empowered to fell trees for purposes of safety or access. Local authorities can cut back or fell trees and bushes which obscure public rights of way, including footpaths, or which obstruct light from street lamps or the sight-lines of car drivers. Railway authorities, land drainage authorities, electricity authorities and British Telecom can require removal of trees or parts of trees which may obstruct railways, river banks (where machines are used for dredging), power lines or telegraph lines. Railway and electricity authorities must pay the costs involved and compensate the owner. Electricity authorities pay a continuing annual compensation for loss of the use of ground. British Telecom does its own lopping, and pays no rent for land occupied by its poles or for wayleaves. Similar powers are available to public bodies that operate water mains, gas mains, oil pipelines and airports, to prevent risk of accident or damage to the installation or to provide access to service routes.

TREES AND BOUNDARIES

The intrusion of the roots or branches of a tree into adjacent properties can become a special form of legal nuisance. The relevant points are as follows:

a If the roots or branches of a tree on one property penetrate or overhang a neighbour's land, this neighbour (who may be owner or tenant) is entitled to cut them off, as long as this is done on their side of the boundary. The boundary is presumed to run vertically up and down from the line at ground level. The neighbour cannot claim expenses from the tree-owner.

b Any cuttings remain the tree-owner's property, and cannot be utilised by the neighbour in any way. The neighbour can, however, place all cuttings on the owner's land. If the owner throws them back, the neighbour can claim for any financial loss incurred.

c If the neighbour must enter the owner's land to cut off overhanging branches, the neighbour must first serve notice of an intent to do so. The owner can then do the work personally if desired. Otherwise, the neighbour cannot be prevented from entering the land unless an injunction is obtained. A claim can however be made for any damages resulting from the neighbour's entry on the land.

d The neighbour must exercise every care to do no injury to overhanging trees when lopping off overhanging branches or penetrating roots.

UNSAFE TREES

Unsafe trees under which the public has access, such as those overhanging highways, may constitute a public nuisance. If the tree appeared sound but then fell or lost branches, the owner would not be liable for damages because he or she could not reasonably have foreseen or prevented the failure of the tree. If the tree had obvious signs of disease or weakness and then failed, however, the owner might be sued for any damage caused. It is therefore very important to inspect such trees regularly to check on their condition. Forestry Commission Arboricultural Leaflet 1, 'The External Signs of Decay in Trees' (revised 1984), and the DoE/Forestry Commission leaflet 'The Recognition of Hazardous Trees' (1990), provide further information on this subject.

WATER RIGHTS AND ANGLING

There are particular responsibilities on the owner of woodland regarding neighbours' water rights. The cultivation of land for tree planting, or the use of herbicides or fertilisers must not damage water rights, fisheries or angling on neighbouring property.

Pests and Diseases

The Plant Health Act, 1967, provides measures to prevent the introduction or spread of plant pests and diseases. Orders may be made by the Forestry Commission on forest trees and timber, and by the Ministry of Agriculture, Fisheries and Food. In addition to orders prohibiting the landing or transport of certain articles or requiring the destruction of plants or seeds liable to aid the spread of diseases or pests, numerous orders have been made which require the felling and burning of affected trees. For example, the Watermark Disease (Local Authorities) Order 1974 gives powers to certain local authorities to order the destruction of diseased willows, with the aim of protecting commercial plantations of cricket bat willow. The order was amended in 1986, and now covers the counties of Bedfordshire, Essex, Hertfordshire, Norfolk and Suffolk.

Under the Forestry Act, 1967, the Forestry Commission may authorise the destruction of rabbits, hares, squirrels and other vermin which are damaging or likely to damage trees. If the landowner does not take sufficient steps to prevent such damage, the Commission may authorise any competent person to enter the land for this purpose and charge the occupier for the work.

Safety, Equipment and Organisation

The following information on safety and equipment is basic to most aspects of tree planting, tree nursery and aftercare operations. As the felling of heavy trees does not come within the scope of this book, only tools appropriate for coppicing and thinning smaller trees will be discussed in the section on felling equipment. For further information on these subjects, consult the Forest Industry Safety Guides published by the Forestry Safety Council.

Safety Precautions

GENERAL

See also pages 108 and 121 for additional precautions when using herbicides, and when undertaking light felling or coppicing.

a Have a suitable first aid kit at the work site (see below).

b All volunteers should have been immunized against tetanus.

c If it is raining heavily, postpone the work. Once gloves, tools and the ground become sodden and slippery, the danger of accidentally injuring yourself or others greatly increases.

d Wear suitable tough clothing (see below). Thorns and brambles are a hazard, especially when weeding and clearing scrub. Most vulnerable are hands and wrists, followed by knees and face. If you occasionally wear glasses, it is best to wear them when working as a precaution against jabs in the eye.

Attend to splinters promptly. Don't ignore even the smallest, as they can cause serious infection. Go to a doctor immediately if you have any serious pain or swelling.

e Never try to lift more than you are capable of. If you can't get help, move logs by rolling or skidding them along the ground. When lifting heavy weights, bend your knees, not your back, and lift using your leg muscles.

f Never walk backwards when you are carrying anything - you may trip. Take particular care when working on a slope.

g Always clear up as you work, and don't leave cut material or debris littering the area.

h If you bring bags with cameras, food and other items in them, put them safely out of the work area. They may either get crushed, or cause someone to trip.

TOOL USE

Further details are given, where appropriate, in later chapters. The following points are basic.

a Never use an unfamiliar tool until you have been shown the proper technique. The information below on care and use of axes is general, but only the use of light axes is discussed in this book.

Chainsaws are not discussed in this handbook, but be aware that only trained operators are allowed to handle them. Training is available through the BTCV, the Agricultural Training Board and agricultural colleges. For general information on chainsaws, see the 'BTCV Chainsaw Policy' (1986). The best publication on chainsaws is 'The Chainsaw - Use and Maintenance', by the National Board of Forestry, Sweden (available through Husqvarna UK Ltd).

b Take care with billhooks, slashers, axes and saws. All edged tools are safest when sharp. Before you begin using one, check that the tool head is secure and that the handle is free from splinters and cracks. Keep a safe distance from other workers (at least two arm lengths plus the length of the tools) when using edged tools.

c Axes, billhooks and other cutting tools are brittle when very cold. Warm them before starting work in hard frosty weather. Sharpening will protect the edge. Avoid cutting icy wood, as it will damage the edge.

d Always make sure that there is a clear path to swing the tool. Even a small twig may deflect it and cause injury. Never cut towards yourself with an edged tool, as it is likely to slip or bounce off the wood. When using a short-handled tool, keep your free hand well away from cutting direction. Be alert for hazards such as wasps' nests, adders, stones and so on.

e Carry edged tools at their point of balance, just below the heads. Carry them at your side with the edges pointing down and slightly away from you. If you trip, swing the tool away from you and let go. Bow saws should be carried with the blade protected by a plastic sleeve, or one made from sacking. Never carry more tools than is safe, which usually means one in each hand.

f Do not leave tools lying about on the ground, as you are likely either to lose them, or discover them the painful way - by treading on them. Never leave edged tools with their cutting edges upward. Prop tools against a nearby tree or stump, or keep them together in a hessian sack. Store your tools centrally so you and any other users know where to find them.

WORKING ALOFT

Only trained and properly equipped people should work aloft, and then only when absolutely necessary. The following points are basic:

a Never work aloft in a high wind, or when branches are wet or covered by frost or snow.

b When climbing in a tree, move slowly and with care. Don't jump on branches to see if they are sound. The branches of some species, such as horse chestnut, Douglas fir, larch and poplar tend to be weak or brittle. Test hand holds before using them.

c Volunteers without special training should only work from ladders. Be aware, however, that working from ladders is hazardous. Limit the work to placing ropes in trees or light pruning of shorter specimens, such as fruit trees.

Before using any ladder, check that it is in a sound condition. Place the top of the ladder squarely against the trunk or main branches of the tree, with the base resting firmly on solid ground. Test the ladder's stability before climbing it. Often it is safest to rope the top of the ladder to the tree. Have a helper stand on the lowest rung of the ladder to steady it.

Clothing

With work clothes, the aim is always safety and comfort first. Special protective clothing is required when using herbicides, a subject fully covered during training on herbicide use (see page 108). For general work, you will need:

a Overalls or close-fitting work clothes. The wearing of loose clothing is dangerous when working with edged tools and among branches and brambles. Don't wear a floppy coat or scarf. Be especially careful when working aloft, as even a belt can snag and cause injury.

b Boots. Heavy leather work boots with spiked or deep moulded soles and protective steel toe-caps are best. In wet and muddy conditions, wellingtons with steel toe-caps are suitable. Plimsolls, light shoes and standard wellington boots do not give adequate protection.

c Gloves. Essential when dealing with thorns and brambles. The handles of edged tools are harder to grip with a gloved hand, so during clearance work, when using a one-handed billhook (never a slasher or axe), wear a glove only on the hand you use for grasping woody growth. Gloves with gauntlets are preferable as they protect the wrists.

d Helmet. A safety helmet complying with BS 5240 will be necessary when working aloft or near machinery, although it is optional when undertaking light felling. If pruning work on taller trees is going on, those working on the ground should wear helmets.

Tools and Accessories

Items are listed by category according to their most important type of use. Many items are used for more than one purpose, but are listed only once.

FOR ALL PROJECTS

First aid kit. Keep this with you at all times. BTCV can supply standard first aid kits which comply with the 1981 Health and Safety Regulations (First Aid). For six to ten people, the contents are:

 1 guidance card

20 individual sterile adhesive dressings

2 sterile eye pads with attachments

2 triangular bandages

2 sterile coverings for serious wounds

6 safety pins

6 medium size sterile unmedicated dressings

2 large size sterile unmedicated dressings

2 extra large size sterile unmedicated dressings.

From experience on projects, the following 'welfare kit' is also found to be useful: 100mm crepe bandage, tweezers (round-nosed), scissors (round-nosed), insect repellent, antihistamine cream for insect bits, sunscreen cream, aspirin, eye lotion, eye bath and mild antiseptic cream. Some volunteers have found that tap water, antiseptic wipes and antiseptic solution are a more effective alternative to antiseptic cream.

A list of local hospitals with casualty departments should also be to hand.

PLANTING AND EARLY CARE

For general use

a Heavy-duty treaded garden (digging) spade

b Heavy-duty garden (digging) fork

c Grubbing mattock

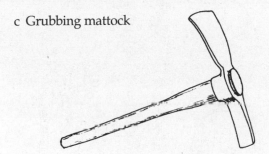

d Lump or sledge hammer (for treeshelter stakes)

Nursery work: additional tools and equipment

a Hessian bags, for seed collecting

b Garden roller, for preparing seedbeds

c Garden rake

d Sharp knife or secateurs, for light pruning

e Wheelbarrow. This should be heavy-duty steel, with a capacity of about .08 cubic metre (3 cubic feet), since larger barrows are hard to handle when full. The barrow should also have long handles and a single wheel, for ease of use. Pneumatic tyres are best for use on soft ground.

f Hoe

Fencing tools

See 'Fencing' (Agate, 1986) for details.

a Mell, maul or 'Drivall' for driving posts (and tree stakes)

b Crowbar, for making pilot holes for fence posts

c Wrecking bar (swan neck)

d Claw hammer

e Fencing pliers

f Wire strainers

g Heavy-duty wire cutter (bolt cropper)

h Tinsnips, for cutting netting

i Shuv-holer for removing soil from straining post holes

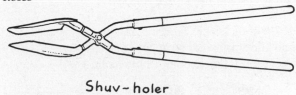

Shuv-holer

Specialist planting equipment

a Schlich or Mansfield planting spade. Both types have a ridge or bulge across the face of the spade which makes a hole for planting when thrust into the ground. Also pictured is the Treeplanter spade, which has a slightly dished, treaded blade.

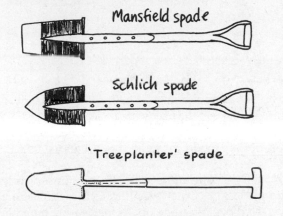

Mansfield spade

Schlich spade

'Treeplanter' spade

Some may prefer a small garden spade, such as a 'lady's' spade, for all-day notch planting work.

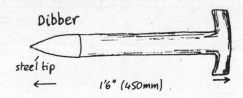

Dibber

steel tip

1'6" (450mm)

b Dibber (dibbler, planting arrow)

c Surveying poles or marker canes, for use in line planting

d Bags with shoulder straps, or buckets, lined with earth or dampened sawdust, for carrying small transplants so that they don't dry out. Bags are lighter and more convenient, and can be made up out of hessian, denim or canvas. Divide each bag into two sections, one for plants and one for fertilizers, if you will be applying fertilizer as you plant. If nothing else is available, you can use the bottom half of a fertilizer sack as a bag, but it must be well washed out to prevent root scorch. A strap of baler twine should be tied to the two corners.

Clearing tools

a Weeding hook or Dutch weeding scythe, for herbaceous and light woody material.

Reap hook (sickle, bagging, fagging or paring hook) and the somewhat stronger bean hook and its variants (e.g. 'Gamekeeper Jungle Knife').

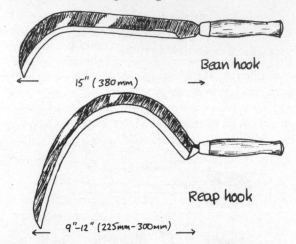

Bean hook

15" (380 mm)

Reap hook

9"-12" (225mm-300mm)

Reap hook handles may be in line with the blade, or cranked to keep the user's hand clear of the ground. If you use a hook with a cranked handle, choose the appropriate model for right- or left-handed use.

Ordinary scythes are useful for cutting grass on rides and glades. The Dutch weeding scythe is sometimes preferred over weeding hooks for clearing brambles because it can be used in a more upright position.

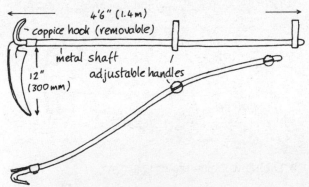

4'6" (1.4m)

coppice hook (removable)

metal shaft
12"
(300mm)
adjustable handles

b Brushing hook or slasher.

The heavy pattern slashers and hooks generally have rather less curve than their equivalent light versions, and are more suitable for tougher, older weed growth. Some are fitted with rings and bolts where the blades sit the handles, to give extra strength. None of them are sturdy enough for use on material over about 25mm (1") diameter.

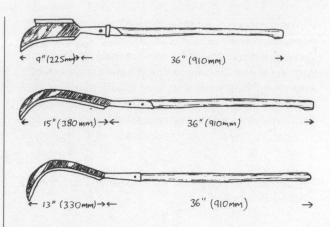

9"(225mm)
36" (910mm)

15"(380 mm)
36" (910mm)

13" (330mm)
36" (910mm)

c Crooked stick, for use with weeding hook.

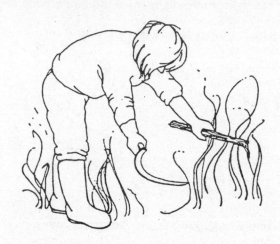

d Power tools (if used): strimmers/brush cutters, Flymo, Aller-scythe.

PRUNING AND WOUND TREATMENT

a Pruning saws. The most useful all-purpose pruning tool is the bow saw (discussed under felling tools, p51). Its main drawback is that it is hard to use on a close-branched tree.

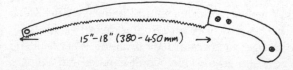

15"-18" (380 - 450mm)

For versatility and accuracy when working aloft, the best additional tool is a one-handed pruning saw, which cuts on the pull stroke. Pruning saws often come with replaceable blades. For a slightly longer reach, the handle can be replaced with a 600mm (2') fawn's-foot handle cut down from an old axe haft. For high pruning, standing at or near ground level, use a two-handed pruning saw. This has a similar blade to the one-handed saw, but comes with a light alloy handle in detachable or telescoping sections, 1-3.6m (3'-12') in length.

b Toggle lopper or long-handled tree pruner. Loppers and pruners, if sharp and in good condition, give very clean cuts and are ideal for use by unskilled workers. They are, however, rather slow if you need to prune many trees over a wide area, and light-weight models can easily be strained or twisted out of alignment if used on material beyond their capacity.

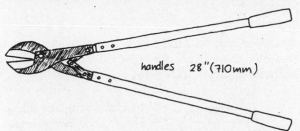

handles   28"(710mm)

The toggle lopper, which is useful for brashing and woodland path clearance, as well as for general pruning, can cut up to 32mm (1.25") branches with ease. The toggle action gives much greater power than ordinary shears.

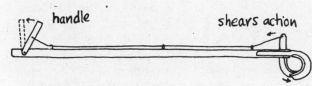

handle   shears action

The long-handled or long-arm tree pruner is useful for cutting higher branches.

c Rope, for slinging and hauling up tools.

d Firmer chisel, 25mm (1") width or larger.

e Ladder, preferably non-rusting light metal alloy.

TOOLS FOR THE DISABLED

Double hoe

Auxiliary grip

For volunteers working from a wheelchair, there are a wide variety of auxiliary attachments and tools available for digging, cultivating, weeding, sowing, planting and pruning. The 'Auxiliary Grip XO', for instance, can be attached to an ordinary spade or fork to facilitate working from a sitting position, while many other tools have longer handles. The Wolf 'Double Hoe' can be used for both infilling and firming of soil while planting.

Although mainly intended for gardening work, many of the tools are also suitable for general nursery, tree planting and aftercare tasks.

Choosing the right tools for the job will mean that

consideration will have to be given to the distance of the soil level from the chair. Appropriate on-site access will also need to be available. Information on these and related considerations is available from Horticultural Therapy (address on p145).

Further information on tools for the disabled is available in the publication 'Equipment for the Disabled', available from Mary Marlborough Lodge, Nuffield Orthopaedic Centre, Headington, Oxford OX3 7LD (tel. 0865 750103). For some manufacturers of these tools, see p147.

FELLING AND EXTRACTION

With the amalgamation of the edged tool industry and changing forestry practices, many traditional felling tools are no longer being manufactured. Some of these, such as certain types of billhooks, are still important in coppice management. Volunteer groups can help keep these tools available by pooling bulk orders to larger manufacturers, and by seeking out blacksmiths willing to experiment with traditional designs. It is also worth keeping a lookout for second-hand tools in patterns which are now out of production.

Note that as felling of larger trees is beyond the scope of this handbook, heavy axes are not discussed here. Both subjects are covered in 'Woodlands' (Brooks, 1988). A wheelbarrow (see above, under nursery tools) will be needed for carrying the tools.

For general use

a Billhook, for very light scrub clearance, coppicing and hedging. There are many patterns, varying in size, blade curvature and balance.

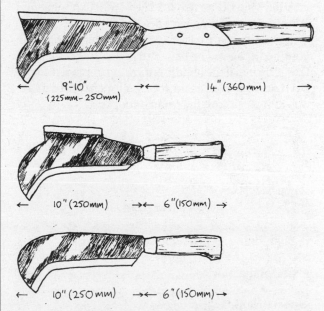

9"-10"
(225mm-250mm)   14" (360mm)

10" (250mm)   6"(150mm)

10" (250mm)   6"(150mm)

For general clearance and coppicing work, a fairly light single-edged tool with a moderate hook is probably best. Some volunteers have trouble managing the heavy Yorkshire billhook one-handed, or must grip the handle so high up that it becomes awkward to use. Never swing a double-edged billhook straight up towards your face!

b Bow saw, for felling and cross-cutting material between 50mm (2") and 300mm (1') in diameter.

The small triangular-shaped 21" saw is best for coppicing and pruning where close-growing stems or branches prevent the use of larger D-shaped saws. The latter are more suited to use on stems in the 100-600mm (4-24") range, the size of material which they can handle being limited by the width and depth of the bow. The 910mm (36") saw is best used as a two-person tool.

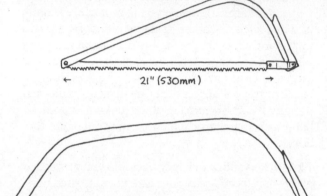

21" (530mm)

24", 30", 36" (610mm, 760mm, 910mm)

Blades are usually hard-point (non-resharpenable and non-resettable) although sharpenable blades are available. In practice, 'throwaway' blades are cheaper and more efficient.

c A light snedding axe for snedding, trimming and coppicing. Snedding axes are usually 1.6kg (3lb 8oz) or lighter, and are easier to use than heavier axes in confined spaces. The hafts are generally 660-760mm (26-30") long. If the handle is too long, replace it. Don't cut it down to size, as the tool is slippery and dangerous to use without the fawn's-foot end.

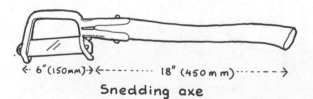

← 6" (150mm) → ← - - - - - - - 18" (450mm) - - - - - - →

Snedding axe

d Sharpening stones (whetstones) and file.

e Chopping block.

Specialist aids

a Sappie, for moving logs or large poles over short distances, and for stacking poles and battens. The sappie can be used as a lever to move the pole over

obstacles, or be driven into the pole to pull it along the ground.

On steep ground, where logs only need occasional nudging, this tool is safer to use than a rope because it can be pulled quickly away from the log.

light hand tongs

b Hand tongs or lifting hooks, for two-person carrying or poles and for handling and stacking logs which have been cut into short lengths. Small, light spring-loaded tongs have a 280mm (11") opening and weigh 0.7kg (1.25lb). Heavy tongs, not spring-loaded, give a 290mm (11.5") opening and weigh 1.7kg (3.75lb).

Take care when using tongs to jam the hooks well in and lift gently at first to make sure the tongs are secure. To release tongs from the log, push downward to open the jaws and twist sideways to clear.

c Pulphook or lumber hook, for lifting, loading and stacking short logs and billets.

To use the pulphook, drive it into the side of the log to pull logs off a stack. Drive it into the end of the log when carrying, to give a good grip.

Tool and Equipment Maintenance

Proper maintenance of tools and equipment is essential for safe and efficient working. People who own their own tools usually take care of them, and volunteer groups which keep a stock of communally used tools should encourage the same attitude of personal responsibility towards their use and upkeep. It is essential to have a tools officer or organiser to take charge of a tool store, ensure that tools go out on task in a good state and check them over afterwards. On task, the leader should be sure that volunteers know how to sharpen, clean and store tools as well as how to use them safely.

This section includes general points on storage, transport and care of tools, and techniques for sharpening edged tools in the field. Jobs for the workshop, such as filing and grinding of edged tools and replacement of hafts and handles are explained in detail in the 'Tools Workshop Manual' (BTCV, 1991).

STORAGE AND GENERAL CARE

a Keep all tools clean and dry. Carry a rag with you to wipe them off in wet weather - especially handles, which are slippery when wet. Keep edges free from mud, as they otherwise dull very quickly. Clean tools immediately after use. If mud is left to harden, the tools will be more difficult to clean, sharpen and oil.

b Oil all metal parts before storing to prevent rust. Although many volunteers swear by used sump oil, this may contain metal fragments that can hurt your hands; it is also thought to be a cause of skin cancer if used frequently. Clean oil is usually a better alternative.

Wipe unvarnished wooden handles with linseed oil when new and occasionally thereafter, as this helps keep them supple. You can also oil with lanolin (which protects metal, wood and your hands all at once!), or even with vegetable oil.

c If handles are scored, rough or splintery, sand them smooth. File out nicks in metal handles.

d Store tools under cover, preferably in racks or on wall brackets. Organise tools by type, with all tools of a type arranged the same way. Keep edged tools stored well out of the way, or provide individual guards for the blades.

e Store bow saws with the tension released.

f Transport tools under vehicle seats or in a trailer or roof boxes to prevent accidents. Don't overload vehicle roof racks, as this can affect vehicle stability. Wrap edged tools in sacking or provide individual guards, for safety and to prevent them damaging each other. Guards for axes and cross-cut saws can be made from old fire hose.

g Hang ladders securely out of the way. Make sure wooden ladders and extension ladders with rope fittings remain absolutely dry. Repair or replace any loose or weak rungs immediately.

SHARPENING EDGED TOOLS IN THE FIELD

Edged tools should go into the field sharp. It is hopeless to try to carry out major sharpening while on task - grinding is a workshop job. Filing usually comes under this category, too, although note point b, below.

a Sharpen tools at least twice a day when in use, or more often as necessary. Some tools, including sickles and scythes, need very frequent honing. A quick touch-up every ten minutes is not excessive. Others, such as axes and billhooks, can be used longer without sharpening but should be checked whenever you stop to rest.

b Although whetstones (see below) are used more frequently, mill files can be used safely in the field to sharpen sickles, scythes, billhooks and slashers, if the following precautions are taken. Set the tool head, with the edge pointing away from you, on the edge of a stump, and hold it securely with your foot. File in one direction, with gentle single strokes, the full length of the file blade. Work from one end of the tool's blade to the other, then turn it over and do the other side. At the curve of the blade, lift the leading edge of the file so that the back edge sharpens the curve.

c If you are using a sharpening stone (whetstone), carry the correct one for the job. Fine cylindrical (cigar-shaped) stones are needed for sickles and scythes. They may also be used for billhooks and slashers, along with flat (canoe-shaped) stones. Canoe-shaped or flat rectangular stones are best for axes. Flat round axe-stones, although commonly used, are dangerous and difficult to hold.

A useful sharpening kit, which consists of a gauge, rectangular sharpening stone and carrying frog, is available. The gauge has slots indicating the correct edge for reap hooks, slashers, billhooks and axes. The stone has two different faces, coarse and fine, for general sharpening and final honing. The canvas frog, which loops over a belt for carrying, is designed to protect the stone and gauge. The set is available from Stanton Hope Ltd.

d Stones are fragile - treat them with respect. Wrap them or carry them separately or in a frog. Broken stones are dangerous and should not be used.

e Always wear a glove on the hand holding the sharpening stone. Place the tool on a firm surface such as a stump, with the edge projecting, or sit down and steady the tool on your knees.

If used dry, the stone will quickly wear away. It should be moistened with water from a stream or puddle; if these are unavailable, spit on the stone to moisten it. Hold the stone at an angle conforming to the existing taper of the blade. Avoid the temptation of using a wider angle to get an edge on the blade more quickly. If using a combination stone, use the coarse side first to eliminate any flaws and bring to an edge, and the fine side afterwards to give a good polish and even taper. Sharpen with small circular motions - this is safer than sweeping the stone along the edge and gives better results for inexperienced workers. Take particular care to sharpen the hooked part of billhook and slasher blades, as this often neglected part does most of the cutting work. On single-bevel tools, sharpen the bevelled side only. To finish, remove the burr on the flat side with a few light strokes.

f Don't touch the blade to see if it is sharp. Instead, check by sighting along the edge. You should see a uniform taper with no light reflected from the edge itself. Reflected light indicates a dull spot, so keep sharpening until this disappears.

SAW MAINTENANCE

a Oil blades frequently. When sawing through resinous trees, keep blades clean and free-cutting by dousing them with an oiling mixture of 7 parts paraffin, 2 parts white spirit and 1 part lubricating oil.

b Sharpen saw blades (see below), or change the blades of hardpoint bow saws, when the saw takes more effort to use than normal, when it produces fine dust rather than 'crumbs' or small chips of wood, or when the teeth have lost their set or become damaged or broken.

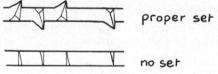

proper set

no set

Top view

To change the saw blade, first release the tension. If the tension lever is hard to release by hand, put the saw on the ground with the frame upright and with the blade pointing away from you, and pull back on the lever, using a metal bar if necessary.

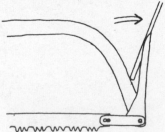

Next, hold the saw vertical with the frame towards you and the lever against the ground. Put your foot on the lever to hold it and push the saw frame away from you.

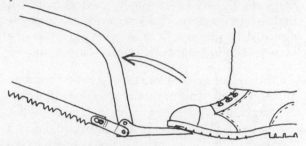

Remove the rivets and put them in a safe place. Position the new blade, replace the rivets and retension the blade by pressing the lever against the ground until it closes.

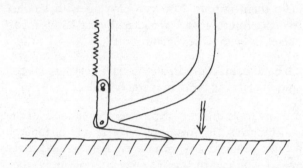

Blades which are to be sharpened in the workshop should be reversed in the saw (points into the bow) to make them easy to identify later. Blades which are beyond help should be taken out of the saw and broken in two, and the pieces removed from the work site for disposal.

c Touch up hardpoint bow saw blades, when dull, by running a whetstone once lightly along each side, with the stone held flat against the blade.

d If a bow saw blade tends to 'run' (cut in a curve), reverse it in the frame. If this is ineffective, adjust the set on the 'gaining' side by running the whetstone over it as for sharpening.

e Sharpenable bow saw blades must be touched up regularly. If they have raker teeth these must be adjusted at each sharpening and kept below the level of the cutting (peg) teeth. Setting is required less often. Cross-cut saws should not be touched up, but used until they require a complete stripping, sharpening and setting. This may be every one to three weeks if in frequent use, or only very occasionally if in infrequent use.

Sharpening and setting is best left to a professional 'saw doctor'. Although volunteers can learn this skill, it requires special files, vices, setting pliers and other tools and is slow, painstaking work. Many ironmongers can recommend a saw doctor or do the work themselves.

Organising Group Work

In the following chapters, organisational points are included where appropriate. The following points are basic to most tree planting and aftercare tasks. The seasonal work in tree nurseries run by volunteer groups is usually organised on a rota basis. See chapter 5 for specifics on the tasks involved in running a tree nursery.

a Volunteers work best if someone responsible for site management is on hand to explain the purpose of the task and to work alongside them.

b Before starting the work, the leader should explain the task (if this has not already been done by the site manager), and set the day's objectives. It helps greatly if the leader has visited the site in advance, and is clear about the job in his or her own mind. The introductory talk should cover the reasons for the work, care of tools and a demonstration of their use, and the standard of work expected (e.g. general tidiness and avoidance of unnecessary damage).

Whenever possible, verbal explanations should be clarified by demonstrations or samples of work. For example, the leader can assemble a tree 'library' in one corner of the work site, consisting of marked specimens of living or freshly cut material. This will help volunteers identify unfamiliar trees as they do tasks such as thinning or heavy weeding. During the winter months, it is especially important to include enough buds on the specimens to ensure accurate identification. A tree key or a good field guide is also useful.

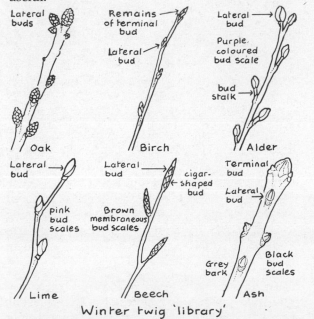

Winter twig 'library'

c Small groups should work methodically on one goal at a time, rather than piecemeal on several things, none of which may get done by the end of the day.

Large groups may, of course, do several things if they are sure of finishing them. It boosts morale, especially on long tasks, to see that a measurable amount of work has been accomplished.

d Some work, such as tree planting or weeding, can be done in teams, while other work, such as heavy pruning, is best done with workers well separated for safety and efficiency. Whatever the division of labour, don't leave anyone out. People of all strengths and abilities must find a place. Give new volunteers instructions and put them to work alongside experienced workers, if possible.

e Keep an eye on how volunteers use tools. Don't hesitate to offer advice to even the most experienced volunteer, as otherwise new workers may pick up bad habits. If the volunteer doesn't have enough skill for the job, tactfully suggest a change of tool or activity. The more 'dramatic' jobs, such as felling, may have more appeal for novice volunteers, but remember that edged tools are particularly dangerous for the untrained. Count out and count in the tools at the start and finish of work and note any which need repair.

f Work situations differ not only with the task at hand, local conditions and the weather, but also with the combination of people present. Flexibility and imagination can help in adapting these 'rules' to the specific occasion. Aim for a balance between high work standards and conditions which are not only safe but also rewarding for the volunteer.

Seed Collection and Tree Nurseries

This chapter discusses the laws surrounding seed collecting and tree nurseries, and the techniques involved in the running of a small-scale tree nursery. (Lifting trees and transporting them from the nursery are discussed in the first part of chapter 6.) Information on running a 'polyhouse' nursery is also included. The BTCV booklet 'Tree Nurseries' (Liebscher, 1984) has been used for most of the information in this chapter. Forestry Commission Bulletin 59, 'Seed Manual for Ornamental Trees and Shrubs' (Gordon and Rowe, 1982), has also been used, and should be consulted for detailed information on the collection, storage, pre-treatment and testing of seeds.

The Forest Reproductive Material Regulations 1977

The following information is from 'The Forest Reproductive Material Regulations 1977: An Explanatory Booklet' (Forestry Commission, 1987a), which should be consulted for details.

Whether you are starting a tree nursery yourself, or buying seeds or plants from an established nursery (p79), it is important to be aware of the Forest Reproductive Material Regulations 1977. These regulations arose from EEC Directives on controlling the physical and genetic quality and the marketing of forest reproductive material (i.e. seed, cones, cuttings and plants) within the EEC. The Regulations apply only to the so-called 'EEC species' listed below, and in general only when material from them is marketed for forestry purposes (i.e. wood production). All other species are exempt, although ash, birch and gean are currently under consideration. Note that the EEC species include eight which are native to Britain: four species of the genus *Populus* (aspen and grey, black and white poplar), beech, pedunculate and sessile oak, and Scots pine.

EEC Species

Austrian and Corsican pine *(Pinus nigra)*
Beech *(Fagus sylvatica)*
Douglas fir *(Pseudotsuga taxifolia)*
European larch *(Larix decidua)*
Japanese larch *(Larix leptolepis)*
Norway spruce *(Picea abies)*
Pedunculate oak *(Quercus robur)*

Poplar *(Populus* spp*)*
Red oak *(Quercus borealis)*
Scots pine *(Pinus sylvestris)*
Sessile oak *(Quercus petraea)*
Silver fir *(Abies alba)*
Sitka spruce *(Picea sitchensis)*
Weymouth pine *(Pinus strobus)*

The Regulations have been put into effect with a scheme administered by the Forestry Commission, which involves the following restrictions:

a Registration of seed sources. Seed of the EEC species can, in general, be collected only from registered woods if the seed, or plants grown from it, is intended to be sold for forestry purposes. Trees in registered woods must be of high quality in forestry terms, i.e. in form, quality of timber and growth rates.

b Seed testing and certification. When seed of the EEC species is bought or sold for forestry purposes, it must be accompanied by a certificate from the Forestry Commission, giving its local provenance (see p58) and the results of tests for purity, germination and viability.

In practice, what do the Regulations mean for the person starting a small tree nursery? First, you are exempt from the restrictions above if you deal only with species other than those in the EEC list. You are also exempt if you collect seeds and raise plants from them for your own use, rather than for purposes of marketing. If you decide at some point that you wish to sell small quantities of seeds or plants of the EEC species, you can do so legally, but only for amenity purposes - and, in the case of seeds, only if the quantity sold will produce less than 1000 useable plants.

However, if you are running a nursery mainly to conserve any of the native trees in the EEC list, and intend to collect the seeds locally and then sell the plants you raise, you may have to make a difficult choice. You will either have to ensure that the people buying the plants will use them only for amenity plantings, or you will have to collect the seed only from registered seed sources. If there are no registered stands of those particular species in your immediate area, you will have to forego your original purpose of conserving the local genetic strain. You may be able to get your seed source registered, but only if the trees are of high quality in forestry terms. If you find yourself in this position, it is best to consult the Forestry Commission.

THE OECD SCHEME

The Organisation for Economic Co-operation and Development (OECD) offers an alternative, voluntary scheme, also administered by the Forestry Commission. The aims of the OECD scheme are the same as those of the EEC scheme, but it differs in that it covers all species and specifies more categories of reproductive material. It is also open to any country that can prove its procedures are workable. Details can be found in the booklet 'OECD Scheme for the Control of Forest Reproductive Material Moving in International Trade' (Forestry Commission, 1982).

Starting a Tree Nursery

Establishing and running a tree nursery is not only fun - it is also a way of ensuring the survival of local genetic strains by raising trees of local provenance. These strains may otherwise be swamped by the widespread planting of trees of non-local, or even non-British, provenance (see below). Small tree nurseries also provide a vital service in the mammoth task of conserving Britain's tree resources.

Much of the following information is based on experience gained in a scheme run by BTCV in northwest England, to encourage schools to establish their own tree nurseries. Tree nurseries, as a means of involving schools in practical conservation work, are well suited to both the primary and secondary levels. Participation in such an activity can be an ideal way of studying botany, among other disciplines, and has the additional benefit of helping children understand the time factor involved in growing trees. Through this, they can begin to see the implications of vandalism in terms of time, cost and damage to the environment. Tree nursery work also naturally leads on to tree planting schemes, school nature reserves and practical conservation work in general.

REQUIREMENTS AND TIMING

The basic requirements for starting a tree nursery are modest. An area of 10 square metres (12 square yards) can produce up to 100 trees a year, so a nursery can be tiny and yet significant. The small area needed also broadens the choice of site. Unused corners or patches of land in fields or even gardens can be pressed into service. Volunteers may, in fact, find that establishing seedbeds in their own gardens both demystifies nursery operations, and ensures that the seedlings will have the best possible care in their vital first year. Ordinary gardening tools (see p49) will be needed periodically, and fencing materials may be required.

Tree nurseries are long-term projects, as trees may need to be in the nursery for several years before they can be moved to their final planting sites. The work involved is little but frequent, and is not heavy. There is something to do all year round, whether it is seed collecting, weeding, sowing or transplanting, and for this reason it is possible to start a tree nursery at any time of year. Spring is the period for sowing seed; winter, for lining out transplants. Most seed is collected in the autumn, although there are some varieties which can be picked year-round. Stratification (p61) where the seed is mixed with sand and buried for a certain period, will mean that for some species there will be a one-year time lag before any seed is ready for sowing. Pre-treatment under controlled conditions (p62), an alternative method, may necessitate even longer time lags.

It is worthwhile to look ahead and make a rough plan of operations. The illustration on page 64 provides one example of how to organise the management of a small traditional nursery. Note that in this illustration, the area allotted to each stage of the work will vary with species chosen, and their rate of growth in local conditions. A polyhouse nursery is illustrated on page 75.

The instructions following should not be regarded as hard-and-fast rules. Experimentation may, in fact, be one of the better ways to learn about trees, and often leads to fascinating discoveries.

Seed Collection, Storage and Pre-Treatment

SEED COLLECTION

With woodland planting schemes, preference should be given to the native tree species. Commercially grown native species are very often raised from imported seed. Maintaining authentic genetic stock is, however, of primary importance for conservation-oriented planting schemes, particularly in nature reserves. To ensure this, use seed of local provenance (i.e. collected from native trees growing locally) instead. Table 5A gives recommended months for seed collection, although there will be variation according to the year of collection and the geographic location.

For those unable to collect seed for any reason, the seed of many forestry species are available from the Seed Branch at the Forestry Commission Forest Research Station.

Remember that there is a need to propagate exotics as amenity trees for towns, parks and gardens. If you wish to grow exotics, the number of species and varieties available to you is enormous. Only the more common trees and shrubs will be discussed in this chapter, however, due to limited space. Those needing information on the more unusual species should see Sheat (1957) or Hillier (1977).

Procedures for seed collection

The general rule when collecting seed is to select the best and healthiest trees as sources. If some trees are stunted, however, this may be the result of management or environmental factors rather than a genetic trait. As maintaining the genetic diversity present in a wood is important for conservation, it is preferable to include some stunted trees as seed sources. Seed should never be collected from trees which are isolated from others of the same species, as the self-pollinating tendency of these trees may cause poor germination, deformity or stunted growth. As a rule of thumb, the minimum acceptable number of pollinating trees of the same species is 20 per square kilometre. Choose trees locally or from an area north of the nursery, as these are more likely to grow well in the area.

Dry days are best for seed collecting. Never use polythene bags, as seed left in them heats up, sweats and blackens. Open-weave hessian sacks that permit the free movement of air are the best choice, but at a pinch paper bags could be used. Bring labels and pens with you, and as you work, label each sack with the species, date and place of collection. During any intervals in collecting, place the sacks in a well-ventilated place away from direct sunlight and rain.

Seed can sometimes be picked directly from small trees and shrubs (e.g. hazel, rowan or hawthorn) and from the lower branches of large trees. Usually, however, seed is borne high up and collection can be a problem. In modern forestry, this is overcome by either felling the trees or by sending trained collectors using specialist equipment up them. As neither method is suitable for volunteers, the following are suggested:

a A long pole with a hook on one end is very useful for bending branches down to within reach.

b A pair of long-handled pruners can be used to cut off terminal twigs bearing seed.

c A small step-ladder is often helpful, but to be safe it must always be steadied by a second person standing below.

d Local tree-felling operations might provide an opportunity for obtaining seed.

The heavy seed of some broadleaves (e.g. oak, sweet chestnut or beech) can be collected from the ground if it is freshly fallen. These trees, however, first shed empty and malformed fruits, usually following the first autumn frosts.

Where light seeds (e.g. birch) fall on concrete or Tarmac, they can be collected simply by sweeping up. This method can also be used on other surfaces, as long as a tarpaulin or polythene sheet is first spread beneath the tree. If, however, the seed is to be stored, and large amounts of debris (e.g. twigs or leaves) have fallen with the seed, it may be better to sort the seeds on site rather than laboriously clean them from the sweepings later. Ash seeds must be immediately separated out from any damp litter to keep them dry.

Seeds which are deposited on the ground are also often attractive to animals, so collections should never be unduly delayed.

Records

You will need to keep ongoing records to build up a picture of the most reliable seed trees in your vicinity. Such records should include:

a Identification of good, healthy specimens

b Their flowering and fruiting habits

c The yield of processed seed from each source

d The exact location of seed bearing trees on a map

e The growing performance of each seed lot collected, on a yearly basis.

TABLE 5A COLLECTION AND STORAGE OF SEED

Notes on columns Column 2 gives the interval in years between good seed crops. Column 3 gives recommended months for seed collection. In most cases these are set out as earliest/normal/latest. Months will vary with different years and with geographic locations. Column 4 gives methods of storage as described in the key on p61. In the case of stratification, the number in column 4 gives the time in months that the seed should be stratified. Column 5 gives information on controlled warm and cold pre-treatment, as discussed on page 62. The numbers refer to time in weeks for warm (w) or cold (c) pre-treatment, while the (m) signifies that seed should be mixed with a pre-treatment medium. Those species with no (m) should be pre-treated 'naked', i.e. without a medium.

SPECIES	CROP	COLLECTION	STORAGE/ STRATIFICATION	WARM/COLD PRE-TREATMENT	NOTES
ALDER	2-3	Sep/Spring	B	c:4	Pick when strobiles (i.e. sections of 'cone') start opening.
ASH	3-5	Aug/Jan	D or C (16-18)	w:8-12 C;8-12 (m)	August for immediate sowing if green. October for stratification.
ASPEN	-	Apr/May	Avoid	-	Collect catkins when the white down appears.
BEECH	1-3	Sep/Nov	D or C (6)	c:4-20	Check nuts are fertile. From January seed may need water spray to remain plump.
BIRCH	1-3	Aug/Winter	A or C (6)	c:4	Pick catkins shortly before they ripen.
BROOM	1	Aug	A	-	Pick pods when black. Pop open by hand.
BUCKTHORN	-	Oct	C (6)	c:2-4 (m)	Pick fully ripe berries.
CHERRY	1-3	Jul/Aug	C (4)	w:2 c:18 (m)	Can be sown immediately. Pick ripe berries before the birds do!
CHESTNUT, Horse	1-2	Sep/Oct	D or C (6)	-	Non-native.
CHESTNUT, Sweet	1-4	Oct/Nov	D	-	Non-native. A warm summer is required to ripen nuts.
ELM, Wych	1-2	Jun/Jul	D	-	Pick when green pigment disappears from wing - sow immediately. Seed of other elms are infertile - propagate suckers.
GORSE	-	May/Jul	A	-	As for broom.
HAWTHORN	1-2	Sep/Nov	C (18)	w:4-8 c:12-16 (m)	Pick fully ripe berries.
HAZEL	2-3	Oct	C (3)	c:12-16 (m)	-
HOLLY	2-4	Nov/Feb	C (16)	w:40 c:24 (m)	Pick fully ripe berries.
HORNBEAM	2-4	Nov/Spring	C (18)	w:4 c:12-24 (m)	Small nut in 3 lobed wing. Pick while still slightly green.
LARCH, European	3-5	Nov/Jan	B	c:4-6	Non-native.
LIME	2-3	Oct	C (18)	w:4-20 c:16-24(m)	
MAPLE, Field	1	Oct/Jan	C (6)	w:4 c:12-24 (m)	Some seeds most years. Pick when seeds are brown
OAK	2-4	Sep/Nov	D	-	
Q. ilex	-	-	-	c:4 (m)	
Q. palustris	-	-	-	c:8 (m)	
Q. rubra	-	-	-	c:4-8 (m)	

SPECIES	CROP	COLLECTION	STORAGE/ STRATIFICATION	WARM/COLD PRE-TREATMENT	NOTES
ROWAN	2-3	Jul/Sep	C (6)	w:2 c:14-16 (m)	Pick fully ripe berries.
SCOTS PINE	2-3	Nov/Feb	B	c:4-6	Collect cones before they open.
SPINDLE	2-4	Sep/Nov	C (6)	w:8-12 c:8-16 (m)	-
SYCAMORE	1-3	Sep/Oct	D	c:6-12	See note, below.
WHITEBEAM	-	Sep	C (6)	As for rowan	-
YEW	-	Sep/Nov	C (16)	-	The seed (not the flesh) and the foliage are deadly poison.

Note: Sycamore is of limited value to wildlife and is sometimes even regarded as a weed where it has invaded woodlands and ousted other species. It is suggested that tree nursery programmes give preference to more important species. The deliberate propagation of sycamore might best be restricted to sites where other trees struggle to survive (e.g. exposed hills in the uplands, windswept coastal sites, etc.).

KEY TO TABLE 5A

A Trees with small dry seeds. These seeds should be stored dry in a sealed container until spring.

B Trees with cones. The small seeds are to be found below the scales of the cones. The cones should be spread in trays and kept warm by a fire or over a radiator, but not left where it is too hot to rest the hand comfortably. As the cones dry, the scales open and the seeds fall out. To separate the seed out, empty all the contents of the tray into a coarse wire sieve or wire mesh drum, and shake vigorously. Store the seed in a sealed container.

C Mainly trees which bear berries. The seed is enclosed by a hard coat within the flesh of the berry. The first step in treatment is the removal of the flesh by maceration, which should be done as soon as possible after collection. The seeds then undergo a period of stratification (see below), which is needed to break down the seed coat. The number following the 'C' in column 4 of Table 5A gives the time in months that the seed should be stratified. If you choose instead to pre-treat the seed under more controlled conditions, column 5 gives the time in weeks that the seeds should be kept at warm or cold temperatures.

D Mainly nut-bearing trees. The nuts are best sown immediately after collection, in a seedbed protected from mice and squirrels. If the seedbed is not ready, the nuts can be stored over winter using the method for berries undergoing stratification. Large quantities of acorns and chestnuts can be stored in hessian sacks and hung up in a cool dry place where there is little circulation of air. The nuts themselves must not dry out, and therefore must be sprayed occasionally with cool water.

STORAGE AND PRE-TREATMENT OF SEED

The fruits and seeds of trees vary immensely in size and shape, from those in husks (beech, hazel) and berries (holly, rowan) to others which are dry and with or without wings. Equally varied are the treatments necessary for each type of seed. Table 5A, column 4 gives the appropriate traditional treatment for each species, as described in the key above. Alternative treatment under temperature-controlled conditions, given in column 5, is discussed more fully on page 62.

Stratification

In their natural state, seeds could remain in the ground, in a state of dormancy, for anything up to several years before germinating. You can imitate this condition in the nursery, but the seedbed will need to be kept weed- and pest-free for at least a year. Seeds can instead be stratified in a container to break dormancy, as follows:

1 Lay berries on a hard surface and crush with a block of wood until the seeds are exposed. The resulting mixture of pulp and seeds can then be put into a

bucket of water for a few hours (i.e. macerated). Alternatively, if the berries are fairly soft, tip them into the bucket and crush and roll them between your hands. In either case, the pulp and non-viable seeds will float to the top and can be drained off, and the heavier viable seeds will sink to the bottom. This process can be omitted, but it does encourage a better percentage of germination. If ash keys are being stratified, do not attempt to separate the seed from the wing, or you are likely to damage the seed.

2 Weigh the seed or count the number of seeds, as appropriate, and record this information. It will be required at the time of sowing (see Table 5B on page 66).

3 Mix the seed with approximately four times its weight of sand, i.e. enough sand to ensure that each seed is separated from any others.

4 Put this mixture into large earthenware flower pots. The holes in the pots must not be plugged with sand. To prevent seed loss and allow drainage, cover the holes with curved pieces of broken pot before you add the mixture.

5 Make the pots mouse-proof by covering with 6mm wire mesh.

6 Bury the pots in a pit full of sand, ensuring that there is 100mm (4") of sand or gravel below the pots for drainage, and about 100mm (4") above. The site of the pit must not be liable to waterlogging or the seed will rot. The pit should be sited in a cool, shady place.

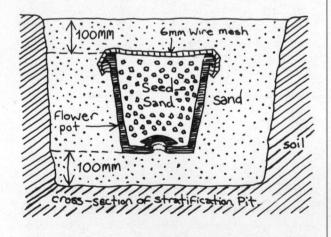

Alternatively, the pots can be covered with a board and placed outside in a cold aspect. This does, however, require careful attention to watering, as the sand will dry out more quickly than if the pot is buried.

The seeds are ready to sow when they are swollen and split, and about 10% of them have chitted (i.e. the root, or radicle, has just emerged).

Warm/cold pre-treatment

Warm and cold pre-treatment are more exact methods than stratification, as the seeds are kept in temperature-controlled conditions. Table 5A, column 5 gives information on pre-treatment for particular species, but these are only guidelines, as each seed lot will have a different optimum treatment period. As with the stratification method, berries should be macerated before pre-treatment, to extract the seeds. A general summary of the procedure follows, but reference should be made to Gordon and Rowe (Forestry Commission Bulletin 59, 1982) for details.

1 Divide the seed into lots according to the seedbeds into which they will be planted, so that the seed can later be sown at the correct density.

2 Place the lots into thick polythene bags and add four to five times their volume of cold water. Label the bags with species, dry weight of seed and relevant dates. Keep at about 3-5°C for 48 hours. The main compartment of a refrigerator can be used for this purpose.

3 Drain the water from the bags.

For seeds which are to be chilled without a medium, leave in loosely tied polythene bags at 3-5°C.

Seeds which need warm treatment or a prolonged cold treatment should be mixed with a medium (a combination of sieved peat and sand), and placed in large, clearly labelled polythene bags. For the warm treatment, put the bags in a place kept at 20-30°C, such as an airing cupboard, for the time specified. For the cold treatment, place bags back in the refrigerator for the required period.

4 Once a week, open the bags, mix the seeds and spray them with water if they seem to be drying out.

5 At the end of the pre-treatment periods, separate the seeds from the medium (if applicable and possible) and lay the seeds out on trays in a cool, well-ventilated place, turning regularly to surface dry. Very small seeds may have to be dried together with the medium. If, immediately after pre-treatment, any seeds show signs of chitting, they must be sown immediately.

Long-term cold storage

You may want to put some seed into long-term storage, for example if it has been a good seed year and you end up with more than you can plant the following spring. You will first have to determine whether the seed species is 'orthodox' or 'recalcitrant', terms which refer to their response to storage.

Orthodox seeds (e.g. birch) are those which can be stored for long periods at low moisture contents and temperatures, and still remain viable. After drying down to about 10% moisture content, these can be stored in plastic bags for up to five years at 3-5°C. Recalcitrant seeds (e.g. pedunculate oak) are killed if their moisture content is reduced below a certain high level, and so cannot be stored successfully for longer than a few months. For full information, see Gordon and Rowe (1982, pp20-22).

Selecting and Preparing the Nursery Site

This section covers the preparatory work necessary for constructing a traditional tree nursery. For a discussion of the construction and management of a polyhouse nursery, see page 75.

SITE SELECTION

There are so many requirements to consider when choosing a site that the ideal location is rarely found. When selecting a site, keep the following points in mind:

a The soil is most important. Heavy soil is difficult to work, and it also makes damage to roots during transplanting likely. A light soil, on the other hand, is more prone to drying out. The best soil is a light loam. A good depth to the soil is desirable, not for the roots but because a deep soil retains more moisture in dry weather. A shallow soil on rock or gravel is unsuitable. Stony soil is troublesome but not impossible. In general, the soil should be fairly fertile, and preferably free of lime.

b A slight slope ensures good drainage, which is essential. Avoid very steep slopes, as soil may be washed away in heavy rain. An easterly aspect should also be avoided if possible, as morning sun can cause serious damage after a frosty night. The best choice is a slight slope to the west or north, or failing this, level ground. Make sure that the site does not lie in a frost hollow.

c Water may be required for the nursery in summer. Ensure that there is a supply near the site.

d Shelter is essential. Failing this, hedges or shelter belts of the appropriate species (see p38) could be grown, but in the interim protect the nursery with screens of wattle hurdles or hessian, or other temporary barriers. Throughout these operations, be careful not to create frost pockets.

e Make sure the site can be used for several years, as most trees will be in the nursery for about four years.

f If individual members of a volunteer group have established seedbeds in their own gardens, the seedlings should be transplanted to the nursery in the winter following their first year.

PREPARING THE SITE

Fencing

The area must be protected from deer, rabbits and dogs, all of which can seriously damage if not destroy tree seedlings. Seedbeds also need protection against cats and birds. An effective rabbit fence can be made with 31mm gauge mesh, 1050mm wide; 900mm (2'11") of the roll stands above ground, and the remaining 150mm (6") is lapped horizontally on the ground in the direction of attack and held down with turves. Rabbits are baffled by their inability to burrow under the visible vertical netting.

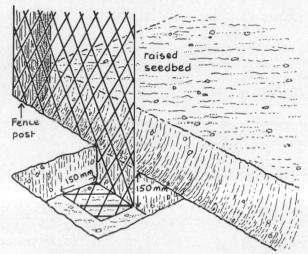

Rabbit-proof fencing: netting lapped horizontally in direction of attack

Some schools have quadrangles completely enclosed by buildings. Siting the nursery within such an area is an easy solution to the problems of dogs, rabbits, vandals and wind - although groups of buildings can, depending on their arrangement, actually create wind turbulence.

Clearance and cultivation

Cut down all the grass and other growth with a sickle. Mark out the seedbeds; then, using a sharp spade, cut and remove the turf in squares and stack them neatly next to the nursery site. In a year or so the turves will have rotted down to a fine loam, ideal for seed sowing. Dig over the site as for a vegetable plot. To do this, dig a trench 300-600mm (1-2') wide at one end of the plot, and barrow this soil to the other end; dig in strips, and turn each one into the trench in front until the whole plot is dug. Use the barrowed soil from the first trench to fill the last one. On heavy soils, break up the bottom of each trench with a fork.

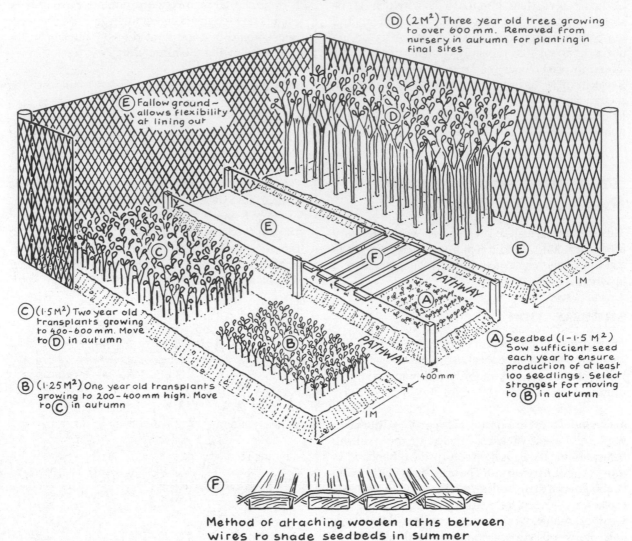

3 × 4 M nursery in early summer

Ⓓ (2 M²) Three year old trees growing to over 600 mm. Removed from nursery in autumn for planting in final sites

Ⓔ Fallow ground — allows flexibility at lining out

Ⓒ (1.5 M²) Two year old transplants growing to 400-600 mm. Move to Ⓓ in autumn

Ⓑ (1.25 M²) One year old transplants growing to 200-400 mm high. Move to Ⓒ in autumn

Ⓐ Seedbed (1-1.5 M²) Sow sufficient seed each year to ensure production of at least 100 seedlings. Select strongest for moving to Ⓑ in autumn

PATHWAY

400 mm

1 M

Method of attaching wooden laths between wires to shade seedbeds in summer

Remove all perennial weeds as you dig. A small piece of couch grass rhizome, if left in the ground, will create havoc among the seedlings when pulled up at a later date. Alternatively, while the wholesale use of chemicals is not advocated, you can use appropriate weedkillers (see p109) to guarantee an absolutely clear area. Keeping the nursery weed-free is of the utmost importance for good seedling growth.

Digging is best done in autumn to allow the winter frosts to break up the clods, but a light soil can be dug at any time in winter or early spring when the soil is workable. Fertilize the soil if it lacks any basic plant nutrients or is excessively acid (see p74).

Constructing the seedbeds

If all plants are to be grown from seed, about 10-20% of the cropped area should be allotted to seedbeds. Seedbeds should be of such a size and shape that one can remove weeds from any part without setting foot on the bed. It is standard practice to make beds 1m (3') wide, and of any length. Pathways, 400mm (16")

wide, should be made between adjacent beds. Set out garden lines to mark the edges of the beds and then remove soil from the pathways and throw it onto the beds on either side alternately (see the section on band sowing, p67) until the beds are 100-200mm (4-8") higher than the pathways. Work in fertilizer (p74) as necessary.

Consolidation

Seedbeds in very sandy soils, constructed early in the year, will consolidate naturally over the winter and should be disturbed as little as possible before sowing. Otherwise proceed as follows. Level out the surface of the beds and then firm them down, either with a roller or with a thick plank on which you should walk up and down. The bed should firm down to about 80mm (3") above the general ground level. Beds must be well consolidated before sowing to allow the soil moisture to reach the surface layers by capillary action, and prevent them from drying out in warm weather.

An effective and simple test for consolidation is to press the bed firmly with the flattest part of a clenched fist. Consolidation is adequate when only a slight indentation can be made. Do not firm down the bed when the soil is too wet, as all the benefit of the previous winter's weathering can be lost by compression and aggregation of soil crumbs. When the soil is in good working condition, however, over-consolidation should not be a problem. Following consolidation, the surface of the bed should be worked to a fine tilth. The seedbed is now ready for sowing.

CONTAINER GROWING

Even without a suitable piece of land, you can still run a tree nursery by using containers. The great advantage of trees grown singly in containers is that they can be planted out at any time of the year without any damage to the root system, although evergreens are best planted in spring.

Seedlings should be started off in a seed tray, or in a Dunemann box or Kember bed (see below), in the same manner as in an ordinary nursery. Containerised plants can dry out very quickly, however, so special attention must be paid to watering. At one or two years old, the seedlings should be potted out singly into containers approximately 250mm (10") deep and 250mm (10") in diameter.

Garden supply stores will have suitable pots available. These may be made of polythene, artificial whalehide, or biodegradable fibre. Empty one-gallon plastic squash containers are ideal if the tops are cut off and holes for drainage are cut. A tree should spend a few years in such a pot before being planted in its final position.

One possible disadvantage of growing trees in containers is root deformation. The lateral roots, which in normal conditions spread outwards, can begin to spiral where they encounter the walls of the container. As these encircling roots will continue to grow in diameter, they may eventually weaken the stem, and they are also liable to create problems of stability in the mature tree. Even when the tree is planted out, the roots may have difficulty in penetrating the root-ball. If your containerised plants begin developing this condition, try to plant them out in beds or, if necessary, their final planting sites as soon as possible, following the procedure on p92.

The Dunemann system

The Dunemann method of growing trees can even be done on a concrete floor. You will need a bottomless, box-shaped structure 1m (3') wide, 300mm (1') high, and of any length. It can be made out of rough wood,

old bricks or concrete blocks. If more than one box is made, leave enough room between adjacent boxes for a wheelbarrow. Site the Dunemann box either where the ground is gently sloping, or where it has a freely draining soil. Frosty sites should be avoided and a good supply of water should be available nearby. The site should also be free of perennial creeping grasses such as couch.

Fill the box up with well broken-down leaf litter. When conifer seed is being sown, a proportion of conifer leaf litter must be included. Otherwise the specialised fungi (*mycorrhiza*), which enable conifers to grow, will be absent. It is important to consolidate leaf litter well by trampling at intervals while the frame is being filled. Before sowing, water the box well. Sow the seed onto the levelled and firmed leaf litter, and cover with 5mm (¼") of sand, free from silt and lime. If protection from animals is needed, lay a piece of 6mm wire mesh of the correct dimensions over the top of the box and secure with a few nails, or bricks placed at the corners. Ensure that the bed does not dry out by watering it from time to time. Additional Dunemann boxes can be used for transplanting.

The Dunemann system lends itself well to variations, of which two are shown below. ('Clinker' is the residue from burnt coal.)

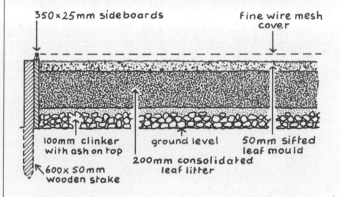

Dunemann box

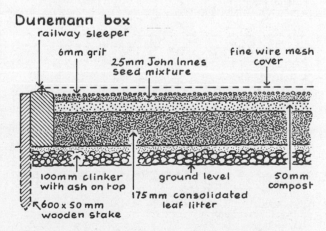

Kember bed

TABLE 5B NOTES ON SOWING DIFFERENT SPECIES OF SEED

% = average percentage germination

Ht = height of seedlings at one year in cm

Den = sowing density as square metres per 100g (3.5oz) of seed

species	%	ht	den	notes
Alder	35	7-20	11.0	4
Ash	61	10-22	1.8	2
Aspen is difficult to grow from seed.				
Beech	60	10-20	0.4	1,3
Birch	30	7-20	22.0	4
Broom	80	8-25	12.5	5
Chestnut, Horse	82	15-25	0.1	1,6
Chestnut, Sweet	67-93	12-30	0.15	1,6
Elm, Wych	44	10-20	7.0	7
Field Maple	54	7-20	2.5	-
Gean (*Prunus avium*)	77	10-15	0.6	-
Gorse	75	-	12.5	5
Hawthorn	-	10-20	0.9	-
Hazel	70	10-15	0.2	-
Holly	80	5-12	3.0	-
Hornbeam	-	5-10	1.2	-
Larch	35	10-20	6.0	-
Lime, large-leaved	70	12-20	0.5	-
Lime, small-leaved	70	15-25	2.2	-
Oak	81	10-20	0.1	1,8
Rowan	70	7-25	9.0	-
Scots Pine	85	5-10	9.0	-
Spindle	71	7-15	4.8	-
Sycamore	40	20-50	3.0	-
Whitebeam	-	7-25	1.8	-
Yew	90	-	9.0	-

Notes to Table 5B

1 Because of variation in seed size, sowing seed 7cm (2¾") apart (i.e. about 200 seeds to the square metre, or about 170 seeds to the square yard) is preferable to sowing by weight.

2 If picked green in August sow immediately. Sow in March if stratified seed has begun to germinate. Otherwise, sow in April.

3 Autumn sowing is satisfactory if soil is free draining and not prone to late spring frosts.

4 Very sensitive to seedbed conditions. Germination is helped by addition of peat to the seedbeds; a smooth, well-formed seedbed surface; an even, light covering; and careful watering up to 5 days after germination.

5 After removing from storage, boil a volume of water not more than 5 times that of the seed. Put seed in a bowl and pour over boiling water. Leave to cool.

6 Can be sown in autumn immediately after collection.

7 Sow on same day as collection. Water after sowing and before covering with earth, and on dry days in the week after sowing.

8 May be sown in autumn if soil is well-drained and bird damage unlikely to be severe, or if netting is provided.

Sowing

Seeds are usually sown in March or April, as soon as ground frosts diminish and the soil becomes workable, or as indicated by the progress of germination in stratification or warm/cold pre-treatments. Species such as oak, beech and birch can be sown in the autumn rather than the spring if desired. This may give better results than storing the seed, provided that the seedbeds are protected from birds and rodents. By the time sowing begins, the seedbeds should have been consolidated and firmed as described on pp64-65.

Seeds should be sown at a density which produces the optimum number of seedlings per unit area. This varies according to the species, the size of the seed and its viability. Calculating optimum densities and expected yields is too involved to detail here, but Aldhous (1972) gives full information. Table 5B (left), gives sowing densities for common species.

SOWING METHODS

Whichever method is used, the seed should be spread as evenly as possible over the seedbed or along the drills or bands. Always leave about 80mm (3") unsown along each edge of the raised seedbed to allow for crumbling of the edge during the growing season. Broadcast and drill sowing are suitable for both large and small seeds. Band sowing and dibbing in are for large seeds only. Broadcasting produces about 25% more seedlings per unit area than the other methods, but weeding and lifting the seedlings may be more difficult.

Dibbing in

1 Make a hole for each seed using a gardener's dibber or a pointed stick. Space the holes about 50mm (2") apart, and ensure they are the appropriate depth for the type of seed.

2 Place and cover the seeds one at a time.

Band sowing

1 Draw trenches 150-220mm (6-8.5") wide and a similar distance apart across the beds, which should be 1m (3') wide with pathways. Make the trenches the appropriate depth for the seed.

2 Sow the seed evenly over the bands, 45mm (2") apart for the largest seeds such as chestnuts and acorns, and 25mm (1") apart for ash and beech.

3 Cover the seeds.

Large hardwood seeds

Seeds of species such as oak, beech and sweet chestnut, if they are to be sown in the autumn, can be sown while preparing the bed (see above).

1 Broadcast the seed over the bed before digging the pathways.

2 Spread soil from the pathways over the beds to a depth of 25-40mm (1-1½"). The pathways may be 100mm (4") below the surface of the seed bed.

3 An extra 80-100mm (4") of soil can be spread over the bed to give the seed more protection over the winter. Rake off the excess in March.

Drill sowing

1 Draw drills 100mm (4") apart, by using the back of a rake or by pressing a board edge-on into the soil. The size and depth of the drills depend on the size of the seeds. For small seeds, use a lath 25mm (1") wide by about 6mm (¼") thick to make a drill 4mm (⅛") deep. For larger seeds, use a board 25mm (1") thick pressed to the appropriate depth.

2 Sow the seed evenly along the drills. This is most easily done by measuring out the right amount of seed for each drill into a calibrated tube or narrow-necked bottle.

3 Cover the seeds.

Broadcasting

1 Divide the seed for the bed into two equal parts, sowing one part from each side of the bed. It can help to first sow a section of a bed, up to about 1 square metre in size. After sowing very carefully, as below, you can memorise the spacing, sowing density, etc. of this section and use it as a model for the rest of the bed.

2 Sprinkle the seed over the bed by hand. Very light seeds such as birch should be scattered from only a few inches above ground level, preferably on a windless day, or the seed may be blown away or onto another seedbed. Mixing the seed with damp sand beforehand often gives better results.

3 Cover the seeds with grit or earth as appropriate (see below).

COVERING THE SEEDS

After sowing, but before covering, seeds must be consolidated into the bed by rolling, spade-pressure, or the use of boards. The seeds must be in close contact with the soil for good germination and subsequent rooting, and in all cases must be covered from view. Cover the seeds as soon as possible after sowing. This is especially important with small seeds, which would otherwise blow away. Note the following points:

a For small broadleaved seeds and all conifers use coarse sand or fine grit, but not nursery soil. The latter will suffice if the others are unavailable, although yields will be lower and germination time longer. Cover the seeds to a depth equal to about one and a half times their length. If the nursery is sheltered you can use coarse sand, but where this is liable to blow away you should use grit which passes through a 3-5mm sieve. Rounded grit is easier to deal with - especially when weeding - than sharp, angular grit. Grit must be silt-free to avoid caking in rain, and lime-free to avoid reducing the soil acidity. Choose white or pale-coloured rather than dark grit, as the latter is likely to heat up in the sun and harm seedlings.

Fifty kg of grit covers about 4 square metres (the equivalent amount to cover 4 square yards would be 92lbs) of conifer seedbed. Grit can be an expensive item, so when drill sowing, cover only the drills.

b Large hardwood seeds (see above) are covered to a depth of 25-40mm (1-1½") with nursery soil. Reserve some seedbed soil for this purpose before sowing these seeds.

SUBSEQUENT CARE

Weeding

Keep the seedbeds scrupulously free of weeds. The old proverb that 'one year's seeding brings seven years' weeding' reflects the importance of this task. The objective of all steps to control weeds should be to break the life cycle of each unwanted species and prevent it from reproducing, whether from seed or vegetatively. If this is achieved, the number of dormant weed seeds and other perennating parts is gradually exhausted. Many weeds can set seed within a few weeks of germinating, and can complete four or five generations in one year. For some weeds there is no dormant season, and with these weed control is a year-round operation. The problem is eased if introductions of weed seeds are prevented. Avoid manures likely to contain weed seeds. Keep fence lines, surrounds of buildings and footpaths clear of weeds.

Large-scale growers use a selection of chemicals to control weeds. Chemical control can also be used in small nurseries (see chapter 7 for a discussion of appropriate herbicides), but is less desirable than other methods. A garden hoe can be used between drills or bands and in the transplant lines. Amongst the seedlings weeds are best removed by hand. Be prepared to weed every two or three weeks in summer, and every month or so at other times of the year, for as long as the seedlings are in the nursery. Do not let the weeds get so big that the seedlings are disturbed when the weeds are pulled up. Caution is required, however, when the tree seedlings are first appearing in the seedbed, as at this stage they may not look very different from weeds.

A good way of keeping weeds down at the same time as conserving moisture in the soil is by applying a mulch. This can be of any material which is itself weed free, such as well rotted compost, grass cuttings or pulverised composted bark. Apply a layer about 20-30mm (1") thick in winter or late spring. Sheet mulches are an excellent alternative to organic mulching. Mulches are fully discussed on pp102-104, in chapter 6.

Shading

Lath shelters or heavy camouflage netting may be needed to prevent the seedlings from drying out, especially if the beds have been sown late (April or May). Construct these screens by threading laths through twisted wires (rather like chestnut paling fences), and laying the screen across two wires supported on two lines of 300mm (1') posts along each side of the seedbed (see illustration on p64). Such shelters can also give protection against late frosts. Light branches can also be used for shading. Lay the branches in an arc over the beds or build them up in 1m (3') high 'hedges' between parallel wires on the sunny side of the beds. Broom and birch are good for this purpose. Conifers are unsuitable because they soon shed their needles.

Protection from mice, birds and cats

If birds, mice or cats are attacking seedlings, stretch fine-mesh (6mm) plastic-covered netting (not galvanised) over the beds on the same kind of support as used for the laths (see above). Bury the edges of the netting 150mm (6") below ground level. Do not allow the netting to sag or the supports to bend over.

Watering

Water the seedbeds in spring and summer whenever the soil begins to dry out below the surface. Use a fine-spray hose. Watering in late spring will help late-sown seed to germinate. Beds of birch or alder seed need frequent watering during dry spells.

Treating nursery diseases and insect pests

There are several diseases and insect pests that may need controlling in a small-scale nursery, as follows:

a Damping-off. This is caused by soil fungi which attack both germinating seeds and young seedlings. Losses may occur scattered throughout the seedbed, or in irregular groups. Drench the soil in Captan or Benlate as soon as you recognise the damage. For environmental and safety reasons, avoid using formulations of Captan which include Gamma-HCH, a persistent organochlorine insecticide.

b Oak mildew (*Microsphaera alphitoides*). This fungal disease distorts and slows the growth of young oak trees, although it seldom kills them. Affected shoots and leaves will be covered with a white bloom. As a preventative measure, collodial sulphur fungicides such as Elosal can be sprayed over the young plants, beginning when the leaves start to flush and continuing at fortnightly intervals, if necessary.

c Chafers (*Melolantha* spp) and cutworms. The grubs of chafers feed on the roots of seedlings and transplants, and may cause trouble in tree nurseries. Cutworms, the caterpillars of various moth species, gnaw at the root collars of seedlings, usually cutting them off at soil level. Nurseries established on agricultural soils are especially susceptible to chafer damage. Beech is particularly vulnerable if left in seedbeds or transplant lines too long, although this is usually only a local problem. Apart from using insecticides, control of both pests can usually be achieved by regularly cultivating the soil and removing the grubs or caterpillars by hand.

Transplanting and Undercutting

TRANSPLANTING

Unless destined to be used as transplants, young plants are usually kept in the nursery until they are large enough to plant out in their permanent quarters as 'whips', when they are between 600mm (2') and 1.2m (3'8") tall, according to species. Since different species grow at different rates, plants may be two to five years in the nursery. Specimen trees are generally left to grow in the nursery for a longer period. As lifting and removing young trees from the nursery is an operation best carried out on the day of planting, this subject is discussed at the beginning of the next chapter.

If left in the seedbed for over two years, seedlings become drawn and spindly through overcrowding. When about two years old, the seedlings should therefore be transplanted to a different part of the nursery which allows increased spacing between the plants for development. Some rapid-growing species are ready for transplanting at one year old. Transplanting also encourages a higher root/shoot ratio, which is desirable for producing more vigorous plants. When lack of time or space makes transplanting difficult, undercutting or root-pruning (see below) provides an alternative.

Recent research indicates that 80% of plant failure on site is the result of bad plant handling. It is therefore vital to follow the steps for lifting and transplanting listed below, to set a precedent for all subsequent handling of the plants.

The age of a tree

A young tree is known as a 'seedling' for as long as it is growing where the seed was sown. Thereafter it is referred to as a 'transplant'. The age of a young tree can be expressed by giving the time spent as a seedling in the seedbed and the time in transplant lines. A transplanting is indicated by a '+' sign. Thus, '2 + 1' means 'three years old', of which two years were in the seedbed and one in a transplant line. Plants which have been undercut rather than transplanted are known as '1 u 1', '1 u 2', etc., depending on the number of growing seasons before and after undercutting.

Time of transplanting

The young trees are usually lifted from the seedbeds at the end of their first or second growing season between October and the end of April. If more than 40% of the trees in a seedbed are less than 40mm (1$\frac{1}{2}$") tall, it is best to leave the bed for a further growing season as such seedlings are difficult to handle. Seedlings can be successfully transplanted at almost any time of year; in practice, however, it is safest to move them during the dormant period, which lies between the formation of buds in winter and bud-burst in spring.

In England and Wales most transplanting is done from October to March. In north-east England and Scotland late March to April is to be preferred, as this is usually a time when the worst of the winter weather has passed, the soil is moist and the plant roots have not yet begun growing. If transplanting takes place too early, repeated freezing and thawing may heave transplants out of the soil. Late transplants run the risk of desiccation. Summer transplanting in June, July or August is practised in many Scottish nurseries after the spring growth has hardened off. The soil must be kept moist and this technique may only be used for seedlings in their second growing season, and only by experienced volunteers. As plants lifted in winter and kept in cold storage have a better chance of surviving than those lifted in summer, this is the recommended method.

Preparation of ground

In September or October (or earlier, if ground is unavailable), preceding transplanting, dig over the area very roughly. If any bulky organic manure is to be added this should be spread on the ground a few weeks before lining out, and dug or rotovated in. This can be done the previous autumn, but more nutrients will be lost through leaching and breakdown. The ground must be free-working, and not hard and compacted. It is usual to cultivate the ground on the same day as transplanting.

Lifting seedlings from the seedbed

Lift the seedlings as follows:

a Always work from the outside of the bed, using a garden fork. Insert the fork vertically to the full depth of the blade and press the handle down until it is at an angle of 45° from the vertical.

b Repeat this movement until the soil is loose, then grasp the seedlings at ground level and lift gently, shaking excess soil from the roots at the same time. Do not remove all the soil, as root damage may be caused.

c Tease the roots apart if they have become intertwined, making sure not to strip the roots. After lifting, the chances of good survival and growth in the new planting site are greater if the maximum amounts of fine fibre and short branched roots and root tips are retained. Roots more than 150-180mm (6-7") long can be a nuisance when lining out and should be cut off. Using a sharp pruning tool, prune any roots that are bent or twisted from growing in cramped conditions, as otherwise the roots will continue to grow in this way for many years and lessen the tree's chances of survival. Avoid too much root pruning, however, as the aim is to help the tree develop a strong root system.

At all times the roots must be protected from drying by placing the plants immediately into buckets or boxes lined with damp moss, or in polythene bags, or by heling the plants in (see p...). Polythene bags, if used, should be co-extruded (white outside and black inside) and must be tied at the top. Always keep the plants out of strong sunlight and drying winds. Plants should not be left with exposed roots a second longer than is necessary.

Lifting and transplanting wild seedlings

Note that under certain circumstances, it may be worthwhile to transplant wild seedlings. If naturally regenerated seedlings would otherwise be cleared, shaded out or trampled in the course of work on a site, you may be able to stage a 'rescue operation'. Follow the lifting procedures for seedlings above, making sure that you retain enough soil around the roots, as there is usually a poor fibrous root system. Line the seedlings out as detailed below. As the growth qualities of wild seedlings cannot be assessed in advance, such plants should not be used later as timber or specimen trees.

Lining out

The density at which transplants are lined out depends on the size they are expected to be at the time of their next move. Read the necessary density from the following table:

Av. height at lifting (cm)	Rec'd growing area/plant (cm²)	Planting density (plants:m²)
below 20	75-100	135-100
20-40	100-125	100-80
40-60	100-150	100-70
over 60	125-200	80-50

When the necessary density has been decided upon, read off the appropriate spacings from the following:

Planting density (plants/m²)	Spacing between rows (cm)	Spacing within rows (cm)
50	20	10
70	15	10
80	17.5	7.5
100	20	5
135	15	5

Only a single transplanting may be required during a plant's time in the nursery. An annual transplanting might, however, be considered, as this can encourage the young plant to develop a good root system. Annual transplanting also enables root pruning (see below) to be carried out as necessary.

The techniques for lining out are as follows. For small numbers of transplants use a garden line and a dibber with which to make a hole, and put in seedlings one by one. Plants must be set upright with roots radiating symmetrically downward. When using a dibber, take care not to bend or cramp the roots. The plant should be pushed downward into the hole, and then drawn upward, so that the roots hang downward. Firm them in to avoid leaving gaps at root level. Plants must always be transplanted to the same depth as in their previous position, as shown by the soil mark on the stem.

For larger numbers of transplants the process can be greatly simplified and speeded up by the use of a simple plank, 1-2m (1-2 yd) long and the width of the transplant lines. Mark along one edge of the plank the appropriate spacing for plants in the row. Use a garden line to set a straight line and lay the plank alongside (see below). Dig a V-shaped trench 125-150mm (5-6") deep with a spade, making the face of the trench nearer to the plank vertical. Secure each plant in place by pressing a handful of soil against the roots, and continue until the length of the plank has been set with plants. Then fill in the trench and consolidate the ground to the side by levelling and treading. Plants which are loose take longer to become established and are also more likely to suffer in dry weather.

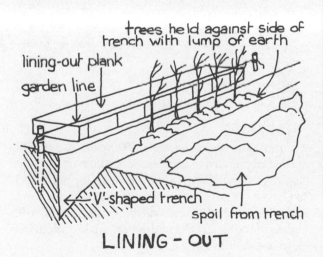

LINING - OUT

UNDERCUTTING

In small-scale nurseries, it is usually better to transplant seedlings and one year old transplants. Two and three year old transplants can be undercut, as described below, if space or time are lacking for further transplanting.

Shoot growth is checked by undercutting or wrenching, especially if this is done before the end of the growing season. Longer roots are cut, and new roots encouraged to develop in a more confined space. The development of long tap roots is undesirable, as this may make the final move from the nursery more difficult and the roots more likely to be damaged. To undercut by hand:

1 Push the spade under the plants as shown below.

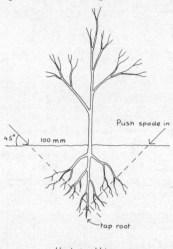

Undercutting

2 Lift the plants slightly before removing the spade. Make sure that you cut to the depth shown. If you cut as close as 50mm (2") below the soil surface, you may kill the plants. If you cut deeper than 100mm (4") you will stimulate little, if any, new root growth.

Work in pairs, one person each with a spade on each side of the row of plants. Excessively long roots on transplants can be pruned using secateurs or a sharp knife.

Remember that, whether lining out or undercutting, you will have to continue weeding. Transplants can be freed from weed competition by regular and light surface cultivation using a hand hoe, supplemented by hand weeding between the plants in the line. Do not allow the weeds to build up at any time, as they will produce seeds.

Vegetative Propagation

Some trees and shrubs can be propagated vegetatively. This is worth doing only if:

a it is quicker, easier and cheaper than raising the plants from seed

b seed is difficult to obtain

c the parent plant does not produce viable seed, or where the desirable characteristics can only be maintained by means of clones.

Only the simplest methods, using no special equipment, are discussed here. The following list gives suitable vegetative propagation methods for species commonly grown in this way. (C = cuttings, L = layering, S = suckers.)

Alder (*Alnus glutinosa*)	C		
Aspen (*Populus tremula*)			S
Beech (*Fagus sylvatica*)		L	
Blackthorn (*Prunus spinosa*)			S
Bramble (*Rubus fruticosa*)		L	
Dogwood (*Thelycrania sanguinea*)	C		S
Elder (*Sambucus nigra*)	C		
Elms (*Ulmus* spp)*			S
Guelder rose (*Viburnum opulus*)		L	
Hazel (*Corylus avellana*)	C	L	
Holly (*Ilex aquifolium*)	C	L	
Honeysuckle (*Lon. periclymenum*)	C	L	
Hornbeam (*Carpinus betulus*)		L	
Ivy (*Hedera helix*)	C		
Pear, Wild (*Pyrus communis*)			S
Poplar, Black (*Populus nigra*)	C		
Poplar, Grey (*Populus canescens*)	C		S
Privet, Wild (*Ligustrum vulgare*)	C	L	S
Wayfaring tree (*Viburnum lantana*)		L	
Willows (*Salix* spp)	C		

*Wych elms can also be grown from cuttings.

SUCKERS

Some trees and shrubs have shallow roots which produce shoots that develop into trees. These suckers can be separated from the parent tree and replanted. To propagate a suckering species, cut through the surface roots all around a sucker with its own cluster of roots. The suckering habit of the parent is continued in the offspring. It is easier to take small suckers (those under 600mm, or 2', high) than to attempt to detach larger plants. Keep the plant's roots moist and follow the transplanting procedure as described above.

HARDWOOD CUTTINGS

These are taken from wood that is fully matured, or hard. They can be used to propagate such species as willows, poplars (other than aspen), dogwood, hazel, honeysuckle and elder. Other species can be propagated, but specialist equipment may be necessary. To propagate hardwood cuttings:

1 Take cuttings in late autumn (after mid-October) or early winter. Choose well-ripened dormant shoots from the previous season's growth. Discard all succulent (soft) cuttings and those which are 'blind' (i.e. lack buds). Cuttings should be fairly typical-looking shoots at least as thick as a pencil, although willow cuttings can be thinner. Some plants root better if they are taken with a heel (see below). This damages the parent tree, so it should only be done using branches which have already been pruned. Poplar and willow cuttings should be unheeled.

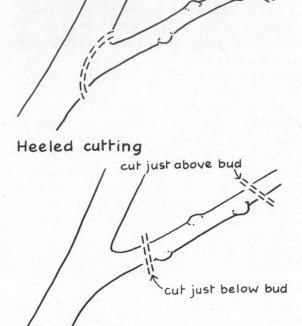

Heeled cutting

cut just above bud

cut just below bud

Unheeled cutting

2 Cut the shoots into sections 200mm (8") long with at least two nodes to each section. Make the top cut sloping, at 30mm (1¼") or less above the top node, and the lower cut straight across just below the bottom node. The sloping top cut will allow water to run off. Unless the cutting is left with a heel, make the cuts as clean as possible using a sharp knife.

3 Store the cuttings until planting time. They can be buried in moist sand or well-drained compost in a cool shed, cellar or garage, where they should survive unless subject to prolonged freezing or warmth. The ideal storage temperature is 4.5°C. Alternatively, hele the cuttings in (see p84) with only their upper tips projecting above ground. Check occasionally that the sand or earth is moist, and that the buds are not bursting. The buds must not burst until the roots have developed. Lower the temperature to ensure this, if necessary. Remember always to insert the flat or heeled end of the cutting into the medium!

4 Transfer the cuttings to cultivated ground any time from early January to March when the ground is not frozen. By this time the cuttings should have formed a callus (a white scabby growth or transparent covering). Insert the cuttings to a depth about two-thirds of their length. Space them 300-370mm (12-15") apart, in rows which are 370-450mm (15-18") apart. Tread well round the stems to firm the soil, and water if necessary.

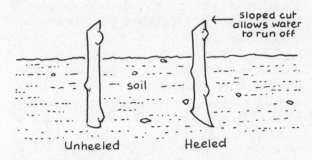

Cuttings inserted up to 2/3 length in the soil

With poplar and willow cuttings, further treatment is necessary. These trees require fertile, sheltered soil with a pH of over 5.5 for the most successful propagation by cuttings. Poplars are heavy feeders and ground which is used to grow them should be fertilized with hop waste at 5kg per square metre (about 9lb per square yard) every second year, plus an annual application of 75g per square metre (about 2oz per square yard) of potassic superphosphate. The following additional procedures apply to poplar and willow cuttings only.

5 By late spring, the cuttings will have produced two or more sprouts at least 150mm (6") long. Cut off all but the strongest sprout on each plant.

6 At the end of the first growing season 'stump' the trees to promote better root formation. Do this by cutting them back to about 30mm (1") above ground level. Leave at least one bud on the stem. Less vigorous plants can be left a second year before stumping.

7 Transplant the rooted stumps any time after stumping. If they have sprouted, single the shoots again (step 5). Space the transplants at 600 by 900mm (2 by 3') intervals if they are to be lifted after one year, or at 900 by 900mm (3 by 3') intervals if they are to remain for two growing seasons. When lifting, take special care to keep the roots moist. Prune long roots with a sharp knife or secateurs.

WILLOWS FROM SETTS

While both poplars and willows can be propagated from long unrooted cuttings or 'setts', this method is tricky with poplars. It is easy with willows, although the resulting trees usually have less good growth and form than those raised as described above. The setts do best if lined out in the nursery for a year or two to root, but they can be successfully planted out direct if the soil remains moist. Proceed as follows:

1 Take cuttings from two year shoots if possible. Older ones take nearly as well but are harder to push into the ground. It is preferable to take setts in early spring. Take them in summer if desired, but in this case clip off all but one or two leaves per sett and continue to trim off leaves all summer long. This helps prevent the plants from losing moisture faster than the new root system can take it in.

2 Trim side shoots from each main shoot as it is cut. Rest the butt ends in water to prevent their drying out. Transplant as soon as possible.

3 Cut the shoots into 600mm (2') lengths, discarding anything less than 10mm ('2") thick. Angle the cut cleanly so that there is no bruising or back-peeling of bark. Where the water table is too deep for short setts, make them 1m or 1.2m (3' or 3'8") long. Use older, thicker shoots for this, although setts thicker than about 50mm (2") at the butt end are hard to push into anything but the softest ground.

4 Push in the setts wearing work gloves, making sure the setts are the correct way up. Force in thick cuttings by leaning on them with a glove or rolled-up jacket between the end of the sett and one's chest to minimise bruising and blisters. Use a crow-bar to punch holes in hard clayey soil or when planting thick setts. Be sure the setts reach moist earth. Push 600mm (2') cuttings in to at least half their depth.

5 After pushing them in, firm down the soil around the stem. If it is uncertain that they are deep enough, or if they seem loose, hammer them home with a wooden maul. Try not to split them. Split setts may grow, but there is the risk that they may develop badly, or simply dry out or rot.

An alternative to the above method is to take shorter setts of about 300mm (1") length from one-year growths. These setts can be inserted through strips of black polythene laid out in rows on the ground, with the edges buried. The advantages of this technique are that there are no weeds to contend with, the plants are easier to lift in the autumn, and more cuttings can be obtained from the mother plant.

LAYERING

Some shrubs spread readily by putting out layers, i.e. side shoots which bend down and root where they touch the ground, forming a new but still connected plant. A number of species can be artificially layered by pegging a shoot to the bare ground and covering it with soil. The bent shoot will form roots during its first growing season, after which it should be separated from its parent shrub by cutting through the shoot. The layer is then left for a further season to establish itself before being transplanted. Further information on this technique will be found in Sheat (1957) and in chapter 7, on p124.

Nursery Soil Fertility

The most important soil nutrients required for tree growth in the nursery include nitrogen (N), phosphorus (P), potassium (K), magnesium (Mg), calcium (Ca) and sulphur (S). These may or may not be available in suitable quantities to begin with, and may become depleted after crops of seedlings have been grown. The most important things to check for are pH (acidity-alkalinity), N, P, K, Mg and Ca. Tree seedlings need much less calcium, on the whole, than garden plants, so don't worry about this factor unless the soil is very acid. Normal calcium and also sulphur requirements are adequately provided by such fertilizers as potassic superphosphate. You can use fairly cheap garden testing kits (e.g. 'Sudbury Soil Test Kit', available from garden supply stores) to assess the pH, N, P and K. Follow the instructions supplied with the kit. Aldous (1972) describes nutrient deficiency symptoms (e.g. of Mg, which is not included in garden test kits).

FERTILIZING METHODS

Using organic fertilizers

Regular dressings of organic fertilizers improve the fertility of all cultivated soils. They ameliorate many adverse soil conditions. The water-holding capacity of sandy soils prone to drought is increased. Soil structure is improved, and the preparation of a good seedbed is easier. Organic fertilizers increase microbial and faunal activity in the soil, including earthworm activity. They also have the advantage of providing a use for industrial and agricultural by-products. The farmyard muck heap contains weed seed and, occasionally, lime. You might want to try farmyard manure anyway, if it is freely available and you already have a weedy site. Farmyard manure needs to be well-rotted, since it will cause a decline in soil nitrogen if used raw. Record the soil pH to make sure it doesn't rise too much. Two organic fertilizers favoured by nurserymen are hop waste and bracken-hop waste compost.

Hop waste is weed-free but low in potassium, which should be added by means of a small dose of inorganic potassic superphosphate or a top dressing of a potassium fertilizer. Hop waste is used raw, not composted, and should be stored undercover to minimise the leaching effects of rain. The usual dosage is 2.4-3.8kg per square metre ($4^1{}_2$-7lb per square yard) dug into seedbeds in the autumn, and about 1.25kg per square metre (2lb 5oz per square yard) dug into transplant beds. These rates apply to ordinary hop waste, but pressed hop waste, which has about half its water squeezed out, should be applied at three-quarters the usual rate.

Bracken-hop waste compost is a balanced NPK fertilizer ideal for seedlings, and like hop waste it is virtually free from weed seeds. It is labour-intensive to make, bulky to store and must be prepared in advance. Make it as follows:

1 Cut the bracken in July just as the tips of the fronds are uncurling.

2 Chaff the bracken into pieces 25-50mm (1-2") long.

3 Site the compost heap on a hard floor, preferably one which has a sump so that seepage from the heap can be collected and returned. Build up layers of bracken and hop waste in the ratio of three parts bracken to one part hops by volume.

4 Moisten the heap and cover it with unchaffed bracken or straw. As the heap ferments, it heats up in a week to 50°C or more.

5 When the temperature starts to fall, uncover the heap, turn it, add water if it is at all dry, and cover it again to heat a second time. When it cools a second time it is ready to use. Apply bracken-hop waste at 5kg per square metre (about 9lb per square yard).

Fallowing and greencropping

Before the advent of inorganic and balanced organic fertilizers, fallowing and greencropping were widely used to restore the soil nitrogen and reduce weed build-up. These days they are really only necessary if you have areas of the nursery which you want to hold over without planting due to lack of time, labour or trees. To keep an area fallow, cultivate it shallowly by hoeing or raking whenever there is a good showing of weed seedlings, or at monthly intervals to prevent the fast-growing weeds from setting seed.

In parts of the country with more than 1000mm (40") of rain each year, it may be hard to cultivate the soil repeatedly without damaging the soil structure. Greencropping can be used instead of fallowing, to 'smother' weeds and improve soil fertility. The best greencrops are oats (for soils with pH above 5.5), blue or yellow lupins or rye-grass (for any soil). Sow Yielder or Castleton potato oats in May at 40-50g per square metre (1¼-1½oz per square yard), and dig them in when the ears are visible but still green. Sow lupins in May or June at 45g per square metre (1¼oz per square yard), and dig them in after the flowers have opened but before the seed has set. Sow rye-grass in April for a summer crop or between a previous greencrop, and in mid-September for an autumn crop. Sow perennial rye-grass at 34g per 10 square metres (about 1oz per 10 square yards). Mow the grass regularly and dig in the summer crop in late August and the autumn crop whenever the ground is to be brought into tree production.

Using inorganic fertilizers

Most commercial nurseries rely on inorganic fertilizers, which have the advantage of allowing you to apply regulated amounts of those nutrients which your soil requires. They are weed-free, easy and compact to store, and easy to apply. One disadvantage of them, however, is that non-renewable resources are required to produce them. Therefore, where organic fertilizers are readily available, their use should be considered instead. The main inorganic fertilizers used in forest nurseries are listed below. For details of how to use them (timing, quantity, etc.), consult Aldhous (1972).

a P and PK fertilizers (potassic superphosphate), e.g. 'Double Season PK'.

b NPK fertilizers, e.g. 'Enmag' and 'Double Season 55'.

c N fertilizers, e.g. 'Nitram', 'Nitro Chalk' and ammonium sulphate.

d N and NK fertilizers.

e Mg fertilizers, e.g. Epsom salts, 'Enmag' and Kieserite.

f Ca fertilizers, e.g. ground limestone or chalk.

Polyhouses

GENERAL

Polyhouses, also called 'polytunnels', are polythene shelters designed for growing containerised seedlings, and have been used for several decades by professional nurserymen. They provide a good alternative to the traditional open-sown tree nursery if the soil in your nursery area is inappropriate for raising seedlings, if the nursery is located in an area of cooler temperatures or constant wind, or simply if you wish to concentrate on container growing. Seedlings raised in polyhouses must be hardened off, like greenhouse plants, before transplanting elsewhere or final planting.

Polyhouses come in many sizes. The smaller models, at about 2.5m wide, 2m high and 3m plus long, are intended for use as garden greenhouses but may be suitable for other small sites. Larger polyhouses available to the retail market come in widths of about 4-10m (14-33') and lengths of 5m (16') plus. Prices will vary with supplier.

Polyhouse frames are hoops, usually made of galvanised steel, which are joined at the top by a steel ridge, or purlin, and further supported by diagonal brace tubes at each corner. The hoops are anchored on foundation tubes, the ends of which are set in the ground and usually concreted. The sheeting used for the cover should be 600 gauge opaque white polythene with a lifespan of three to four years. Any rips that occur in the cover during that period can be repaired with matching patches or tape. You will, of course, need to include regular replacement of the cover in your costing estimates, although the frame should last about 30 years.

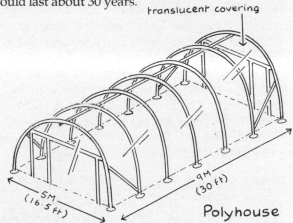

Polyhouse

The simplest polyhouses have a treated timber-frame or roll-up door at one end which serves as both access and ventilation. Suppliers of polyhouses and the equipment designed for use in them are listed on p148. Note the following points:

a The size of polyhouse you choose will depend mainly on the space available. The next deciding factor is the number of seedlings you require, not only during the first year but at peak times in the future. For example, if the requirement is 16,000 seedlings sown in Sherwood-sized Rootrainers (see p76), 500 trays containing 32 cells each will be needed, and this will occupy about 44 square metres (400 square feet).

b Pathways 450-600mm (1'6"-2') wide are required down the length of the polyhouse so that all trays of seedlings can be reached by hand.

c The polyhouse must be situated near a source of water and erected, if possible, in an east/west orientation.

d Access by vehicles will be necessary.

e A flat space adjoining the polyhouse is useful for storing seedlings during the hardening-off period.

If erecting the polyhouse yourself, line the hoops up with each other, sink and secure the ends in the ground, and attach the supports, following the manufacturer's instructions. Choose a sunny, warm day to put the polythene cover on, and stretch it tightly over the hoops. The reason for this is that polythene expands in warm weather and, if put on in the cold, will later loosen, flap about and eventually deteriorate.

CONTAINER GROWING IN POLYHOUSES

Single rigid pots are suitable only for small-scale growing. Two types of container commonly used in polyhouses are the following:

a Paperpot system JPP ('JPP' signifies 'Japanese paper pot'). These pots are made of biodegradeable paper and resistant fibres which are formed into series of hexagonal paper tubes, held together with a water-soluble glue. They come in a range of sizes which vary in both diameter and depth, and therefore in the number of cells per set. Paper pots arrive flat, and each set needs to be pulled out like a concertina and clipped into a 600 x 400mm plastic tray to be ready for use. The trays have sides which open out to allow access to the pots when the seedlings are ready to plant. The pots themselves are easily detached from one another at the time of planting.

The three grades of paper used in the pots are:

B Grade, for 4-6 week propagation

V Grade, for 7-9 week propagation

F Grade, for 3-12 month propagation.

F Grade is the one most suitable for growing trees. The most likely size for growing hardwoods is the F515, which has a 50mm diameter and a depth of 150mm. There are 130 pots to a set.

b Rootrainers. These are moulded plastic pots or cells which come four or five to the set, or 'book'. Because the books are hinged and can be opened out, it is possible to observe soil condition and root systems without harming the seedlings, and to remove the plants easily when they are ready. The lengthwise grooves in each cell promote straight root development. They range in size from 80-200mm in depth, and 65-350ml in volume; a 1000ml-volume cell is now also available. Rootrainers arrive flat and opened out. They should be closed and placed in 360 x 210 x 90mm trays to be ready for filling and sowing. The number of books per tray varies between 8 and 14.

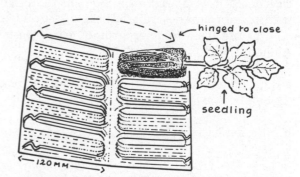

Rootrainer (Sherwood size) 'book' shown opened out

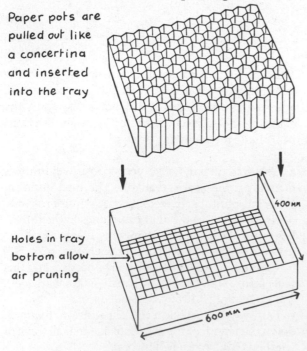

Paper pots are pulled out like a concertina and inserted into the tray

Holes in tray bottom allow air pruning

Japanese paper pot system

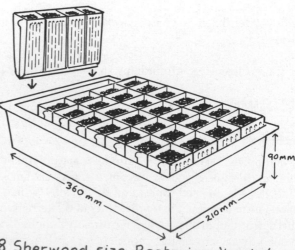

8 Sherwood size Rootrainer 'books' fitted into tray, shown after sowing

The best size for growing hardwoods is the Sherwood, with a depth of 120mm and a volume of 175ml. This provides eight books with four cells each to accommodate 32 seedlings per tray.

Suppliers of both types of container are listed on p148.

PRODUCTION OF SEEDLINGS

1 Seed. Seed must be obtained ready for sowing in late March to early April, but no later than May, as this may not leave time for hardening off at the end of the season. Moreover, if seed is sown late, temperatures in the polyhouse can induce dormancy and reduce germination.

Seed will normally have to be stored from autumn until the sowing period - ideally, in a store at a temperature of 2-5°C, e.g. the main compartment of a refrigerator. Only good quality seed should be used in container growing. Seed should also chit before sowing, as every pot or cell should have a viable seed in it to prevent waste of time and money. As with seed grown in traditional nurseries, some pre-treatment may be required. For detailed information on pre-treatment of the seed of most common species, refer to Gordon and Rowe (Forestry Commission Bulletin 59, 1982). Page 62 and Table 5A on pages 60-61 of this chapter, also give rough guidelines on pre-treatment.

2 Filling/sowing. Put the sets (paper pots or Rootrainers) into the trays and fill and compact the cells to approximately twice their volume. Use a prepared medium which includes fertiliser, such as a container compost. In view of the destruction of peatlands, peat-based composts are not recommended.

For large seed, fill the cells to within 50mm (2") of the top. After sowing, add more medium until the seed is just covered. For small seed, fill the cells to within 10mm (1/2") of the top. Sow the seed on the surface and cover with a layer of lime-free washed grit or sand. If you are using paper pots, make sure that you fill them so that no paper is visible at the top of the pots on the inside, as otherwise the paper draws moisture out of the medium.

Very small seed may have to be sown in groups and thinned out later. Remember to sow more seed than is necessary, as not all seed will produce acceptable seedlings.

3 Placing of sets. The sets may be placed on sand or gravel, but if so the roots of the seedlings will require pruning at regular intervals. Alternatively, the sets can be placed on open mesh benches, where rooting is controlled by 'air pruning', or exposure to air.

4 Germination environment. The pots require a thorough watering. Small seed should be covered with polythene until germination starts, but large seed does not require covering.

5 Watering. Water is necessary once germination starts, but only enough to keep the medium moist.

6 Fertilizing. The sowing medium will normally contain enough fertiliser for the start of germination, but a top dressing of soluble fertiliser will thereafter be needed to maintain good growth. When choosing a fertiliser, remember that it should contain nitrogen, phosphorus, potassium and organic compost. For further information on fertilisers, see p74.

7 Disease. Close attention to hygiene must be observed to reduce the risk of disease. Fungal diseases and oak mildew will be the most common problems. For treatment, see p68.

8 Pests and insects. Mice are usually a problem, and the polyhouse should be kept clear of them before sowing and while the seeds are still vulnerable. Always be on the lookout for any insects that can cause damage to the seed or seedlings.

9 Hardening off. After approximately 16 weeks, some of the faster growing species will need to be taken out of the polyhouse to harden off before planting. The others will follow at intervals. Regularly check all seedlings to monitor their health.

RECORD KEEPING

As the people staffing the polyhouse may change periodically, it is important to keep records. Always try to choose the same day each week for a full inspection of the polyhouse.

A record sheet might contain the following information:

1 Where seed was obtained

2 How seed was stored until needed for pre-treatment or sowing

3 Method of chitting, and results

4 Date sown, including types of container and medium

5 Time taken for seeds to germinate

6 Dates of fertiliser applications

7 Stocktaking - number of trees and average heights

8 Date hardening off commenced

9 Date of despatch, and destination

10 Daily weather conditions (if possible)

11 Any other comments for future reference.

Planting and Early Care

Like most other aspects of working with trees, planting cannot be considered in isolation. The sources for the trees, the care with which they are handled before planting, and the protection and early care they receive post-planting are all as important as the planting process itself. This chapter looks at all these concerns, covering the purchase of plants from a commercial nursery, site preparation, lifting of young trees from the nursery, planting methods, tree protection and early care. Aftercare is discussed in chapter 7.

Buying from a Nursery

If you have successfully established your own tree nursery (chapter 5), your supply of quality planting stock of known provenance (p58) is assured. Buying from an established nursery will save you the time and expense involved in seed collection and raising trees, but you will have to carefully check the provenance of the native trees you buy, as much native stock is of foreign origin. The quality of the trees, and their condition on arrival, will also need to be assessed. Prices for trees will vary according to their species and size, with discounts for quantity purchases. Packing and transport charges may be extra.

A cheap alternative to purchasing larger plants is to buy seedlings wholesale from a nursery and line them out (p70) for a year or two before transplanting. This could be worthwhile if you need a large number of trees, provided that you have a suitable lining-out site and can plan the programme in advance. See p148 for a list of nurseries.

Checking provenance

If the nursery is unable to supply information on provenance, be wary. Some nurseries list the provenance of each species in their catalogues, and many now have a policy of increasing the use of seed from British seed sources. A few may also engage in 'contract growing', i.e. raising plants from seed of acceptable provenance for you, if you collect and supply it (see p58).

The Forest Reproductive Material Regulations 1977 (p57) can provide a check on provenance, depending on the species and the objectives of your planting scheme. For example, you may want to buy beech or pedunculate oak transplants, both species covered by the Regulations, for a scheme aimed primarily at timber production. In this case, the nursery you buy

them from must give you a suppliers' certificate, which contains information on the origin and provenance of the trees, within 14 days of sale or delivery. The Forestry Commission, which administers the Regulations, should be contacted if you have any questions about the information on the certificate.

Checking quality

It is best to visit the nursery beforehand to check on the overall quality of the plants on offer, as you will then have a basis for complaint if the plants they deliver are of inferior quality. If this is not possible, it is a good idea to ask for a sample from the nursery beforehand. Check to see that the sample has a well-developed fibrous root system and reasonable recent shoot growth, which you can gauge by the spacing of the buds. Poor growth in the nursery is indicated by tightly clustered buds on the leader (Hibberd, 1989, p75).

Be especially wary of cheap, end-of-season nursery 'bargains'. Poor-quality plants, or those in bad condition, will need to be returned after delivery. For inspection of the plants' condition on delivery and pre-planting care, see pp85-86.

ORDERING NURSERY PLANTS

Local suppliers of trees may be listed in the Yellow Pages under 'Nurseries-Horticultural' or 'Garden Centres', but most of these will be suppliers of container-grown ornamental stock. For native trees in quantity, your best starting point is to contact the local tree officer at the County or District Council, who should be able to give you the names of local suppliers. Look in the 'countryside and farming' section of your local newspaper, and for larger growers, in the national forestry and horticultural magazines such as 'Forestry and British Timber', 'Horticulture Week', 'Nurserymen and Garden Centre' and 'The Grower'. Each August, 'Horticulture Week' publishes a booklet of 'Nursery Stock Suppliers', which gives current details of the majority of suppliers in the UK. Although mainly for amenity stock, this includes information on suppliers of forest seedlings. The National Farmers Union and the Horticultural Trades Association will advise on specialist suppliers. The Forestry Commission sell surplus planting stock through their various conservancy offices.

It is best to place orders as early as possible, but at least by July or August for supply in the late autumn/winter. Lifting of open ground stock will take place from October/November, depending on the species concerned, and the season. If mild weather continues late into the autumn, lifting will have to be delayed as this cannot be done until cold weather has stopped plant growth and hardened shoots. When placing an order, request delivery by a certain date if necessary, but be prepared to be flexible, as either mild or very wet weather can affect lifting, just as very wet or cold weather can delay planting.

Preparation for Planting

SIZE OF TREES TO PLANT

The table following gives the nomenclature for trees of various sizes, along with the usual planting distances for each size. Other criteria for determining planting distances are given on p86. This metric system is standard throughout the nursery trade.

'Feathered' trees are well furnished with branches from low on the stem. 'Standard' trees have a specified length of clear stem below a crown of branches.

Name	Overall Height	Planting Distance
Seedling (one year old in Rootrainer/Japanese paper pot)	variable	2-3m
Transplant	20-40cm	2-3m
Whip	60-90cm	3-4m
Whip or feathered whip	90-120cm	3-4m
Feathered whip	150-180cm	4-5m
Feathered whip	180-210cm	6m
Light standard	250-275cm (150-180cm stem)	10m +
Standard	275-300cm	10m +
Selected standard	300-360cm (180-215cm stem)	10m +
Extra heavy nursery stock	5m +	20m +

When deciding the size of tree to plant, keep the following points in mind:

a Trees for forestry use are usually planted as '1+1' or '1 + 2' transplants (p69), as these are much hardier than plants of equal size which have not been moved prior to final planting out. Some broadleaves (e.g. oak), however, may be of adequate size as '1 + 0' plants.

One year seedlings in Rootrainers or Japanese paper pots (p76) are becoming more popular, as their use maximises the benefits of using tree shelters. Planting

with the root-ball intact results in high survival rates and strong early growth, as well as an extended planting season. In addition, heling-in is not required, the plants will not dry out if planting is delayed, and the evenly sized rootballs ensure easier planting. They are, however, more expensive and bulky to transport than plants supplied bare rooted.

Small trees survive transplanting better than larger ones of the same species, as large plants may check after planting and be slow in establishing. The optimum size for most broadleaved species is 25-30cm. More important than the height is the root collar diameter, as thin, spindly plants are more likely to die than shorter but sturdier ones. For plants in the 25-50cm range, the root collar diameter should be at least 5mm.

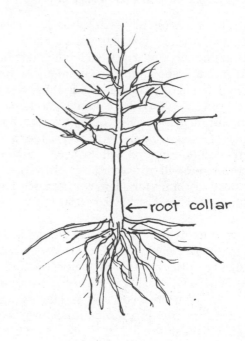

←root collar

An exception is alder, which should be 45-70cm ('1 + 1'). Alder seedlings grow rapidly but '1 + 0' plants are not recommended because survival is often poor (Evans, 1984, p31). Plants which are '1 u 2' (p69) are acceptable.

Container-grown transplants appear to be more successful than field-grown transplants in difficult soils, as well as allowing for early or late season planting.

b In shelterbelts or hedges, '1 + 2' or '2 + 2' plants, 30-60cm tall, are often planted instead of the somewhat smaller and younger trees favoured in forestry. If you will be using hawthorn, '1 + 2' plants should have been cut back to 225mm (9"), and should be bushy plants with a diameter of 10-12mm at the root collar.

PLANTING SEASON AND WEATHER PRECAUTIONS

Plant fully hardy trees any time over the season (October to March or April) other than in hard frosty or cold windy weather. Hard frost is most likely in January and February. Plant half-hardy species (suitable only for western coastal districts) in spring.

Hardy deciduous trees are best planted before Christmas. They will survive spring planting but are more likely to suffer from drought than if planted in the autumn or early winter. Birch and beech, especially, are bad risks if planted after the end of February.

Evergreens are best planted either early or late in the season, when their roots are somewhat active. Spring planting should take place when the soil has begun to warm but before the first flush of new growth.

In dry areas, early autumn planting is best for most species, other things being equal, to give the tree a chance to become established before spring droughts. In wet areas, early spring planting is generally best, to minimise the risk of uprooting in winter gales. Spring planting is also considered better in western locations, as the combination of moister soils and frost often causes excessive frost heave in winter which can expose roots and even lift the entire plant.

Avoid planting in sunny, windy, drying weather. Choose cloudy and drizzly weather if possible. Be sure to firm up trees (p105) if hard frosts or storms occur in the weeks after planting.

Although container-grown plants can theoretically be planted at any time of year, the above guidelines will give best results. A mulch (p102) should be applied if planting is done in late spring or summer, and the plants should be watered during dry spells for the first growing season.

SITE PREPARATION

Clearance, cultivation and drainage

On any planting site, large-scale clearance, cultivation or drainage is costly, requiring equipment and skills which are usually beyond the scope of volunteers. The disturbance to sites created by such operations can also be very destructive environmentally. To avoid the need for such measures, choose suitable species for existing site conditions (p20) and do not plant under heavy shade or in boggy patches where trees will do poorly. On grassland sites, spot clearance will be necessary. Grass competes strongly with young trees for moisture and nutrients, so the sward should be destroyed at each planting position by scraping or applying herbicide (p108) on an area about 1m in diameter. See Blatchford (1978, pp22-7) for further information.

If the site is completely overrun with woody growth, shrubs and brambles, however, some clearance and weed control may be unavoidable. This can be done by hand or machine clearance, or with herbicides formulated for use on woody weeds (p112). Simply cutting a small area for each tree is not sufficient, as cutting stimulates growth, and any gaps made by uprooting will soon be filled by the growth of surrounding shrubs. The action taken will depend on the species present, the type of site, and the objective of planting. Aside from rhododendron, Japanese knotweed, cherry laurel and some other species, existing shrubs may well have some wildlife value, and the best approach may be to clear areas and plant groups of trees. Where woody shrubs are cut rather than uprooted, the stumps will need to be chemically treated (p112) to prevent re-sprouting.

On some sites it may be possible to use farm animals to help with clearance. Pigs will dig out roots as well as clear top growth. Cattle, sheep and goats may also be useful, depending on the type of growth and the fencing. Cattle, for example, not only graze on unwanted vegetation but also tread down bracken very effectively. Be aware, however, that animals can become poisoned by eating unusually large amounts of broadleaved plants and shrubs in lieu of grass. Sheep grazing on brambles may also become entangled in them.

Other sites, on farmland and in urban areas, may also need specific treatment. As indicated in chapter 2, urban sites can be more problematic than others, not least because compaction, waterlogging and poor, toxic or non-existent soil are often found on them. Compaction can be caused not only by heavy machinery, but also by pedestrian traffic, especially when the soil is wet. Faced with a large, heavily compacted new site, the most that you can do, in the absence of bulldozers, is to dig larger planting pits than usual and refill them loosely to the appropriate planting depth. When you plant the tree, the looser earth in the pit will allow the roots to establish more easily. In such an extreme case it is, however, preferable to arrange for the treatment of the entire area by hiring equipment and labour to rip or subsoil the ground in summer, when the soil is dry. Heavy metal toxicity is very difficult to treat and may make soils unusable, but soil which is full of rubble or lacking in nutrients can be planted with tolerant species (Hibberd, 1989, pp44-7).

On farms, most land will be in good condition for tree planting, provided the soil is not waterlogged. If it is, mound planting (p90) is a useful technique which does not require the use of heavy machinery unless the planting area is very large. Pastures are suitable for transplanting but, as mentioned above, grass must be removed at each planting position. If the soil on the site has been repeatedly cultivated for many years, a 'plough pan' (compacted underlayer of soil) may have developed. This can lead to unstable root systems and reduced growth, and so should be broken up, if feasible, by overal\l deep cultivation of the planting site (Hibberd, 1988, p30).

Fencing

It is usually necessary to fence around newly planted or coppiced trees, to prevent damage by rabbits, livestock or deer, and to reduce trespass. Design and materials are given in the BTCV handbook 'Fencing' (Agate, 1986), and Pepper and Tee (1986). For details of individual tree protection, see p96.

Keep the following points in mind:

a Note the points on on the most economical shapes to fence, and on comparative costs of fences and individual guards, on page 95.

b Post-and-wire fencing is usually the cheapest and most effective type, especially against rabbits and deer. Ordinary strained wire is often adequate but high tensile spring-steel fencing may be preferable, as fewer posts are required to erect a taut and stock-proof fence. This is especially useful in either stony or very soft ground where it is difficult to erect posts.

Although it is an unusual problem, it is worth noting that incidental damage can occur to young trees from new galvanized wire netting. Zinc dissolved from the netting by rainwater may leach through the soil and kill the roots of small trees. If you are using such netting, choose lengths which have been stored long enough for the zinc plating to have oxidised, as it will not then be so toxic to plants (Hibberd, 1989, p114).

Where rabbits and deer are not a problem, consider renovating and maintaining any existing hedges or dry stone walls rather than replacing them with fences. See 'Hedging' (Brooks, 1975) and 'Dry Stone Walling' (Brooks, 1977) for details. Post-and-rail or chestnut paling fences may be more appropriate in parkland or amenity areas, or on ground where straining posts cannot be secured firmly.

c Include gates and stiles where necessary for access. If you have to put netting across an existing badger run, put in a badger gate. It is advisable to patrol any new netting lines regularly for the first two to three weeks to check for badger holes, as these will indicate other locations for installing gates. See Rowe (1976) or Neal (1982) for details.

d When fencing against rabbits, make sure the bottom 150mm (6") of netting is turned outward, to prevent rabbits from burrowing underneath. Hold the netting down with thick turfs, stones or wire pegs, or bury it when you set the fence up (p63). Rabbits must be eliminated from the fenced area before you plant.

e Do not use barbed wire in deer fences, nor as the top wire when fencing against horses, as these animals are easily injured by the barbs. Also avoid using it in fences which line public footpaths.

See page 95 for information regarding the height of fence required against different animals.

LIFTING, TRANSPORTING AND PRE-PLANTING CARE

Every year, thousands of trees are planted which are already dead, due to careless handling while being lifted and transported to their planting site. Plants are extremely vulnerable to damage from any drying out, heating up or rough handling they may undergo during this stage. Unless great care is taken, the work of several seasons in a tree nursery will be lost.

In order to try and prevent these losses, the Joint Liaison Committee on Plant Supplies, which represents various professional organisations, has issued the 'Code of Practice for Plant Handling' (revised 1985). This three-part code comprises the following - Part 1: Specifications for packaging and transporting nursery stock; Part 2: Recommendations for plant handling from lifting until delivery to site; Part 3: Recommendations for plant handling from delivery to site to successful establishment.

This code is a useful practical guide for all aspects of plant handling if you are growing your own plants. If you are buying in, the Code is a good form of protection, as any plants received from a commercial nursery should be packaged, handled and transported in accordance with it. If this is not included by the nursery as part of their normal terms of business, the purchaser can stipulate that the supplier adheres to the Code in any contract to supply plants. Copies of the Code, in a booklet called 'Plant Handling', are available from the Horticultural Trades Association.

During lifting and transporting, it is essential to:

a Prevent drying of the roots.

b Keep as much short fibrous root on the trees as possible.

c Avoid damaging the roots, breaking the stem tops or stripping bark from stem or roots.

d Prevent heating, by maintaining air circulation around the stems and foliage of trees in storage or transit. Heat is generated by bacteria and microorganisms on the plants, especially on the leaves of evergreens. Plants are seriously weakened and may be killed if they become warm to the touch at any stage between lifting and planting.

Ideally, plants should be lifted while dormant, packed and immediately despatched to the planting site without any period in store. Temporary storage is sometimes necessary, however, and in this case you will have to hele the plants in or place them in plastic bags (see below).

If you are running your own tree nursery, the points on lifting listed below should be followed when the plants are ready for despatch to the planting site.

Lifting small trees

1 The method for lifting transplants and whips is the same as that used for lifting seedlings for transplanting (see pp69-70). Transplants and whips should be lifted and shifted as bare rooted plants, i.e. with no ball of soil around the roots. Remember to use a garden fork, as a spade may damage the roots.

2 Once the plants have been lifted, put them into plastic sacks or lay them in a barrow or trailer with the roots covered with plastic. Take them immediately to a cool shed, or behind a screen out of sun and wind, for sorting. As with seedlings for transplanting, cut off any roots over 150-175mm (6-7") long. Avoid over pruning the roots, aiming instead for a balanced root:shoot ratio. Prune off any multiple leaders to leave a single strong leader on each tree. This step is particularly important for trees with two strong leaders which form a tight fork, as in mature trees such forks are vulnerable to cracking and infection at the join. Ruthlessly cull and burn all diseased, spindly or damaged plants and those with inadequate root systems, as these are not worth planting.

3 Count and bundle the plants into suitable units while sorting. Tie the bundles loosely with natural fibre (e.g. bailer twine) or soft synthetic fibre - not polypropylene, which can cut the bark very easily. If the plants are going to be transported to the planting site within about seven days, they can be packed directly into plastic bags (see below). If there is going to be some delay before the plants are despatched, they must be temporarily stored. Bare-rooted plants can be heled in (see below), or for shorter periods, kept outside in a moist, cool, sheltered, shaded place, with the roots covered with damp compost. Protect against damage by rodents. Alternatively, plants can be kept in an unheated shed for a week or more, out of the sun and with the roots covered with damp compost. If storage is needed for a few days only, put the plants in plastic bags tied at the top, and store upright in a cool shady position or shed. Check once

or twice to find out transpiration rates; if excessive, open up the bags to allow the foliage to dry.

Lifting larger trees

Trees over 90cm (36") tall require more care than smaller transplants. Broadleaved trees may be planted bare-rooted but are more safely planted with a ball of earth around the roots. Conifers of this size should always be planted with a root ball.

The limiting factor when moving large trees is the size and weight of root ball required. For a tree of 38mm (1^{1}_{2}") diameter at 150mm (6") above ground level, the ball should be 450mm (18") in diameter. A root ball this size weighs about 115kg (250lb), and this is about the maximum which volunteers should attempt to move.

A general rule of thumb when deciding on the size of the root ball is to dig around the tree at the drip line, under the outermost branches, where most of the feeding roots are concentrated. Keep the following points in mind:

a If the soil is so dry that the root ball is likely to crumble when lifted, water it thoroughly two days before lifting. If the soil is too wet, postpone the job! Extra water means extra weight.

b Prune any limbs which may get in the way during lifting and transport, or wrap them in hessian and tie them to the main stem to keep them from rubbing. If lifting the plants by sling or tractor, protect the main stems with sacking.

c If the tree has a large crown, prune it before moving to reduce the demands of the branches and leaves on the root system (p114). Evergreens may benefit from a spray of anti-desiccant, e.g. S600 or Foliguard. These are non-toxic plastic materials which form a film on the foliage and reduce transpiration.

d As with small trees, avoid lifting in hot sun or drying, windy weather.

Two people are needed. Follow this procedure:

1 If the ground is soft, score a deep circle around the tree at the diameter of the root ball to cut most of the lateral roots. Use a pointed spade. If the soil is hard or stony, dig a trench, using a mattock if necessary.

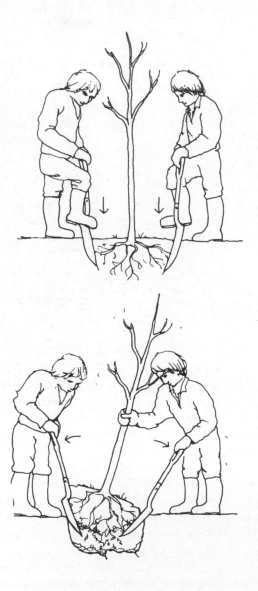

2 The two people should stand on either side of the circle. Push the spades as far under the root-ball as possible to lever the tree up. Don't pull on the trunk or limbs to loosen the tree, since this may shatter the root-ball.

If the tree remains anchored by long bottom roots, loop a winch cable around the roots and tighten to sever them.

3 When the tree and its root-ball tear free of the earth, keep the spades underneath to hold up the ball. If the ball falls apart, quickly wrap the main roots in damp sacking or hessian to keep them moist. Use one piece of sacking on each major root. This way, if a piece comes loose only part of the root system dries out.

4 Lay a square of sacking or hessian, big enough to wrap around the root-ball, to one side of the hole. Then gently manoeuvre the tree out of the hole, remove the spades and fasten the cloth tightly around the ball with rope.

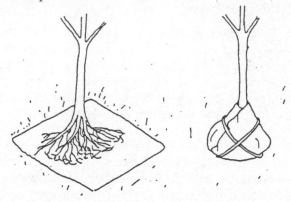

If the tree is to be loaded into a vehicle, push a stout round rod into the ball next to the stem before wrapping it up. The rod should project a few inches beyond the end of the stem to protect the tip.

Heling-in

If plants need to be held for some weeks or even months before planting, the best storage method is to hele-in (customarily, though incorrectly, spelt heel-in), known as 'sheughing' in Scotland. Plants may be heled-in loose or in counted bundles.

1 Dig a trench in good fresh moist soil which will not dry out or become waterlogged. Cultivated nursery soil is ideal. Dig the trench with a sloping back, deep enough so that the plants can be put in and their roots completely covered.

2 Trees in bundles should be separated and spaced along the trench, to keep the plants in the centres of the bundles from drying out or - in the case of evergreens - from heating up. It is convenient to place a marker stick every 50 or 100 plants to save counting later. Place the plants with their roots completely in the trench but with their tops mostly out. With standards, make sure that they are laid close to the ground to avoid being blown about by the wind.

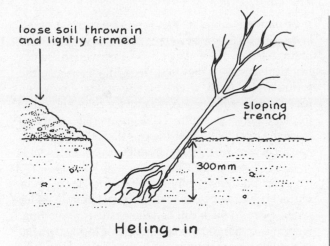

loose soil thrown in
and lightly firmed

sloping
trench

300mm

Heling-in

3 If you anticipate having to lift the plants in very frosty weather, cover the roots in a thick layer of straw to prevent the soil from freezing to them.

4 Throw soil over the roots to cover them and lightly firm the soil around the roots by treading.

Packing in bags

Where plants are going to be no more than about seven days from lifting to planting, they can be packed in polythene bags. Use bags of 250 gauge polythene, or 500 gauge if you want to re-use the bags. Co-extruded polythene (black inside, white outside) is the recommended choice.

If possible, try to sort and pack the plants so that the bags don't have to be opened or re-packed again before planting, as this will save a lot of time and trouble, and will also minimise drying of the roots. If, for example, three teams will be planting mixed species in different areas of the site, bag up the plants needed in three lots and affix labels. It is easiest to write the labels out beforehand, with the aid of the planting plan. Use plastic plant labels (or old plastic jerry cans cut into strips) and waterproof pens, and include species name, number of plants, planting team or code which refers to the planting plan, and any other relevant information. To minimise delays, try to organise all the lifting, sorting, counting, bundling, bagging and labelling with a small team of workers.

1 Pack all plants with their shoots in the same direction. Plants up to 45cm (18") tall can be entirely enclosed in the bag, which should be tied at the top. Needles or leaves of evergreen plants should be dry when put into bags, as otherwise they may rot. Thorny plants, and all plants over 45cm (18") should have just the roots enclosed, with the bag securely tied around the stems. Plants 60cm (24") and taller may have roots too large to bag easily. Keep the roots moist and protected by covering them with straw and wrapping them in plastic.

2 Squeeze the bags gently to expel excess air, and tie them with string. Attach labels (as above) or mark the bags with indelible felt pen to avoid confusion.

3 Store bagged trees in a well-ventilated shed or shelter, which should be kept at below 5°C. Bags must not be stacked for more than a few hours or the trees may heat up, and there is also the danger of the trees becoming crushed or otherwise damaged from over-stacking. If you stack at all, stack the plants no more than two or three layers deep, and ensure that air can get to at least one side of the bags. If stored for more than two or three days, bags should be opened and kept upright. Check periodically to see that the trees are not drying out. Keep bagged plants out of direct sunlight at all times to prevent them from heating up.

Transport

Bare-rooted plants should always be transported with at least their roots protected in plastic bags. Simply fixing a tarpaulin over the trees will not give them enough protection, either during the journey to the planting site or afterwards, when there will be inevitable delays before the trees are actually put into the ground. Remember that even a few minutes of exposure to wind or cold can damage the roots. Leave the plants in the bag until the moment you plant.

Keep the vehicle well ventilated and unheated. Placing bagged plants no more than two layers deep is the ideal. If transporting the plants on an open wagon, cover them with opaque sheeting so they are shaded from sunlight.

Root-balled trees should be packed individually in straw and secured in the vehicle by means of rope around the stems. Keep the rootballs covered and moisten them if the trip is long or in hot weather. Evergreens can be protected from water loss during transport by wrapping the crowns in opaque sheeting secured with string or rope.

Inspection of plants after delivery

If you buy plants from a nursery, inspect them on delivery. After checking numbers, species and quality (p79) of the stock, look for the indicators of condition listed below. Return any individual trees to the nursery if:

a The plants look dry and shrivelled. Plants in torn bags, for example, can dry out or, if the weather is cold, become vulnerable to frost damage.

b There are any signs of serious mechanical damage (e.g. broken or scarred stems).

c There is any evidence of fungal growth or insect pests.

Further examine any suspect plants by nicking the bark with your thumbnail. If the underlayer is greenish, the plant is still alive; if white or brownish, it is dead or dying. Where more than 5% of the plants are in poor condition, consider returning the entire consignment (Hibberd, 1989, p76).

Pre-planting care

a If only the roots of some plants appear dry, soak the roots in a tank of water for a few hours before planting.

b If you cannot plant the trees as soon as delivered, it is best to unpack them and hele them in, preferably in trenches dug in advance.

c If you receive the plants during a very cold period, wait until the frost ends to plant them. Place the unopened bundles in a dry, frost-free shed or cellar, where they will survive for two to three weeks if well covered with straw, bracken, sacking or newspapers. Check the bags for rodent damage periodically - mice have a preference for hawthorn, ash and hazel roots.

If the frost seems likely to continue for longer than this, undo the bundles but leave the packing around the roots and hele the plants in a trench, if you can manage to dig in the frozen ground. Ensure that no frozen soil touches any of the roots when you hele in.

PATTERNS, SPACINGS AND MIXTURES

Some patterns, spacings and mixtures have been suggested in chapter 2, under the headings for various types of planting sites. General guidelines follow.

Planting patterns

Trees may be planted in rows or in irregular clumps or random spacing. Row planting is best with transplants and small whips because it makes the trees easier to find later for weeding, although straight planting lines are not aesthetically pleasing and may not be suitable for many situations.

Of the various possible patterns, the simplest and most satisfactory is planting 'on the square', where the distance between rows is the same as the distance between trees in a row. In practice, this is never quite so uniform as might be expected, due to irregularities and obstacles on the ground. For planting on the square, the number of trees required is given by the formula:

$$N = \frac{A}{2d}$$

where N is the number of trees required, A is the area to be planted (in square feet or square metres), and d is the distance between trees in the row (in feet or metres). Where the distance between rows is different from the distance between trees in a row, use the formula $N = A/dl$, where l is the distance between rows. Where you need to account for rides and other unplantable areas, subtract 15% (an average estimate) from the total. Note that 1 acre = 43,560 square feet, and 1 hectare = 10,000 square metres.

Irregular patterns are more suitable for large, individually guarded trees which are planted at wider spacings and which can be seen easily for weeding. Here it is easier to take advantage of topographical variations. For example:

a On exposed sites, plant trees on the north or east side of sheltering stumps, boulders and hummocks for protection from prevailing southwesterly winds.

b On dry sites, or with moisture-loving trees, plant in dips, hollows and furrows.

c On damp sites, or where trees need good drainage, plant on hummocks, hillocks and ridges.

Spacings

Trees are usually spaced according to their size (see the table, p80). Bear in mind the following points:

a Conifers for timber production are now usually spaced not less than 1.8m (6') apart and normally 2m (6$\frac{1}{2}$-7'). Broadleaved trees are sometimes planted at the traditional distance of 1.2-1.5m (4-5') but 1.8m (6') or wider is more common. On weedy sites, plant at the wider spacings to minimise costs, as the fewer trees to weed, the lower the cost. Plant at closer spacings where lower survival rates are anticipated. A few broadleaved timber trees are planted at very wide spacings, e.g. 7.5m (24') for poplars and 9m (30') for cricket bat willow.

b Conservation and amenity trees can be planted at wider spacings, e.g. 3-3.5m (10-12'), where you expect the survival rate to be high and where you want the trees to develop spreading lower branches. Wide spacing also allows a herbaceous layer and self-seeded wild trees to grow up.

c Mature specimen trees, in parks, gardens or roadside situations, should be spaced widely so that they can develop a full crown. To prevent the site looking bare in early years, you can plant a variety of species that grow to different heights, or plant slow- and fast-growing species together. Alternatively, plant closely and thin later to give some of the trees sufficient room.

Broadleaved trees vary greatly in crown spread, but a total spread of about 40% of the mature height is usual. Crown spread of broadleaved trees can be increased in relation to height by lopping or pollarding, or restricted by fairly frequent pruning of side branches. Bear in mind, however, that it is always better to plant a tree with a smaller crown spread than to subject a tree to regular lopping or pollarding, as these practices can make the tree more vulnerable to infection.

WORK RATES AND ORGANISATION

Work rates

Rates vary greatly, depending on the size of the trees planted and the method used, the terrain and the experience and organisation of the planters. Rates for volunteers are about 80-100 notch-planted transplants (50-75 if in tree shelters), 15-20 pit-planted whips, or 4-5 pit-planted, staked and individually guarded standards, per person per day.

Organisation

The following points apply to mass plantings of small trees, where proper organisation can make a big difference to the work rate and the survival of trees:

a Each volunteer should have a plastic sack, a bag with a shoulder strap, or a bucket or other container, lined with moist earth or dampened sawdust (p49). This is used to carry the trees.

b Mark the line to be planted, using poles or stakes. For long lines, use at least three poles. It is usual to plant in echelon, with the leader setting the spacing along the sighted row, and the others following along adjacent rows a few plants back.

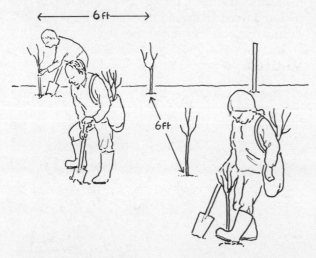

Use your planting tool, or a stick cut to length, to measure the distances between plants or to pace the spacings.

c It is often easiest for volunteers to work in pairs, with one person measuring the spacing and cutting the notch and the other person planting.

d On large tasks, one or more volunteers should act as couriers to keep the planters supplied with trees, stakes and guards as necessary. Provide extra containers so that some can be refilled while others are in use. It may be worth storing or heling-in the trees and stockpiling materials in several places around the site for convenience. Overnight storage of the plants on-site is not advisable, as rabbits can nip the tops of the trees if these are near ground level.

e When planting mixtures, stake out the boundaries of the bands or groups in advance. Then let people plant the rows within the bands or groups as for single-species planting.

f One person should always be allocated the job of following the planters, so that they can check and firm-in the trees if necessary.

The following points apply to pit-planting tasks where larger trees are used:

a When planting trees which do not need staking, work in teams of about six people, with four digging the holes and two planting the trees.

b When planting trees which need staking and extra protection, minimise the number of tools required by working in a production line. For example, three teams of two people dig the holes, two people put in stakes, two people plant and two people fix rabbit guards and tree ties, water the trees and help the others as needed, in that order.

Planting Methods

GENERAL RULES

a Keep fine root fibres moist at all times. If bare roots are exposed to the air on a hot, sunny or frosty, windy day, the root fibres can be killed within a minute or so. Even on a rainy day the trees' survival changes are greatly reduced if bare roots are exposed for more than a few minutes.

b Make planting holes big enough for the roots, as otherwise the trees grow poorly and develop weak root systems. Trim excessively long roots with a clean cut before planting, or make the holes deeper.

c Plant trees to the same depth at which they were growing in the nursery, shown by the soil mark on the stem at the root collar (see the diagram, p80). Trees planted too shallowly may dry out or be loosened by the wind. Those planted too deeply may rot.

d Plant trees with the stems vertical, as otherwise they tend to grow weak near the base and have poor form.

e Firm the soil around the plants by treading in with the heel. This fills in any air pockets and firmly anchors the roots. Take care not to scrape the bark when treading in, and be sure the trees stay vertical. Avoid leaving a depression around the stem where water can collect. Test for firmness by tugging the stem; the tree should not shift.

Check the trees again for firmness at least once in the first weeks after planting, and more often if there are heavy frosts or high winds.

f Protect and care for the trees as necessary after planting (see p102 and chapter 7).

NOTCH PLANTING

Notch or slit planting is the quickest method, but not the most reliable. It is generally suitable for the mass planting of bare-rooted transplants and whips under about 90cm (3') high. It should not be used in wet soil or for large and expensive trees or where failures must be minimised. There may be problems if it is used in heavy clay soils, as the notch can re-open in dry weather (Hibberd, 1989, p78).

The technique varies somewhat, according to the tool used (see p49). The choice of tool depends on the ground conditions as well as on personal preference. A small garden spade is the usual tool in most conditions, although the cranked blade may make it difficult to get a vertical slit. A Schlich or Mansfield planting spade can overcome this difficulty, as its blade is vertical. These specialist tools are also stronger than a garden spade and may be better for T-notching, although they can make it harder to plant trees firmly. When using a Schlich or Mansfield spade, firm up the roots by re-inserting the spade to one side and levering soil below ground towards the roots, which removes air pockets. A grubbing mattock is better in hard, stony, ploughed or steeply sloping ground or where much scarifying is needed. A dibber is useful when planting small trees in very light or sandy soil.

Basic procedure

Where there is a thick grassy mat or a mass of herbaceous weeds, the first step - whatever the planting tool used - is to clear a bare patch about 450mm (18") in diameter where the tree is to be planted by scarifying with a spade or mattock.

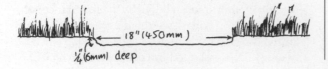

Use the following technique for planting with a garden spade:

1 Cut an L-, T- or H-shaped notch in the ground where the tree is to be planted. L-notching is usual, but use whatever system seems best to you. Make the cuts 150mm (6") deep or more, according to the length of the tree's roots. Make at least one of the cuts vertical so that the tree is held upright in the soil.

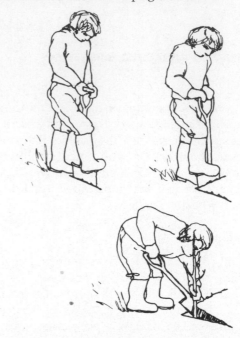

2 Lever the soil up with the spade to create a notch.

3 Take a tree from your bag or bucket and insert it in the notch a bit too deeply. Don't cram it in - use a wiping motion to get the roots well in, and then pull upwards a little to bring the root collar level with the soil surface, helping to straighten the roots. Don't pull too hard or you'll strip the roots.

4 Pull the spade out, taking care not to dislodge the tree, and tread in around the stem to firm the roots. Ensure that you leave no air pockets.

Variations

a When planting small trees in soft ground with a spade, make a notch simply by jamming the blade down and levering back or working the handle to and fro. Insert the tree, remove the spade and close the notch by treading.

b To L- or T-notch with a grubbing mattock, make the first cut with the tool's axe blade, then make a cross-cut with its adze blade and lift.

In suitable soil you can just jam the adze blade down and pull up on the handle to make a hole for planting. In very stony ground, you may need a pick-ended mattock to make a hole.

c To use a dibber, simply push the tool into the soil, work it around to make a conical hole, and drop in the plant.

With any of these variations, remember that it is essential to tread in carefully, to avoid leaving air pockets around the roots.

TURF PLANTING

This method is useful for planting small trees in wet ground, especially peaty soils, as it improves the drainage around the roots.

Planting in individual turfs

When you are cutting drains by hand, or where drainage has not been carried out, use the following method:

1 Cut turfs using a garden or planting spade. Cut them at least 300mm (12") square, and 100-150mm (4-6")

thick; preferable dimensions are 450mm (18") square, and 230mm (9") thick. The bigger the turf, the better the tree growth. Cut the turfs from the lines of the drains or wherever convenient, and place them grass-side down where you want to plant the trees.

2 Cut the slit in the side of the turf from the middle outward. It is usually recommended that the slit be made in the side of the turf facing the prevailing wind, so that the wind pushes the tree against the uncut part of the turf. Edlin (1984, p45), however, suggests cutting on the opposite side to prevent the wind from drying the turf around the slit, which may then open and allow the roots to dry out.

Cut through fairly thin turfs down to, but not below, ground level. With thick turfs, cut 150mm (6") or so into the turf, but not through it. When planting oak it is best to cut deeper so that the roots can go through the turf into the ground.

3 Insert the tree as shown below.

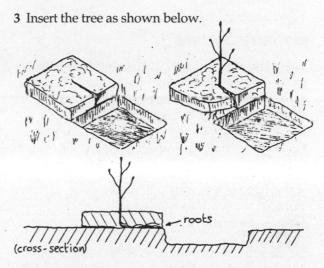

(cross-section) roots

4 Remove the spade and tread in around the tree to firm it.

Planting in ridges

Where a ridge has been created by ploughing, plant in the ridge. There are three methods, as follows:

a Using a garden or planting spade, cut a slit in the top of the ridge, insert the tree and firm it as when planting in individual turfs (above). If the ridge is more than about 230mm (9") high, slice the top of it where you intend to plant and cut a slit in the platform.

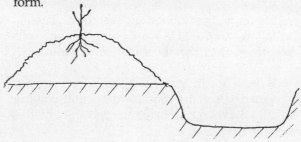

b Cut a V-shaped wedge of turf out of the side of the ridge away from the wind, with two strokes of the spade. Then place the tree in the notch and replace the wedge, trampling it down to make sure the roots are held firmly in the turf.

c Use a semi-circular spade to twist out a plug in the ridge to make a suitable hole. Replace the plug after positioning the tree.

MOUND PLANTING

Mound planting is slower than turf planting but gives the trees extra inches above the wet soil. It is most useful where drainage has not been carried out and where turfs are difficult to cut.

1 Make a mound by heaping up loose soil or spoil from drainage ditches. It is preferable to work with mineral soils such as clay, as peat dries out too quickly. The mound should be 230mm (9") high or more, so that the tree roots will be above the level of badly drained soil. Firm the mound as much as possible by treading.

2 Cut a slit in the top or side of the mound as for turf planting (above). Insert the tree at the correct depth and tread in to firm.

PIT PLANTING

Pit planting is the slowest method, but one which ensures plenty of room for the roots, especially on compacted ground. It is essential for trees over about 90cm (3') tall. It is also worth doing when you are planting only a few trees or where failures would be expensive or difficult to replace.

Treading in is most important when pit planting. Most failures are due to lack of firming. In heavy soils don't firm so much that the soil becomes compacted.

If you dig a pit in frosty weather, don't leave it overnight. The frost that forms on the bottom will stay there all winter, and damage the roots of any tree planted in the pit.

Small trees

Pit planting trees under about 1.5m (5'), or 1.2m (4') in exposed conditions, can be done without staking:

1 In grassland, cut a square of turf about $1^{1}2$ spade widths wide. Lift the turf out and put it to one side.

2 Dig the soil out to the depth of the spade's blade (a 'spit'), to make a square-sided hole. Place the spoil neatly in a heap nearby, or, for ease of retrieval, onto a plastic sheet. Keep the topsoil separate if it is noticeably better than the subsoil, and remove any big stones from the spoil. Loosen the soil in the sides and bottom of the hole using a spade or fork, to make it easier for the roots to grow out and down.

3 Hold the tree vertically in the centre of the hole, checking that the soil mark at the root collar is at ground surface level. A cane or other straight stick held across the hole makes it easier to check. Working quickly but thoroughly, shovel or push the best soil, usually the topsoil, around the roots. You may need to shake the tree gently to work in the soil and prevent air pockets among the roots. When the roots are covered, firm the soil with your hands or boot, taking care not to damage the roots or stem. Backfill with the remaining spoil, and then cut the turf in two and put it upside down around the stem, making sure that the turf is slightly raised above ground level to prevent water from collecting around the stem.

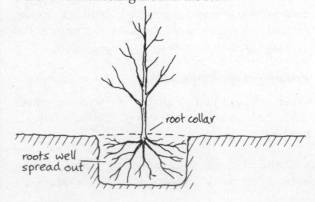

root collar

roots well
spread out

Larger trees

Before pit planting larger trees, note the following points:

a Trees over 1.5m (5') tall will normally need staking (see p92). The bigger the tree, the more care is needed in planting, but the method is essentially the same for all. The work is best done by two people, or more when planting large trees with heavy root balls.

b Soil ameliorants such as compost, a loam-leaf-mould mixture or well-rotted manure are often used in pit planting with the intention of improving soil fertility and structure. Recent research (Arboriculture Research Note 69/87/SILS), however, indicates that many organic and proprietary ameliorants have no positive effect, on certain species at least. The use of peat and some other organic materials can even cause problems, as in dry weather the edges of the pit may open up and expose roots. In any case, using peat is not now recommended on conservation grounds, as there are few remaining peat bogs in Britain. In clay soils, organic ameliorants should not be used, as they may exacerbate anaerobic conditions (Hibberd, 1989, p79). Generally, ameliorants should be used only if the soil is very sandy and free-draining. On other soils, the best course is to plant species that will be able to utilise the available structure and nutrient levels in the soil.

When you are ready to plant, follow this procedure:

1 Dig a hole large enough to take the roots comfortably when spread out, and deep enough for the soil mark to be at ground level. Roots should never be coiled or bent to fit the hole, but instead the hole should be enlarged. Put the turf, topsoil and subsoil in separate heaps beside the pit.

When planting on a slope, cut a level shelf before digging the hole.

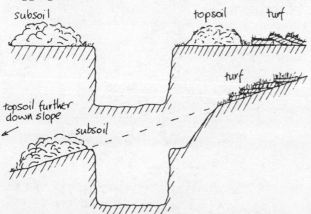

It is best not to dig the hole more than a few hours in advance of planting, as it may fill with water which will then need to be emptied before planting can be done. If the hole fills with water as you are digging,

the site is too wet and tree roots will 'drown'. Find an alternative site, unless the waterlogging is the result of unusually rainy weather, in which case delay planting until conditions improve.

2 Fork over the soil on the sides and in the bottom of the hole to loosen it thoroughly. If you decide to use a soil ameliorant (see above), fork it into the bottom of the pit, and mix some in with the soil for back-filling. Mound some of this planting mixture into a rough cone in the base of the pit.

3 Position the stake and drive it in (see p93).

4 If the tree has a root-ball, place it in the hole with the ball intact. Then loosen the wrapping if it is a material which degrades very quickly, or remove it if it is plastic or heavy canvas. Don't break up the root ball. If the tree is bare-rooted, one person should hold it while the other spreads the root crown over the cone of topsoil and works the soil in among the roots. It is a good idea to shake the tree gently up and down to help the earth settle between the roots as you lightly tamp the soil by hand.

5 Fill the hole in stages, starting with topsoil and adding subsoil nearer the top. Some volunteers prefer to break up the turf and put the pieces into the hole before adding the topsoil. Make sure the stem of the tree is vertical and the soil mark at ground level. Firm around the roots after the addition of every 100-140mm (4-6") of soil, since treading in may not be effective beyond this depth. Light soils need to be firmed much more strongly than heavy soils. Where practical, firm heavy soils minimally if wet at planting time, and then tread them in strongly when the soil is drier. Continue adding soil until the pit has been filled and slightly mounded at the level of the root collar.

Unless you have used the broken-up turf in the planting hole, it is usually best to replace the turf grass-side down around the stem (see p90) so that it rots down to provide a mulch around the tree. Where watering by hand is possible in dry soils, form a dam around the tree by putting the turfs upside down in a circle 600-900mm (2-3') out from the stem or at the drip line. Where the tree is planted on a slope, build up a higher, semi-circular dam downhill of the tree.

6 Tie the tree to the stake, position a guard, water the tree and carry out other aftercare as necessary (p102).

CONTAINER-GROWN PLANTS

As described in chapter 5 (p65), it is possible to run a tree nursery by growing seedlings of many species in containers. In large commercial nurseries, container-grown stock often include evergreens such as holly and yew, and ornamental trees such as garden cultivars of native species. Containerised plants do not have a large root-ball, and, with the exception of evergreens (see below), should be treated as for bare-rooted stock and planted only in the dormant season.

The following points should be noted about container-grown trees and shrubs:

a Evergreens are best planted in late spring to avoid frosts. In theory, other container-grown trees can be planted at any time when soil conditions are suitable. In practice, however, planting in late spring or summer is risky unless provision is made for regular watering.

b Container-grown trees often have a large amount of top growth for the size of the root-ball. This is made possible by careful cultivation in the nursery.

To transplant successfully, the tree will normally need to be staked so that the roots have a chance to grow out of the root-ball and into the surrounding soil. If this is not done, the root-ball will be loosened. Until such rooting takes place, the tree will also need regular watering during the growing season to sustain the amount of top growth.

c Container-grown trees and shrubs are normally grown in a light compost, as this promotes rapid root growth. If the root-ball is put directly into a heavy soil, the roots will have difficulty penetrating the soil and may simply continue to grow round the root-ball, as if pot-bound. Plants which have already developed encircling root systems in the container (p65) will be even more likely to develop in this way. The tree may put on some growth, but then die as it is starved of water or nutrients, and even after several seasons in the ground may be found to have made no new growth beyond the original root-ball. It is therefore very important, when planting container-grown stock, to encourage the roots to grow slowly into the surrounding soil. Do this by digging a planting hole twice the diameter of the pot and half as deep again, and back-filling it with a mixture of half soil to half garden compost.

Pots such as Rootrainers (p76) are designed to help the plant develop a straight fibrous root system. Seedlings grown in them are much less likely to suffer the problems outlined above.

d Research by H. Insley and D. Patch (Arboriculture Research Note 22/80/ARB) indicates that some biodegradable containers may not rot down as quickly as previously thought, especially in poor or disturbed soils. As trees raised and then planted in these containers may be particularly liable to develop the

problems discussed in c, above, it is advisable to remove all containers at the time of planting. The exception is one year old seedlings grown in Japanese paper pots, as the plants are too young to develop encircling roots, and the pots themselves are open-ended and easily biodegradable.

e If you are buying in, note that container-grown stock is more expensive than the same stock grown in the open ground, because of the extra work and materials involved in growing them and the higher cost of transporting them. Most species establish much faster from small bare-rooted stock, or seedlings grown in Japanese paper pots or Rootrainers, than from larger container-grown stock.

Staking and Tying

The recommendation for staking trees has changed in recent years, as the result of studies on the effect of wind sway on trees, and experience of what happens to staked trees. Trees tied to tall stakes at a point just below the crown are still a common sight, so much so that they are regarded as the norm. This practice was once thought to discourage vandalism and support the tree, but for the reasons detailed below it is no longer recommended.

The information below is in part from D. Patch (Arboriculture Research Notes 40/89/ARB and 77/89/ARB).

a The stem diameter growth of a tree is stimulated when it sways in the wind. If a tree is left unstaked, the whole tree - including the stem - will sway, stimulating maximum diameter growth at or near the root collar. Over time, this swaying will help form a stout, firm tree with a stem that tapers evenly from base to crown. The unstaked tree will thus develop a structure which can flex under the force of wind or vandalism. As roots at the root collar also increase in diameter from the movement of the stem, the tree is given added stability.

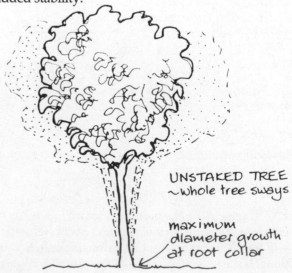

UNSTAKED TREE
~whole tree sways

maximum diameter growth at root collar

It has also been found that stem diameter growth towards the base of the tree is increased by planting 'feathered' trees, rather than trees with clean pruned stems. If feathered trees are used, they can be pruned progressively over the following years, as necessary.

b Conversely, if a tree is staked and tied just below the crown, the stem cannot sway, and little increase in stem diameter occurs from base to crown. The stem may in fact become thicker above the tie than below it, because diameter growth increases in response to the movement of the crown. A supported tree will initially gain height faster than the unsupported tree, but the stem will be thin and weak up to the tie, and then taper rapidly. As the tree can flex only over the height of the crown, it is all too easy to snap the crown off by using the tie as a pivot.

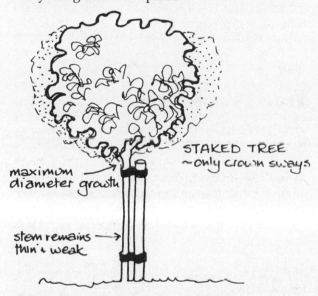

When the time comes to remove the stake from a supported tree, it may lean or even bend down to the ground because of imbalance between the crown and lower stem.

c There are two other disadvantages to staking. Regular maintenance will be needed to check on the ties, as these can abrade and even strangle the stem if not adjusted from time to time. Stakes and ties also cost money. Where possible, it is usually better to use smaller trees which do not need staking.

d Nursery grown trees have a relatively limited root-spread, which makes them vulnerable to wind-throw or vandalism when they are planted in cultivated soil. For trees 1.5m and taller, using stakes and ties is therefore justified - but only as a means of stabilising the root collar until the root system develops to anchor the tree.

Stakes

Where it is necessary to stake a tree, aim to anchor the root-ball in the ground while still leaving enough stem free to sway in the wind. The stake should ex-tend no higher than a quarter to a third of the way up the stem. Tie the tree with a single tie, preferably of a flexible material which allows some movement. Commercial tree ties with spacers (see below) are best, as home-made ties (e.g. of old inner tubes) may allow the stem to abrade against the top of the stake. The tie must be placed near the top of the stake to prevent this type of abrasion.

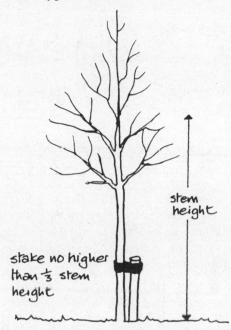

Provided that soil or weather conditions do not impede growth, sufficient root growth should have occurred to anchor the tree by the end of the growing season after planting. It is suggested that the stake be removed at the beginning of the second growing season. For this reason, it is unnecessary to use stakes pressure-treated with preservative unless you can ensure that they will be re-used after removal.

Trees which were planted with tall stakes or which have been staked for a number of years may need to be gradually weaned from their supports. For each such tree, assess the need for support by freeing it from its stake and manually shaking the stem. If the crown remains firmly upright, it should be safe to leave the stem unsupported. If the tree leans, reposition the tie at a point where the tree just remains erect. The tie will need to be lowered successively for a few years at the start of each growing season. Cut off the extra piece of stake each time to prevent it from rubbing against the stem.

Ties

There are several types of commercial tree ties available, designed for different types of uses, sizes of tree and degree of exposure. They are generally easier to adjust, stronger and more acceptable looking than their home-made equivalents, therefore justifying the extra expense.

Prices vary from about 15p each for small chainlock ties, to 50p and more for large buckle and collar ties.

Types include:

a Chainlock ties, which are threaded through and twisted to lock in place. Available in 25m rolls. Similar locking ties are available in packs of five, each 450mm (18") long.

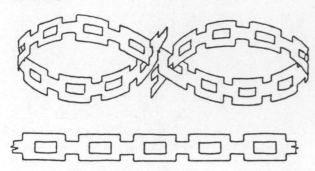

b Nail-on or buckle ties with collars or pads, which prevent the tree from chafing against the stake. Buckle ties can be loosened to allow adjustment for the tree's growth, or re-use. Nail-on ties can only be adjusted by removing and re-nailing.

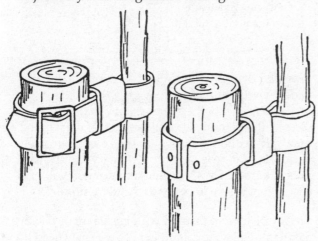

c Three-point ties, for use with guy wires to anchor extra-large transplanted trees with trunks of 100mm (4") or more diameter.

Procedural points

1 Position the stake so that it will be on the side of the tree towards the prevailing wind. This reduces the likelihood of chafing in storms. Position the tree so that it is 25-50mm (1-2") from the stake.

2 For ties with pads, first fix the pad about 75mm (3") from the top of the stake by driving two tacks into the countersunk holes. Then thread the belt through, and either fasten the buckle, or tack as shown to leave space for adjustment as the tree grows. It is important to have the right size pad for the tree, as pads which are too small can split as the tree grows. When fitted correctly, the belt should form a loop as shown, and

not be drawn in tightly by the pad to make a 'figure of eight'. Some pads have four slots instead of the normal two, so that they can be used on different sizes of tree. J. Toms Ltd manufacture a range of ties and pads.

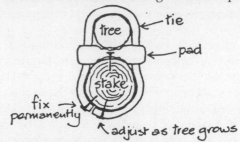

3 Ties with collars can be fitted to most sizes of tree. The tie should be tacked to the stake to prevent it slipping. Inspect trees at least twice a year to make sure they are secure and not chafed or constricted by the stakes and ties. Loosen ties as necessary to accommodate stem growth.

Tree Protection

Trees may need to be protected against damage by wild animals, livestock, machinery or vandalism. Urban trees are not exempt from damage by mammals. Voles, for example, can be a particular problem around plantings on motorway verges (Hibberd, 1989, p84). Additional hazards common to the urban environment may necessitate further special protection (see p102).

The main types of protection available for trees are fences; individual guards made of timber, plastic or metal; and treeshelters, which were originally designed to increase tree growth rates, but also protect against deer, hares and rabbits. In group or woodland planting, perimeter fencing may protect against all or some of the more common damaging agents, depending on the type of fence and the situation. Whether to use perimeter fencing or individual guards, or a combination of both, needs to be carefully weighed up.

The subject of tree guards is covered in Arboricultural Leaflet 10, 'Individual Tree Protection' (Forestry Commission 1985). 'Fencing' (Agate, 1986) contains detailed information on fencing.

Fences and tree guards are costly to build in terms of labour and materials. Needs must be assessed carefully, as failure can mean loss of the tree, as well as time and energy wasted in trying to maintain a badly designed system. Individual tree guards nearly always cost more than the tree itself, but it is never worth planting trees unless you can give them adequate protection.

Fences or guards?

The cost of individual tree protection increases directly with the number of trees protected, whereas the cost of fencing relates to the size and shape of land enclosed, regardless of the number of trees. Shapes which are complex or long and thin are the most uneconomic to fence, with squares and rectangles being the cheapest. The following formula for calculating the 'Critical Area Index' is given in Arboricultural Leaflet 10. If the answer is greater than 1, individual tree protection is cheaper. If the answer is less than 1, a perimeter fence is cheaper.

$$\textit{Critical Area Index} = \frac{F \times P}{N \times C}$$

where F is the fencing costs per linear metre; P is the perimeter of area in metres (lengths of fence-line); N is the number of plants per hectare to be protected; and C is the cost of protecting individual trees.

Factors to consider

When designing or choosing the type of tree protection, the following factors should be considered:

a What are the threats to the tree? Are there rabbits or hares in the area? What type of livestock may have access around the tree?

b How long is protection required? Tree guards can be designed for a long, maintenance-free life, or to disintegrate after a few years. Some tree guards will themselves restrict and damage the tree if left in position too long.

c Does the guard allow access to the tree for weeding, loosening of tree ties and so on?

d Is the guard in a situation where its appearance is important?

e Do you want the guard to be conspicuous, for example to aid weeding, or inconspicuous, to reduce vandalism?

Damage by animals

There are many ways in which wild animals and livestock can damage trees. Leaves can be browsed during the growing season, or buds and twigs chewed off during the winter. Horses, sheep, hares, rabbits, deer and voles can all damage trees by stripping the bark, normally during winter and spring, when other food is scarce. In areas of heavy snowfall where deep drifts can reach the level of fence tops, this type of damage can occur high up on the stem. If a tree is 'ringbarked', i.e. bark is removed all the way around the stem, it may die. All sizes of tree may be vulnerable, and thin-barked trees such as beech, hornbeam and sycamore are especially so. Although squirrels are one of the more enthusiastic bark strippers, they cannot be controlled by any form of guard (see p117).

Deer may fray trees by rubbing their antlers against the stems during the build-up to the rut. Cattle, horses and sheep can damage trees and guards by rubbing against them, and also eat young shoots. Where livestock gather around trees, compaction and poaching of the ground can cause waterlogging and damage to tree roots.

Tables 6A and 6B give information on suitable dimensions to protect trees against different types of animals. Use of a mulch or herbicide on the grass within a tree guard will not only aid tree establishment and growth, but will also mean there is less inducement for animals to lean through to graze.

TABLE 6A HEIGHT OF GUARD REQUIRED (in metres)

zone A [   ]   zone B [   ]

Distance from tree (in metres)	0-0.25	0.25-.5	.5-0.75	0.75-1	1-1.25	1.25-1.5	1.5-1.75	1.75-2	2-2.25	
Horses	2.50	2.25	2.00	1.75	1.50	1.15	1.15	1.15	1.15	
Cattle	1.85	1.70	1.50	1.15	1.15	1.15	1.15	1.15	1.15	
Man	2.25	1.90	1.70	1.50	1.35	1.15	1.15	1.15	1.15	
Red Deer	2.10	1.75	1.45	1.20	1.20	1.20	1.20	1.50	1.80	HEIGHT
Fallow Deer	1.80	1.60	1.25	1.10	1.10	1.10	1.35	1.80	1.80	
Goats	1.85	1.70	1.35	1.20	1.15	1.15	1.15	1.15	1.15	
Roe Deer	1.60	1.35	1.10	1.00	1.00	1.00	1.60	1.80	1.80	
Sheep	1.10	0.90	0.90	0.90	0.90	0.90	0.90	0.90	0.90	
Hares	0.85	0.85	0.85	0.85	0.85	0.85	0.85	0.85	0.85	
Rabbits	0.75	0.85	0.85	0.85	0.85	0.85	0.85	0.85	0.85	

For further information on identifying and controlling damage by wild animals, see the 'Wildlife Rangers Handbook' (Forestry Commission, 1985).

Table 6A shows the height of the guard required against various animals, and the distance it should be from the tree. In zone A, the barrier must be of netting or timbers which are close enough to prevent the animal putting its head through and reaching the tree. In zone B, the barrier need only be sufficient to prevent the passage of the animal. The spacing of the horizontal and vertical members of netting or timber are shown in Table 6B. Note that in Table 6A the height of the barrier against deer increases as the distance from the tree increases. This is to prevent deer jumping into the exclosure.

TABLE 6B SPACING OF NETTING/TIMBER VERTICALS AND HORIZONTALS

	Vertical & horizontal spacing (mm) zone A	Horizontal spacing (mm) zone B
Horses	100	500
Cattle	100	500
Deer	75	225
Goats	75	225
Sheep	50	150
Hares	30	30
Rabbits	30	30

Plastic spiral guards

These are designed to protect young trees against bark-stripping by rabbits and voles. They are easy to install, being simply wound around the stem of the tree, and are suitable for trees of between 10 and 40mm stem diameter. Trees smaller than this may bend over under the weight of the guard, and the space between the guard and the stem may be large enough to give access to voles. A cane should be used inside the spiral to support the stem. Stems larger than 40mm diameter will not be properly protected, as gaps will form in the spiral. Spiral guards are unsuitable for trees which are multi-stemmed, and those that are strongly feathered or branching.

When fitting the guard, push the end into the ground around the base of the tree, to lessen the chance of the wind or animals dislodging it. Guards should be checked every year to make sure that they are still properly fitted, and that they are free to expand as the stem thickens. Any side shoots protruding through the holes in the guard should be freed or cut off, or they will prevent the guard from expanding with tree growth.

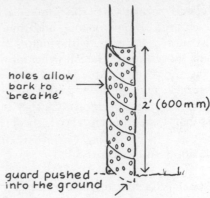

Spiral guards give no protection against animals other than rabbits and voles, and are often used in addition to a timber or other guard, or perimeter fence. They are available in white, green, grey or black. White guards draw attention to the trees, and are therefore useful for identifying young trees that need regular weeding, but inadvisable for use in areas where vandalism is likely. Spiral guards should last five years or more, but they will eventually become brittle.

Tubular plastic guards

These serve a similar purpose to spiral guards, but are made of rigid plastic. They cannot be fitted to trees with side branches below the height of the guard. They are more durable than spiral guards, but also more expensive.

Plastic mesh guards

Plastic mesh tree guards have a wider application than spiral guards, as they can prevent browsing and bark stripping by rabbits, ponies and deer. Details on these guards are available in H. W. Pepper, 'Plastic Mesh Tree Guards' (Arboriculture Research Note 5/87/WILD).

'Netlon' guards are available in two types: preformed guards, 75mm diameter x 1.2m; and in rolls 450mm wide x 50m, for cutting as required.

The smaller guards can be used whole to protect against roe deer, or cut in half to protect against hares and rabbits. When fitting guards to small transplants, ensure that the guard is erected vertically with the tree in the centre, and fasten the guard to a supporting stake. The stake should be about 25 x 25mm (1 x 1"), and long enough to hold securely in the ground. This stake should be removed when the tree is large enough to support the guard. Use a staple gun or small fencing staples to fix the guard to the stake.

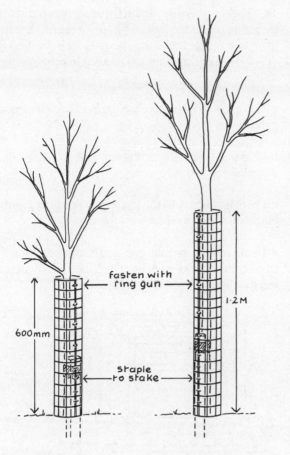

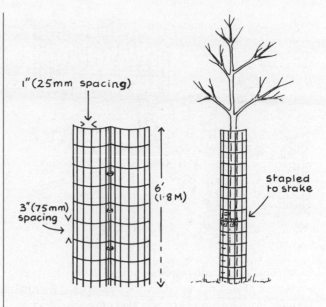

With larger trees, the tree itself provides the support, making stakes unnecessary. Fasten the guard with netting rings or wire ties. Check the guards occasionally to ensure they are still fitted correctly, and that the leading shoots are not growing out through the mesh. Undo and re-fasten as necessary. The guards are designed to degrade at between 5 to 10 years, so they do not need to be removed from the trees.

To protect amenity and parkland trees from deer, rabbits and hares, use the larger guards. Cut the required length (usually 1.2-1.5m) from the roll, then form it into a tube of 150mm diameter. Fasten it to the tree stake, or, for established trees, to itself.

Wire mesh guards

These guards are expensive but durable, and are especially useful for protecting urban trees from mechanical damage, or established trees from damage by horses or cattle. If used around young trees, any side shoots which grow through the mesh must be pruned off before they become entangled, as otherwise the wire will eventually 'strangle' the branches and will become difficult to remove. You will also have to check to ensure that the stem of the tree does not become abraded when it grows above the top edge and sways in the wind. If you see this happening, it might be worthwhile to substitute a plastic guard, as these have been shown to be at least as effective against vandalism.

Timber guards

Timber guards are suitable for long-term protection of trees in parklands and pastures, to prevent cattle, sheep, horses and deer causing browsing damage to young trees, and to protect against bark damage throughout the tree's life. If properly built of preserved timber and regularly maintained, timber guards should have a life of at least 20 years. They are only worth doing well: poorly constructed guards or those of weak timber will soon be damaged by leaning or rubbing animals.

Note the following:

a Use Tables 6A and 6B to find the required dimension of the guard. Make sure that all likely damaging animals are taken into account, as it is difficult to upgrade the protection at a later date.

b Unless vandalism is a problem, a section of climbable fence is useful for tending the tree.

c As for all young trees, use a mulch or herbicide to keep down grass and weeds in a 1m radius around the stem. This will have the added benefit of lessening the inducement for animals to reach in through the tree guard.

d It is not possible to build an exclosure simply of three or four posts with strained wire or netting, as sufficient strain to keep the wire taut will cause the posts to move. Horizontal rails, preferably rebated, must be included.

e Where netting is to be fitted to an enclosure, it is not usually a good idea to increase the distance of the top rail from the tree by slanting the posts outwards. This makes it difficult to fit the netting neatly and securely.

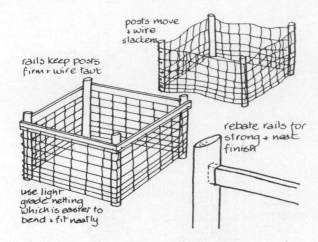

f Don't automatically top the exclosure with barbed wire, except against vandals, as this does not stop animals from leaning over and also makes it difficult to climb in to tend the tree.

Some designs for timber tree guards are shown below. These should be adapted, using Tables 6A and 6B, to fit the space and materials available. All guards can be made rabbit-proof by fitting rabbit netting (900mm hexagonal mesh, 31mm gauge), with the bottom 150mm (6") of netting turned out and pegged to the ground, or held down with heavy turfs or stones.

Tree shelters

The following information is based partly on J. Evans and C. W. Shanks, 'Treeshelters' (Arboriculture Research Note 63/87/SILS).

Since 1979, over 6 million tree shelters have been used in Britain and overseas. They are now probably the most common form of tree protection for plantings of less than a hectare, above which perimeter fencing against rabbits or deer usually becomes cheaper. Tree shelters have been less widely used in built-up urban areas, as they are supposed to attract vandalism, and are less suitable for use on the taller trees normally planted in such areas. Further experiments with their use in such areas may be worthwhile, however, due to their value as aids to tree establishment (Hibberd, 1989, p85).

Most broadleaved species benefit from tree shelters, although there are occasional problems with beech, as the leaves can stick to the inside surface of the shelter and scorch in sunlight. Plastic mesh guards (p96), which allow the free movement of air, are therefore probably a better alternative for use with this species. Table 6c (p99), is the result of Forestry Commission experiments using tree shelters on different species.

Tree shelters were designed to promote rapid growth by acting like a mini-greenhouse, and growth can be from two to five times the normal rate in the first two years. Tree shelters are also useful in other ways, as follows:

a Tree growth is less likely to be held back in drought conditions.

b Young trees are protected against damage by animals (see below).

c There is less risk to the tree when spray or granular herbicides are used around the base.

d Being readily visible, even in bracken or brambles, tree shelters make it easier to relocate newly planted trees for weeding and maintenance.

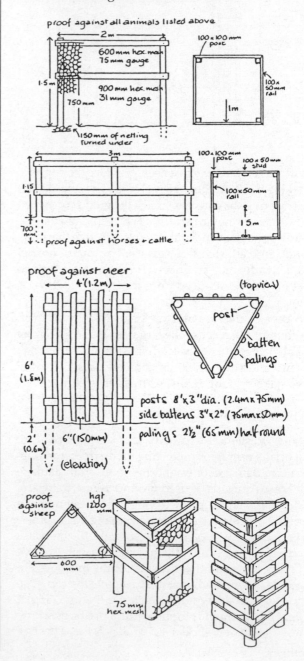

98

TABLE 6C EFFECTS OF TREE SHELTERS ON GROWTH BY SPECIES

SPECIES [a]		OVERALL GROWTH RESPONSE [b]				
Common name	Scientific name	1	2	3	4	Comments
Alder, common	*Alnus glutinosa*			x		
Alder, Italian	*Alnus cordata*				x	
Ash, common	*Fraxinus excelsior*		x			Few early experiments
Beech	*Fagus sylvatica*	x				Occasionally slow/poor response
Birch	*Betula pendula*			x		
Cherry	*Prunus avium*			x		Rapidly outgrows shelter
Hawthorn	*Crataegus monogyna*	x				
Holly	*Ilex aquifolium*		x			
Hornbeam	*Carpinus betulus*		x			Variable, site-sensitive
Horse chestnut	*Aesculus hippocastanum*				x	
Lime, large-leaved	*Tilia platyphylos*		x			Often very good response
Lime, small-leaved	*Tilia cordata*	x				Occasionally poor response
Maple, field	*Acer campestre*		x			Variable
Maple, Norway	*Acer platanoides*		x			Variable
Oak, pedunculate	*Quercus robur*	x				
Oak, sessile	*Quercus petraea*	x				One or two trees often fail to respond
Rowan	*Sorbus aucuparia*			x		
Sweet chestnut	*Castanea sativa*	x				Rapid initial response only
Sycamore	*Acer pseudoplatanus*		x			
Whitebeam	*Sorbus aria*				x	

Notes

a Omission of a species from the table should not be interpreted as being unsuitable for growing in tree shelters. Many species have simply not been formally evaluated. For information on other species tested, see J. Evans and C.W. Shanks (Arboriculture Research Note 63/87/SILS).

b Overall growth response:

1 Very good. Species show consistently good response to shelters, usually more than doubling rate of height growth in first two to three years after planting.

2 Good. Generally show a significant improvement in growth on most sites but not as marked as in 1, above.

3 Initial. Species which initially respond well to shelters but, because of early emergence from the top (at the end of the first, or during the second, year) and naturally fast growth rates, do not sustain a large significant improvement beyond the third year.

4 Some. On average, growth appears somewhat improved by shelters, but either there is great variability or, in the experiments in question, the improvement was not statistically significant.

Shelters currently on the market are made of corrugated polypropylene, extruded polypropylene or PVC. The corrugated type are probably the most popular, being stronger than PVC but having the advantage over the extruded type of being supplied flat-packed. Extruded tubes are very strong and only require a short stake, but are bulky to store and carry. Various colours are available, including white, green and pale brown, and should be chosen according to whether the shelters need to be easily visible or inconspicuous. Note that in underplantings, where light levels are lower, paler colours should be used.

Shelters are best used on transplants 150-400mm (6-16") tall, as these are cheap, transplant well, and can benefit the most from the improved growing conditions in the shelter. The transplants should have a single strong leader, and any spreading side branches should be pruned at the time of planting, to enable the shelter to be fitted. Transplants with multiple stems or many side branches are not suitable. It is not worth using shelters on taller whips, as they will soon outgrow the shelter.

Although the diameter of the shelter is unimportant, the height can be critical when protection from animals is needed. The following sizes are recommended:

Shelter	Stake	Animals
600mm	800mm	Rabbits and hares
1.2m	1.5m	Sheep and roe deer
1.8m	1.8m	Fallow, sika and red deer
1.8m heavy duty		Cattle and horses

Tree shelters used on steep slopes may have to be taller, as deer may otherwise be able to browse off the emerging tree tops from the high side of the slope.

Where there is heavy pressure of deer or sheep, shelters and stakes may get damaged or destroyed by animals rubbing against them. In a sheep paddock, this can be reduced by providing other posts for the animals to rub on. In areas with high fallow deer populations, use extruded shelters, as these deer can swiftly demolish corrugated polypropylene with their antlers.

Trees in fields grazed by cattle, horses or sheep will need protection for longer than the five-year life of a shelter. Fences or timber guards are the best protection against stock, but if shelters are to be used as an interim measure, support them with proper fence stakes. The 'Bull Toob' (see supplier on p147), an extra heavy duty shelter suitable for areas where cattle and sheep are kept, was designed for use with such stakes.

Most suppliers of shelters can also supply the stakes, although this can be an expensive option if you are erecting many shelters. A square 25 x 25mm stake is suitable for the most commonly used 1.2m shelter. On exposed sites, a 32mm x 32mm stake will be needed. Ensure that the stakes are long enough to knock securely into the ground and hold the shelters firmly against wind and weather. Untreated timber such as sweet chestnut, larch or western red cedar is sufficient for a five-year life. Single chestnut pales can also be used. Shelters 1.8m tall should have a quarter-sawn, split or round stake. Knotty or otherwise weak stakes should be rejected, as they will not last five years. As vandalism to shelters has been limited largely to the pulling up of stakes, use stronger stakes in urban areas.

The method of fixing varies with the make of shelter. Shelters with an integral tie which can be quickly attached to the stake by hand are easy to use. Those designed with a tie that fastens the shelter to the stake without encircling the tree (e.g. 'Tubex') are useful, as the tie will fall harmlessly to the ground when the shelter eventually disintegrates. If shelters with encircling ties are used, the ties will have to be removed when the shelter falls apart to prevent them from 'strangling' the trees. Other types have non-encircling wire ties which are twisted to fasten, although problems have arisen from the wires breaking or causing the shelter itself to split and fail early on.

It is also important to ensure that the top edge of the shelter is rounded or can be folded back, as a sharp edge can cut into the emerging leader of the tree when this is blown about by the wind.

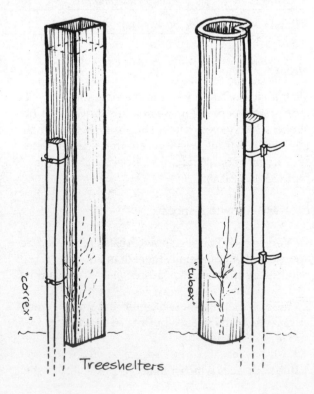

"correx" "tubex"

Treeshelters

Of the many types of shelter available, 'Correx plus' are widely used. These are made of corrugated polypropylene, with a folded top and non-encircling wire ties, and are supplied flat-packed. The 'Tubex Treeshelter', also shown, is a twin-wall extruded shelter with nylon straps. 'Correx' and 'Tubex' have been found to be the quickest to erect, and both can be easily removed for tree maintenance. It is, however, best to shop around and find the type of shelter to suit any particular requirements. Prices vary with make and with the number ordered.

The procedure for erecting a shelter of the Correx type is as follows:

1 Prepare the planting site by applying a pre-planting treatment to kill all perennial weeds (p108) on an area at least 300mm (12") but preferably 900mm (3') square. Alternatively, scarify or dig the soil on an area of the same dimensions and to a depth of 100mm (4") to kill all the weeds.

2 If pit planting (p90), prepare a planting hole about 300mm (12") in diameter in the middle of this weed-free area.

Drive the upright stake firmly into the ground at the edge of the hole, preferably on the northern side so that it does not shade the transplant. On exposed sites, it may be better to place the stake on the side of the prevailing wind. Use a small lump hammer on 25 x 25mm stakes. The stake should be knocked in far enough to leave about 50mm (2") above the upper wire of the shelter, so use the shelter itself as a gauge.

Then, laying the shelter aside for the moment, plant the transplant at the correct distance from the stake, so that it will be in the middle of the shelter. Firm the soil, but leave a level surface covered with about 20mm (1") of loose soil.

If using the notch or T method (p88), cut the notch away from the side where you place the stake. Knock the stake in firmly as above, then plant the transplant.

3 Prune off any spreading side branches.

4 Place the shelter over the transplant, with the folded edge to the top, wires towards the stake and the plant central in the shelter. If the weather is very cold, avoid handling the shelter too roughly, as polypropylene becomes brittle at low temperatures and may break. The bottom of the shelter should be pressed firmly into the soil to exclude voles, which may otherwise eat the bark or nest in the bottom of the shelter. Do not push or press the shelter in further than about 40mm (1¹₂"), however, as more can make lifting for weed control difficult.

5 Fasten the wires around the stake, bending the ends in neatly as shown to prevent them from snagging on people or animals.

Some volunteers prefer to knock in the stake after planting the transplant and positioning the shelter. This method makes it much easier to get the stake in exactly the right position, but does involve some slight danger of damage to the roots. The choice of method is really up to you!

Tree shelters should last at least five years, and should be left to disintegrate. Do not remove them from around the protected tree, as rapid growth will have produced a slender stem that may not be strong enough to support the crown if conditions suddenly change. After the shelters disintegrate, any large pieces should be removed from the site to prevent a litter problem.

Check the shelters regularly to make sure they have not come loose due to wind or animals, and replace any broken stakes. In the first years of growth, before the trees have emerged from the top, check periodically also to ensure that no small birds have become entrapped within the shelter.

Tree shelters are not a substitute for weeding. It is important to check early in the growing season that the shelter is not becoming choked with weeds. If it is, remove the shelter to clear the weeds and then reposition. It is, however, recommended that an area at least 1m (3') in diameter around the base of all newly planted trees be kept weed-free for the first few years. An easy method of doing this is to fit a mulching mat (p103) at the time of planting, but granular herbicides applied around the shelter will also help control weeds within it.

Chemical repellents

Chemical repellents are contact chemicals which protect young trees from winter browsing damage by mammals. They are usually applied over several winters to give the trees a chance to establish. Repellents may be cheaper than tree guards or fencing for small (under 2 hectares) or awkwardly shaped areas, such as plantings on motorway verges. For larger or more regularly shaped areas, chemical application will be less suitable because of the labour intensity involved and the need to apply over several years.

The repellents should be applied to the tree in early winter, after which they last two to three months. They should not be used when trees are in active growth. The Forestry Commission have found that 'Aaprotect' and 'Dendrocol 17' are effective, and other products are currently being tested. Some care must be taken when applying both these products. For further information, see Pepper (1978).

Other deterrents

Other methods that have been used against mammals, particularly deer, include tying rags soaked in creosote at entrances to small woods, paths, crossing points and so on. Tie the rags at deer head height (about 1m for roe and fallow, 1.2m for sika, 1.3m for red deer). Deer are also discouraged by strips of brightly coloured plastic tied near new plantings or at intervals along perimeter fencing, particularly if the siting and colours of the strips are changed from time to time. Neither of these methods will give permanent protection, but may be successful for a few months over the winter, when food is in short supply.

Deer fences are described in 'Fencing' (Agate, 1986). A single strand of electric fencing at deer head height on an existing stock fence is an effective deterrent, or fences of two or three electrified strands can be used. Low electric fences can also be used against rabbits and hares.

Deer management is necessary on sites used for commercial timber production. This is described fully in the 'Wildlife Rangers Handbook' (Forestry Commission, 1985). Information on mammal control in established plantings can be found on p117.

Extra protection for urban trees

On some urban sites, newly planted trees are likely to need extra protection from vandalism and collision with cars or machinery, even if they have been protected with wire mesh guards. The following information is from Rushforth (1987, pp42,91). Protection of established trees from construction work is discussed on p120.

a If trees are planted on sites in close proximity to cars (e.g. along streets or in areas abutting onto car parks), serious wounding may occur to their stems when cars repeatedly reverse into them. Traditional wire mesh guards may not withstand repeated collision. To protect trees around car parks, surround them with

bollards, or with railway sleepers or logs laid out horizontally. Either should be placed so that there is at least a 1.5m clearance on all sides of the tree, and bollards should also be tall enough to be seen by the reversing driver. Street trees should be planted as far back as feasible from the kerb.

b In addition to using strong stakes and tree guards, effective protection against vandalism can be provided for specimen trees if they are planted in beds of thorny shrubs, such as barberry. Mulching mats (see below) or other forms of weed control will still be needed for trees planted in this way. Tending the trees may pose difficulties unless you remember to bring protective clothing!

If trees do become vandalised, assess te damage to see if they can be saved. Trees with their stems broken off high up may make considerable regrowth by the end of the first season, with the aid of judicious pruning. Try also to tidy up the broken stakes, guards, etc. Trees or sites which look neglected may be incentives to further vandalism.

Early Care

Early care should aim at helping the young trees adjust to a new environment, so that they can begin to reach a natural equilibrium with the existing conditions on the planting site. Artificial 'boosts' in the form of regular watering and feeding, for example, are not normally needed. The main priority in caring for all young trees immediately after planting and for some years afterwards is weed control. Mulching, as a method of controlling weeds from the time of planting through the first few years, is discussed below, along with the situations in which other forms of early care may be needed. Remember that stakes, ties, guards and shelters will all need to be checked regularly during the first one to five years.

Details on weeding in general and the other methods of weed control are given in chapter 7.

MULCHING

The following is in part from R. J. Davies (1987, pp28-31).

As a way of suppressing weeds around trees, mulching is both simple and effective, and all mulches have the added benefits of keeping the ground surface moist and fairly stable in temperature. Note that before mulches can be used, all weeds must first be killed around the base of the tree on an area 1-1.5m in diameter.

If practicable, organic or sheet mulches are excellent for use with most newly planted trees. Mulching is standard practice for poplars, although other forestry trees are not usually mulched. With turf-planted trees the turf itself acts as a mulch. Pit planted trees can benefit from the same 'instant mulch' if the turf from the pit is replaced grass-side down around the tree. Weeding will still be needed with turf and other organic mulches.

Sheet mulches

Sheet mulches have some advantages over traditional organic granular mulches. They are generally better for weed control, are less bulky to transport, and are easy to fit quickly around the base of the tree. On dry sandy soils they are especially effective, as they reduce nutrient loss due to leaching in wet weather. Sheet mulches also raise the temperature of the soil, thus stimulating root growth. Used on waterlogged soils, however, they may cause anaerobic conditions and lead to root death. There may be problems with voles, which can nest under the sheet and gnaw the base of the tree. Voles may also attract foxes, which may tear the mats as they hunt. Firmly anchoring the sheet (see below) should prevent this.

Black polythene, roofing felt or old carpets can be used as sheet mulches. If carpeting is used, the jute-backed variety is preferable, as it will eventually decompose. The material must allow no light to penetrate or weeds will grow under it, so perforated material is unsuitable. If black polythene is used, at least 500 gauge is required, with thicker material needed for rougher ground. To prevent the sheet from going brittle in sunlight, use only polythene made from virgin polymer, containing 2-5% carbon-black.

For use around transplants, cut the sheet into mats 1m square. Standards will require 1.5m-square mats. On each mat, cut a slit from the middle of one edge to the centre so it can be fitted around the base of the tree. If the tree is staked, cut a small slit in the appropriate

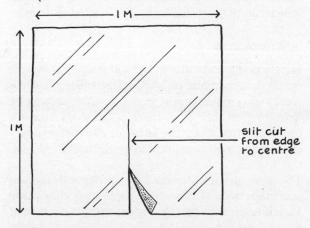

Black polythene mulching mat

place on the mat.

To anchor the mat and keep voles out, use a spade to push the edges into slits in the ground, or place clods of earth or stones all around the edge. You may wish to put a layer of chopped bark on top of the mat to mask its appearance and further anchor it. Weeds tend to be invigorated around the edges of mulching mats and can root underneath them, so it is best to control such weeds periodically with herbicides.

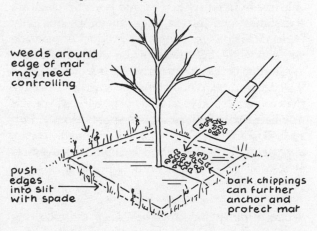

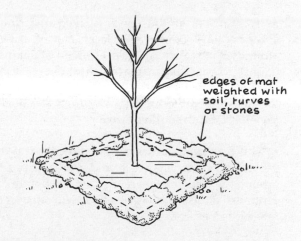

Ready-made mulching mats composed of thick polythene or bitumen are available from forestry product suppliers (see p147). These mats are usually 600 x 600mm or 750 x 750mm square, with slits already cut.

Mats should be left in place until they disintegrate, usually after five years or so. Regular checking during that period will be necessary to ensure that none are damaged to the point where they need replacement. Sheet mulches generally work out cheaper than two or more annual applications of herbicide; but their main advantage is that they present no environmental hazard.

Organic mulches

Organic granular mulches can gradually improve the soil as the mulch breaks down, and can also aid trees in compacted or eroded soil. Although they can become quickly colonised by weeds, these are easily uprooted from the loose mulch. As with sheet mulches, fine-ground organic mulches should not be used around trees on wetter soils, or anaerobism may result.

Many types of bulky organic matter are suitable mulches. If you are planting in existing woodland, you can simply rake up leaf litter around the planted stems. Spoiled hay, which is excellent, may be available free from farms. Leaves and lawn clippings are sometimes available in large quantities from city parks departments, or as a by-product of roadside verge mowing, but they must be well-rotted before application or they will deprive the tree of nitrogen as they decompose. Wood chips and sawdust will have the same effect and so should not be used; sawdust is also hazardous, as it can ignite spontaneously. Pulverised, composted forest bark is reasonably cheap, and useful if available in bulk locally. Garden centres also stock it by the sack, although this is more expensive.

When using organic mulches, keep the following points in mind:

a To mulch around a newly planted tree, simply spread a 100-150mm (4-6") deep layer of material around the stem in a circle of about 900mm (3') diameter. Don't heap up the mulch too deeply - it may generate too much heat as it rots, which can damage the trees. Keep the mulch away from the stem to prevent rot from starting there.

b Mulch around mature trees in the same way, but spread the material over a wider area, especially around the drip line where the feeder roots are concentrated. If the soil is very compacted, fork over the few top inches first.

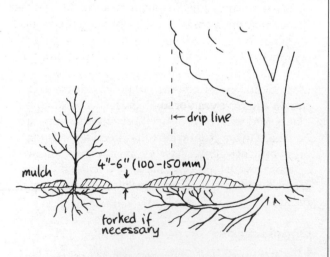

c Use sticks to weigh down hay or other lightweight material which may blow away.

d Avoid using inflammable mulch in high fire-risk areas.

e One application of mulch is adequate, but trees benefit from mulching in later years if they grow where there is little natural build-up of plant litter.

f If it is not possible to spread the mulch at the time of planting, in winter, spread in spring when the ground is moist. Do not spread after a period of drought, as this will only inhibit moisture from reaching the roots.

FERTILIZING

With some exceptions (see below), fertilizers are generally unnecessary for tree growth once the tree has been planted in its final position. Inorganic fertilizers can even be detrimental to trees and the environment if used in excess. Unless the soil is extremely poor, tree failure is more likely to be caused by other factors, such as bad handling or planting practice, waterlogging or drought. If compaction has not been rectified at the pre-planting stage, this can also be damaging to trees. Note that weed control may have to be stepped up for trees which have had fertilizer applications, as weeds are generally very responsive to fertilizers.

Forestry trees on poor soil

If timber production is a prime objective but the soil on the site is very poor, it may be necessary to apply phosphate fertilizer as the trees are being planted. The usual dose is 60-80g (2-3oz), or one level handful, sprinkled around the base of each transplant. Note that alders will need another 60g (2oz) six years after planting.

Occasionally, trees need phosphate at the pole stage or later, but determining this requires expert knowledge. Very occasionally, trees show signs of potassium deficiency (e.g. uncharacteristic yellowing of leaves), which can be corrected by an application of potash.

Specimen trees

Newly planted specimen trees on poor sites benefit from a dose of combined NPK fertilizer (see p74) a few weeks after planting. At least 60g (2oz) should be forked lightly into weed-free soil around the base of the young tree. Keep the fertilizer a foot or so away from the stem to avoid scorching the roots.

The same sort of treatment may reinvigorate mature specimen trees which show signs of decline. Late March is the best time for application. As a rule of thumb, use 1kg of fertilizer for every 50mm of stem growth (1lb for every 1"). To apply the fertilizer, dig small holes (or use a dibber) about 1.5m (5') apart under the tree's crown, where most of the roots are. Put about 250g (8oz) of fertilizer into each hole and refill with earth.

WATERING

Except during droughts, most newly planted trees should not need watering, provided that the roots are kept moist during the planting process and the trees are mulched at planting. Too much watering can induce surface rooting, making the roots more susceptible to scorching in dry weather. With such trees, once watering has begun it may have to be continued at every dry spell. Judicious watering during droughts will, on the other hand, encourage roots to penetrate further out and down, which will help the tree's overall development.

Watering may be essential in a few cases. Specimen trees, transplanted wild trees and large container-grown trees should be well watered at planting time and during any periods of drought in the first growing season. Trees planted late in the planting season may be especially vulnerable to the effects of spring droughts. In all these cases, water before any actual drought damage to the tree occurs, as afterwards it may be too late. If possible, use approximately 50-75l (10-15gal) of water - about five to eight buckets - per square metre of root area on a weekly or fortnightly basis (Rushforth, 1987, p87). Always pull up any emerging weeds immediately after you water.

FIRMING UP

In the weeks following planting, and especially after storms or hard frosts, check to see if the trees need treading in again. Check again in early spring, before the leaves flush. Wind-sway can cause a hollow to form around the root collar of the tree, and frost or mole activity can cause the ground to heave, thus loosening the roots. Tread around any loose stems to keep the soil firm and the stems upright. Trees in shelterbelts, at windy corners and other exposed locations are most likely to need repeated firming, so check these often.

PRUNING AT PLANTING

Nursery plants of high quality should already have a balanced root:shoot ratio which should obviate the need for much pruning at planting time. Transplanted wild trees, however, usually need pruning when planted to reduce the amount of crown in relation to the root system. With these, prune weak and damaged branches and any limbs which cross or rub together. Cut back the side branches by at least one-third of their length. Do not cut the leader. For trees

that grow in a spreading shape, make each pruning cut just above an outward-facing bud. For upright or columnar trees, cut just above stem-facing buds. Shelterbelt trees occasionally need pruning to reduce their wind resistance during the establishment phase.

See Chapter 7 for details of relevant techniques and information on formative pruning, and the pruning of established and mature trees.

BEATING UP

'Beating up', also known as 'filling up', is the replacement of any trees that fail. Before any new planting stock is purchased, however, it is worth finding out the cause of failure. A change of species may be indicated. Good plant handling and planting practice will greatly reduce the need to beat up.

In schemes where timber production is the prime objective, beating up should be done only if more than about 20% of the planted trees fail, assuming the failures are distributed evenly through the crop, or if more than 10-15% fail when the failures are concentrated in groups or when the original spacing was wide. A rule of thumb is to put in one replacement tree where three have failed together. If spacing between trees is 3m or more, it is usual to replace every tree that fails.

Beating up should be done in the autumn or winter after planting and, very rarely, again in the year after that. On sites where trees grow slowly, it may be worth waiting until the second year to do the beating up. Later than this, it is not normally worth replacing failures since the new trees cannot catch up with the main crop and are suppressed.

For plantings of specimen trees, and in hedges, screens and shelterbelts, beating up may be necessary even if failures are few, in order to preserve the required effect. Hedge and shelter trees may need replacing over as long a period as four or five years if growing conditions are difficult and the effects of gaps serious.

Use good quality plants as replacements, since they must catch up to the main crop. They should be at least as large as the originals or of a faster growing species. This is especially important when replacing hedge and screen plants after several years.

When beating up, check the surviving trees for firmness, and tread them in as necessary. Remember that beating up will make weeding necessary for a longer period.

PREVENTING SUN, WIND OR FROST DAMAGE

Specimen trees and transplanted wild trees which are moved from relatively shady or protected situations to more exposed sites may suffer damage to the bark from sun, wind or frost. Thin-barked trees such as beech, hornbeam and poplars are particularly susceptible to sun scorch (Rushforth, 1987, p126). In cases where such damage is likely, protect the trees during the period of adjustment by wrapping the trunks and main limbs with tree-wrapping paper or hessian before or immediately after planting. Wrap the material in overlapping spirals, tightly enough to stay in place, and tuck in the ends to hold.

Aftercare and Maintenance

Aftercare is crucial to the success of tree planting schemes. Given that the trees were healthy to begin with, and were carefully planted out in a site with conditions amenable to good growth, the work involved in aftercare should not be heavy. The prime requirement is regularity of care through the establishment phase, and it is in this that many planting schemes fail. It has been estimated that approximately one-half of the trees planted do not survive after the tenth year, often as the result of simple neglect (Sinden, 1989, p55).

This chapter covers weeding during the establishment phase, the control of woody weeds, pruning and wound treatment, the treatment required for pests and diseases, and prevention of damage to mature urban trees. Light felling in relation to thinning, coppicing and pollarding is discussed, although in less detail. Techniques for propagating coppice are also included in this section. For discussions on weeding at the pre-planting stage, and early care, see chapter 6.

Weeding through the Establishment Phase

Research conducted by the Forestry Commission in many parts of Britain indicates that weeding is necessary if young trees are to establish successfully, whatever the type or location of planting scheme. Effective weeding promotes both more rapid growth and greater health in the young trees, whereas unchecked weed growth around a tree will at the least lead to water stress, and may well result in tree failure.

The best way of establishing young trees is to maintain a weed-free area of at least 1m in diameter around the base. All sizes of planting stock - standards as well as transplants - grow faster or survive better with weed control. Standards usually require a larger weed-free area of 1.5m to establish well. Mulching (p102) and the use of chemicals (see below) are the two main methods of control.

The following information on weed competition, and the timing and duration of weed control, is based on 'Trees and Weeds' (Davies, 1987).

HOW WEEDS COMPETE

Weeds, and in particular grasses and clovers, compete with trees for water, light and nutrients in the following ways:

a At the early stage of growth, trees rely on moisture in the soil's surface layer. If weeds are allowed to grow around the base of a young tree, they will compete strongly for this water by drawing it up and transpiring it through their leaves. During dry weather, weeds continue to transpire and draw up moisture from deeper in the soil. An unweeded tree avoids the moisture stress caused by this competition by reducing its area of foliage, for example by producing smaller leaves. This reduces the tree's capability to photosynthesise, which in turn slows root growth. As root growth is needed for the uptake of water, the unweeded tree will be caught in a 'vicious circle', and will eventually die back or fail.

On an area of bare soil, by contrast, the rate of water lost through evaporation will be much lower and the tree will be much less affected. Evaporation will slow further during dry weather, when a 'skin' of dry soil forms at the surface.

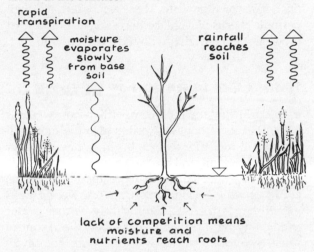

Benefits of 1M weed-free zone

b Nutrients are only available to the tree through the mechanism of water uptake. Thus, a tree which appears to be suffering from a nutrient deficiency in the soil may in fact simply be losing water - and nutrients - to competing weeds. In the cases where fertilizer must be applied (p104) it is even more important to eradicate herbaceous weeds, as otherwise the extra nutrients will simply stimulate their growth at the expense of the planted tree.

c In effect, regular mowing or scything around the base of trees is not a method of weed control, as repeated cutting simply stimulates grass growth. In addition, mown grass eventually forms a thick mat which prevents rainfall from reaching the soil. Maintaining a short sward of grass around the stems of young trees will therefore only make moisture and nutrient deficiencies worse. Incidental damage to bark from mowers, scythes or grazing animals can also occur to trees in this situation.

d There are cases where weed control should be modified. Too heavy a weeding of woody and herbaceous growth should be avoided, as this can encourage grasses. Bluebells and some other low herbaceous woodland flora can be left, as they do not harm trees. Mosses, which have no roots, do not appreciably lower the soil's water content and may help to stabilise and protect the soil around the tree by forming a natural 'mulch'.

In some cases, tall weeds can also be beneficial. In general, these weeds are intrusive, as they compete with young trees for light, can interfere with roots or distort stems, and may harbour bark-gnawing rodents. Bracken, for example, competes strongly with young trees for light in the first part of the growing season, and later collapses, often smothering or even flattening small trees. However, brambles, nettles and many tall herbaceous plants with sparse growth may protect trees from drying winds and damage from deer, hares or vandalism. These can be left, although periodic checks will still be necessary to ensure that they are not interfering with the trees' growth.

TIMING AND DURATION OF WEEDING

a In April, May and June, competition from weeds is usually at its strongest. April is also the month in which soil moisture deficits begin to develop over much of England, and the transpiration from weeds left after this date will result in greater deficits for the entire growing season. Thus, even one week's weed growth in April can significantly reduce water availability right through to October. Weed control must therefore begin early in the year. For newly planted trees, weeding during the first spring and summer is vital.

b Timing will vary with the season, the locality and the method of control. Sheet mulches (p103), for example, are fitted at the time of planting and then left in position for several years. Some herbicides work better at particular stages of weed growth, so application must be carefully timed. In general, however, weed control measures should have been taken by the middle of March, and earlier in the south or in mild winters. Grass can grow at any time of year, if the weather is mild enough.

Given that this initial weeding was thorough, the trees may be able to withstand some weed competition later on in the season, although they will grow best if kept weed-free until autumn.

c The number of years that weed control will be needed will depend on the site, the species planted, the spacing of the trees and other factors. Three years from the time of planting is usually the minimum.

Single trees in open ground and trees at the edges of planted areas need weeding for a longer period than trees within woodlands, where the relative lack of light and other conditions do not encourage the growth of grasses.

A 1m weed-free area should be maintained around trees planted in grassland for five or more years. The ground under trees cropped for fruit in orchards and gardens should be kept permanently bare.

CHEMICAL CONTROL

The Control of Pesticides Regulations 1986, which were brought in following the Food and Environment Protection Act 1985, cover all aspects of the development, advertisement, sale, supply, storage and use of pesticides. To help implement the Regulations, a series of codes of practice are being published. These include the 'Code of Practice for the Use of Pesticides in Forestry' (HMSO, 1990), available from the Forestry Commission, and the `Code of Practice for Safe Use of Pesticides on Farms and Holdings' (HMSO, 1990), available from offices of the Ministry of Agriculture, Fisheries and Food. It is generally recommended that pesticides be used only when absolutely necessary, so it is important to give some thought to alternatives such as mulching (p102) or appropriate hand or mechanical weeding (see below).

Volunteer groups that have used or are contemplating using pesticides will need to be aware of the following:

a The Recommendations cover proprietary products rather than active ingredients, and classify these products according to approved use. The two classes of product relevant to voluntary bodies are 'professional' (formulated for use mainly in agriculture, horticulture and forestry) and 'amateur' (formulated for use primarily in garden or household). Amateur products may contain the same active ingredients as those in the professional category, but at lower strengths. This does not affect their performance, but merely means that less dilution is necessary before application.

b Two categories of people need certificates of competence if they intend to use professional pesticides: contractors, and all those born on or after 31 December 1964. These two groups can be exempted from certification only if they use the products under the direct and personal supervision of a certificate holder. Volunteer groups are classed as contractors, and therefore need to meet the requirements if they intend to use professional products.

Training, which fully covers protective clothing, transport of chemicals, storage, etc., is offered by the

Agricultural Training Board and other bodies approved by them. The National Proficiency Tests Council issues the certificates, although testing is carried out locally. The ATB and NPTC should be contacted for details.

c Amateur products, while more expensive than professional products, can be used relatively freely by volunteers. They may therefore provide a viable alternative to the professional formulations, for smaller-scale schemes (e.g. in parks) at least. The amateur products which might be substituted for professional products are shown in the table below. Note that Amcide is the only amateur product discussed in this handbook; the other products covered belong in the professional category.

Chemical	Professional product	Amateur product and manufacturer
Ammonium sulphamate	Amcide	Amcide (Battle, Hayward & Bower)
Glyphosate	Roundup	Tumbleweed (Murphy Chem.)
Triclopyr	Timbrel	Tumble Nettle (Dow Chem.)

The other chemicals discussed below - asulam, atrazine with dalapon, and propyzamide - are not available in amateur formulations, although dalapon (for use on coarse grasses only) is available in the amateur products Synchemical Couch Grass Killer and Dalapon Herbicide.

Techniques for using ammonium sulphamate and triclopyr are discussed in the section on woody weeds (p112).

The professional pesticides listed below are suitable for use in non-commercial woodlands. They are discussed in brief, as detailed information on safe working practice is covered by the certificate. Suppliers are listed on p147.

Chemical control of weeds is fully covered in 'The Use of Herbicides in the Forest' (Forestry Commission Field Book 8, HMSO, 1989), which details suitable treatments for the control of grasses and grass/broadleaved mixtures, bracken, heather, woody weeds, gorse, broom, and rhododendron in mixed woodlands and coniferous plantations.

Asulam

Asulam is available as the liquid herbicide Asulox, and is specific to bracken. It is taken up by the foliage and transferred to the rhizomes, usually stopping growth in the season following application. Where other weeds such as bramble also need treatment, glyphosate (see below) can be used instead. Pre-planting control is best, as if used post-planting, the dead bracken stems will still need clearing by hand to prevent them from smothering the young trees.

Bracken should be treated when the frond tips have unfurled, in July or August. If you use Asulox, allow at least six weeks to elapse before planting.

Atrazine with dalapon

This is available as the granular herbicide Atlas Lignum, and is active against nearly all types of grasses. Atrazine acts on soft grasses, while the dalapon component kills coarse grasses. The herbicide is mainly soil-acting, so grasses absorb it through their roots. Activity is dependent on rainfall, which dissolves the granules into the soil. Atrazine remains active for up to six months; dalapon, for up to three months.

Atlas Lignum can be applied either pre-planting, at the time of planting (provided it is kept away from tree roots), or post-planting. If applied when trees are in leaf, it should only be used when the foliage is dry, to prevent the granules from sticking to and acting on the leaves.

Although the optimum period for application is mid-March to May, Atlas Lignum should be applied as soon as weed growth starts, which may be as early as February. Applying later may entail risk from an early spring drought, which will render the herbicide ineffective and thus lead to even more water stress on the trees. If applied at the time of planting, note that effectiveness will be reduced if you plant in November or December, as the dalapon will be inactive by the time spring arrives.

Glysophate

Glyphosate is a liquid contact herbicide, effective against grasses, broadleaved plants, bracken, heather, and woody weeds, including rhododendron (see p112). Its professional formulation is Roundup, and it is also available as the amateur product Tumbleweed. Roundup is mixed in water and then applied by sprayer, drench gun or weed-wiper (see below). Absorbed by the leaves, it is then transferred through to the roots, killing the plant. A red dye, available from Hortichem Ltd (p147), can be mixed with the solution to make treated areas more obvious and thorough control easier. Glyphosate can be used up to three days before planting, or post-planting, if the following precautions are taken.

As glyphosate can damage conifers and broadleaves (including their buds in winter, bark and foliage), any spraying must be done in calm weather, and directed carefully onto weed vegetation. Spray guards can be used to shield trees not already protected by tree shelters. Tall vegetation around small feathered trees should not be sprayed. Glyphosate works best on moist vegetation in warm and humid conditions, but its effectiveness may be reduced if rain is expected within 24 hours.

Because weed-wipers allow more accurate application, they are better for use on tall weeds around smaller trees, although control will be reduced on weeds over 300mm (1') in height and where many seed heads are present. Weed-wipers have reservoirs for the herbicide, which is fed through a wick and brushed on both sides of the weed foliage in a sweeping motion. The tree must not be touched.

Although glyphosate is most effective from July to September, it is better to apply it in March or early April when weeds start into active growth. This will protect the tree at the most vulnerable period of water stress, and make application easier as the weed vegetation is not so high. If needed, another application can be made from July to September. Depending on site conditions and weed types, this may obviate the need for a new application the following spring. Remember that water for mixing with the chemical will need to be transported to sites without a supply; Roundup needs to be mixed with tap water rather than water from ponds and streams.

Propyzamide

This is a soil-acting herbicide, available as granules (Kerb Granules), suspension concentrate (Kerb Flowable) or wettable powder (Kerb 50W). Propyzamide slowly volatilises in cold soil, and is taken up by germinating weeds and the roots of existing weeds, particularly grasses. It is not effective on peat soils. As good control depends on persistent low temperatures following application, it should be applied from October to December (or January in upland Britain). It remains active for three to six months.

Propyzamide can be used either pre- or post-planting. Because some users have experienced problems with it when used around trees in the winter of planting, it is best to use it only in the second and following seasons.

HAND WEEDING

As has been explained previously, scything or mowing is more likely to hinder a tree's establishment than help it. If you scythe some types of herbaceous growth, such as nettles or thistles, this will increase the available light and thus stimulate the growth of grasses, which will then need herbicide treatment.

The most effective manual method of weeding herbaceous growth is cultivation by hoe or mattock. This is very labour-intensive, however, and will be suitable only for smaller planting schemes in parks or gardens. You may need to hoe up to seven times annually if the site is fertile and conditions are damp, and skill is needed to avoid damage to the tree's surface roots.

If you choose to scythe herbaceous growth, only scythe an area large enough so that when the surrounding growth collapses it does not smother the tree. The cut weeds should be left spread on the ground as a mulch to suppress further growth.

As an alternative to scything, weak herbaceous growth such as nettles, creeping thistle or bracken can simply be trampled. This suppresses rather than stimulates growth, but may need to be repeated a few times through the season. Avoid treading the soil too heavily, or it may become compacted. Bracken can also be 'whipped' with a stick as the fronds open, to weaken the growth.

Goose-grass (cleavers), a rapidly growing, clambering annual, should be controlled before it smothers the tree or goes to seed, by pulling it away and compacting the unwanted growth into a heap. Persistent perennial climbers such as clematis (e.g. old man's beard), bindweed, honeysuckle and ivy should be cut back in late winter or early spring, and any young plants pulled or dug up. It may be necessary to treat bindweed with glyphosate, as this plant is very difficult to dig up, and grows very rapidly to smother young trees in a matter of weeks during the early summer.

The weeds present will determine the choice of tools. Weeding hooks or scythes can be used on herbaceous growth, as outlined above. Where there is up to a year's growth of climbers, brambles and other woody weeds, use a light brushing hook (curved slasher) or a bean hook. Where there is a heavy growth of woody weeds, use a heavy pattern slasher. Occasionally, you may need to use a billhook for heavy coppice regrowth. Felling of small trees and shrubs is discussed at the end of this chapter. (See p50 for details of tools.)

Procedural points

a If the trees are difficult to see, mark out the row to be weeded with poles stuck in the ground at intervals of 30m (30yd) or so. In the first year, clear lanes 600-900mm (2-3') wide along each row of trees, leaving the weeds between rows untouched unless they are likely to become tall enough to fall on the trees, in which case they should be topped. In the second and third years, weed around each stem as necessary to control grasses and keep the leader free from over-arching growth.

Where deer are present, you may decide to weed between the rows, to avoid vegetation topping the trees, but leave the weeds in the row uncut to help protect the trees. If these weeds begin seriously out-competing the trees, however, clear them and use another method of protection from deer (pp94 &117).

b Ensure that you find each tree before you cut around it, to avoid decapitating the stems.

c It is safest and easiest if each volunteer has a band of several rows to work on. Keep at least one row of trees between you and other workers. Take extra care where weeds are tall or the terrain difficult.

On moderate slopes work up and down hill. On steep slopes it is safest and easiest to work uphill only, so allow extra time for walking down to the bottom to begin each new row.

d If you have the time, shift the cut growth into piles around each stem to act as a mulch. Otherwise, leave it where it falls. Keep major drains, footpaths and rides clear of cuttings. Where herbaceous growth is exceptionally heavy, pile the cuttings between the rows. Lay woody weeds and climbers between the rows.

e Tread in around any trees which seem to be loose or growing at a slant.

MECHANICAL WEEDING

Mechanical weeding is less laborious than hand weeding where conditions are suitable, and may be appropriate for sites where herbicides are not acceptable. It has several disadvantages, however, in addition to the high rental or purchase cost of machinery.

It is necessary to design the planting layout and spacing with the type of weeding machine in mind, especially if a tractor-mounted machine is to be used. For efficiency and to prevent damage, the area should be cleared of large rocks and high stumps before planting. Access across drains must be prepared in advance.

Operators of weeding machinery, including portable brush cutters, must have proper training in safe use of machinery.

Supplementary hand weeding is usually required in inaccessible spots, on steep slopes or places missed by the machine.

Frequent mechanical weeding will result in a change in the weed species on the site, usually resulting in the formation of grass cover. Selective hand weeding of a site may be more appropriate than overall mechanical weeding, by maintaining the less competitive herbaceous growth, and allowing a woodland-type flora to establish instead of grass.

Types of machines include: portable brushcutters (scrub cutter or portable clearing saws); pedestrian-controlled motor scythes, rotating blade machines and flail mowers; and tractor-mounted blade mowers, chain mowers and flail mowers.

Portable brushcutters allow the operator to work standing up, out of the clutches of dense and thorny vegetation, and to weed in a more confined space than when using a larger machine. They are most suited for use on woody vegetation under 35mm (1½") in diameter, although they may be used on larger material. Brushcutter attachments, which apply herbicide to the cut stumps, are available. Brushcutters are very tiring to use. It is essential for other workers to keep well away from the operator while the machine is going.

Pedestrian-controlled machines (e.g. Aller-Scythe) are designed for purposes other than forest weeding, so they tend to have too little clearance and to be hard on the operator in rough terrain. They are, however, useful where a machine is needed for clearing rides, paths and glades. Care is needed on slopes and where stumps and other obstacles may require extra manoeuvring. Motor scythes are best limited to use on grass, bracken and other herbaceous weeds. Flail mowers are rather easier to manoeuvre than the other types and tend to chop the material more finely.

Tractor-mounted machines are very efficient, provided the rows are wide enough and at least 90m (100yd) long, and clear of obstacles over about 100mm (4") high. They cannot work where the ground is rutted or on heavy soils if the ground is wet. On hillsides, they should only be used up and down slope. Side sloping is dangerous. Where trees are small, spot weeding by hand or herbicides should be carried out beforehand around the trees so that the tractor operator can see them. Tractors can also be used to pull rollers to crush bracken and wood small-weed (*Calamogrostis epigejos*). For best effect, rolling should be done just as the weeds achieve maximum growth.

Controlling Woody Weeds

Woody weeds are less harmful than grasses to the growth of young trees. A continuous cover of vigorous woody shrubs will, however, compete strongly with young trees if the soil is very poor, with water and nutrients in short supply. In planted areas where timber production is important, many native and non-native plants may need to be cleared because such competition will reduce the quality and thus the value of the trees.

In woodland planting schemes where the primary aim is conservation and amenity, any native shrubs and trees which eventually colonise the planted area are usually very desirable, as they provide greater variety of species, structure and cover. It may be necessary, however, to control them for several reasons. These include keeping rides and glades open, allowing the more desirable trees to thrive, maintaining a full range of woodland structure, and allowing access for management and recreation.

Certain invasive introduced species such as sycamore and rhododendron, and invasive native species such as birch, willow and wayfaring tree, may also require controlling. Rhododendron is a particularly problematic presence in woodlands with more acid soils, as it propagates vigorously, both thrives in and casts heavy shade, and creates toxic conditions in the soil when its leaves fall and rot.

If you cut woody weeds by hand, you will need to treat the stump to prevent regrowth. You can remove the stump by hand or winch, or kill it with an herbicide. Another method of control is to apply herbicide to foliage or stem. The control of one year old seedlings by pulling or herbicide application, and removal of seeding trees, can also be useful measures.

Techniques for cutting smaller trees and shrubs are covered at the end of this chapter. Herbicides for use in non-commercial woodlands are briefly discussed below (see p108 for general information on herbicide use and training requirements). 'The Use of Herbicides in the Forest' (Forestry Commission Field Book 8, 1989) should be consulted for full details.

HERBICIDES FOR WOODY WEEDS

Foliar treatment

This is the cheapest and easiest method to use on shrubs which are in leaf, and of a size which is accessible to spraying. However, it has several disadvantages which makes it generally unsuitable for conservation management, with the exception of rhododendron control (see below). Great care has to be taken to treat only the weed species, as desirable broadleaves and ground flora will be damaged if sprayed. The treated plants will go brown and die, leaving unsightly dead growth which can make access and future management difficult, as well as being a fire hazard.

If using the foliar method on rhododendron, only young plants less than 2m (6'8") tall should be treated, as their foliage will be less resistant to the chemical. Glyphosate (Roundup) plus Mixture B wetting agent can be used in summer, or triclopyr (Timbrel) can be applied diluted in water as a summer foliage spray, or diluted in diesel as a winter shoot spray. Where foliar control of other woody weeds is thought necessary, glyphosate is effective on most except for gorse and broom.

Stem treatment

This method involves applying herbicide to the stems of standing shrubs and trees, either by injection or by applying the herbicide to a notch or frill cut around the stem. This technique is used on woody weeds which are too tall to spray, or where treatment has to be done in winter. Although avoiding damage to desirable species, this method still creates the problems of the standing dead trees.

Where treatment is thought appropriate, ammonium sulphamate (Amcide) can be used as a spray onto a frill cut around each stem, or the dry crystals can be placed into individual notches. Alternatively, glyphosate (Roundup) can be applied by injection to individual notches.

Cut stump treatment

This method involves applying the herbicide to the cut stump, to prevent regrowth. It can be a useful technique for non-commercial woodlands as it only affects the treated stump and there is no unsightly dead material left standing. It is labour intensive, in that clearance still has to be done first by hand or machine, and the cut material removed, stacked or burnt. Stump treatment avoids the ground disturbance caused by stump removal, although the cut stumps may be a hazard for machinery or for amenity use of the area.

Ammonium sulphamate (Amcide), an amateur herbicide, can be applied by watering can or spray, or placed as crystals. If using Amcide crystals, drill 25mm (1") diameter holes, 50mm (2") deep, and fill them with the crystals. A 150mm (6") diameter stump should have four holes. Cover the filled holes with stones or bung with wood to keep the rain out, or the crystals will become diluted and ineffective. This measure also prevents birds from eating the crystals. Alternatively, glyphosate (Roundup) can be applied by paint brush or knapsack spray.

If using this method on rhododendron, treat the stumps of mature plants over 2m (6'8") in height. Amcide can be used as above. Otherwise, either Roundup plus Mixture B wetting agent, or triclopyr (Timbrel), can be applied at any time of year except spring.

Pruning and Wound Treatment

This section outlines basic aspects of tree surgery which volunteers may be required to carry out, usually on amenity trees. Pruning over shoulder height should only be done by experienced volunteers. More complex operations, such as the wiring of limbs, require professional skills and may be hazardous for volunteers. The Arboricultural Association maintain a List of Recommended Contractors and Consultants.

The following information is from Capel (1987), Shigo, Vollbrecht and Hvass (1987) and Hibberd (1989).

PRUNING

Where trees are grown for timber, 'pruning' means the removal of branches for a considerable height up the stem in order to encourage the formation of knot-free, high-quality timber. This treatment is most suitable on potentially valuable broadleaved trees such as oak, ash, cricket bat willow, wild cherry, sweet chestnut and sycamore. Slow-grown Scots pine and a few other conifers grown for joinery may also be pruned. This type of pruning is laborious, so it is important to treat only those trees which are to form the final crop or late thinnings.

Early pruning of timber trees is important, as it helps prevent the formation of knots and reduces the risk of disease. The stem should be pruned up to a height of 3m (10') before the first thinning, and up to 5-6m (16-20') before the second thinning. Pruning reduces the diametric growth of the stem temporarily, until the crown grows larger, so over-pruning (i.e. over half the height of the tree) will inhibit growth unacceptably and should be avoided for the final crop of trees.

Pruning of amenity trees usually involves crown management, with the aim of producing a strong branch system able to withstand high winds or other natural disasters, as well as an attractive shape. Dead, diseased or damaged parts will need to be removed to keep the tree in a safe condition and maintain its health as far as possible. Branches that cross through the tree or rub against other branches will also need pruning, as otherwise structural damage can occur, or decay can enter through any resultant wounds. The overall size of the tree may need to be reduced to keep it from overcrowding its living space. Urban trees may also need to be pruned to allow more air to circulate and more light to reach nearby buildings.

General points

a With all but small forest trees, formative pruning usually begins in the nursery to promote a balanced shape and optimum health in the growing tree. After planting, you should prune to the point of active growth any shoots which die back, as these may otherwise become entry points for decay organisms. Any surplus, crossing or broken branches should also be removed regularly. The leader should normally be retained and encouraged.

It is very important to reduce potentially weak forks by pruning to a single shoot, particularly on trees prone to producing them, such as Norway maple and sycamore. This treatment is also vital on tall trees, especially brittle species such as locust tree. If left to develop, weak forks can later crack and rot under the weight of snow or in wet conditions, making the tree unsafe and necessitating either expensive cabling operations or removal.

Flowering crab, cherry, hawthorn and some other ornamentals tend not to produce strong leaders and are best left to develop open crowns. Some of these trees should be pruned to maintain flower-producing spurs, as with fruit trees.

b For trees beyond the establishment phase, prune little and often rather than waiting until drastic measures are needed. Light pruning is relatively easy, requires less skill and is usually less hazardous than heavy pruning. It also involves much less threat to the tree's health and powers of recovery. Trees generally respond less well to pruning as they age, although species vary greatly. London plane and lime remain very tolerant. Beech, birch, cherry, sycamore, walnut, and on occasion oak and ash must be treated very carefully after maturity. If any of these species require heavy pruning, spread the work over two or three years. In any case, never remove more than one-third of a tree's branch system at a time.

As a rule of thumb, restrict the size of pruning wounds on the main stem or a large branch to no more than one-third the size of the stem or branch itself. Avoiding the need to make multiple wounds on a single stem or branch will also lessen the chance of extensive decay developing. Note that trees which are already stressed from drought or other factors are more likely to experience dieback following pruning (Hibberd, 1989, p97).

c For most species, the best time to prune is in the spring, before the period of leaf expansion. This will allow the protective growth of callus, which is fastest in spring and summer, to be well advanced by autumn. The timing is less significant for large wounds on over-mature trees, as callus growth on such trees is very slow regardless of the season. Species such as horse chestnut, walnut, hornbeam, birch and maple 'bleed' profusely if pruned in spring, and so should be treated in late July or August. Prune cherries and plums in early summer, by mid-July at the latest, to reduce the risk of silver leaf infection. Pruning live branches of conifers should be done in late spring as growth is beginning.

Crown treatment

a If you must limit the size of the tree, the best method is crown reduction ('drop crotching'). This is a tricky job, as you will need to trim back the crown to the main branch system without spoiling the symmetry of the tree.

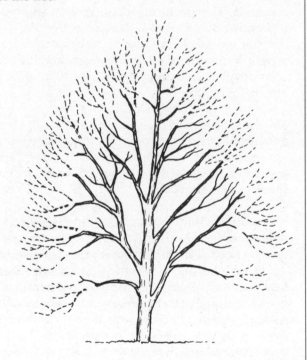

To allow the tree to recover quickly, reduce the crown before the tree achieves its maximum height. Repeat the job whenever regrowth reaches the previous limits, usually about every four or five years.

b 'Lifting' the crown may be necessary where you need to let people or vehicles pass beside the tree. Remove the bottom side branches, but leave the upper part of the crown untouched. As with crown reduction, it is important to try to preserve the general shape of the tree.

c Crown thinning - lessening the bulk of branches in the crown - is a skilled job best left to the professional.

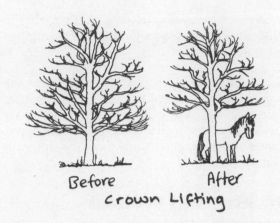

Before   After
Crown Lifting

Over-thinning is difficult to avoid, for example, and this will simply encourage extensive regrowth. Where a tree is vulnerable to wind-throw, however, crown thinning is worth arranging, as it increases the tree's stability by reducing the crown's weight and wind resistance. It is also a useful procedure where more light is needed beneath or near a tree. As with crown reduction, this job needs to be repeated regularly.

Crown thinning

d Note that if you need to prune aloft in an urban area, any overhead telephone or electricity cables passing through the tree's crown may be hidden by the tree's foliage. Always check to locate any overhead cables before you start work, as any contact with them is obviously very dangerous. Also take care to ensure that the branches you cut do not fall on cables or become entangled with them.

Pruning techniques

See page 50 for tools which are used in pruning. Note the following points:

a All pruning cuts of live wood expose tissue to organisms which may cause decay. To minimise the

114

chance of such decay, it is important to make cuts at the optimum position on the stem or branch, as detailed below.

b Twigs and small branches under about 12mm ($\frac{1}{2}$") diameter at their base which need pruning to remove damaged tips or to encourage further growth should be cut cleanly back, preferably to just above a node where they will re-sprout. You can cut straight through these branches with secateurs or a fine pruning saw.

too long   too short   too slanted   right

c Larger branches are normally cut back to the trunk or to the main branches, and the positioning of the cuts is more specific. Extensive research by Dr Alex Shigo in the USA and Europe has shown how trees form natural protection boundaries against decay, which has led to new recommendations for 'natural target pruning'.

Two of these protection boundaries are easily identified on branch and stem. The 'branch bark ridge' is the point where the tissues of the smaller branch separate from the major branch, and is clearly visible as a raised ridge of bark. Make all pruning cuts to the outside of it, as shown.

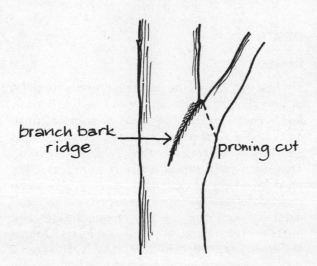

branch bark ridge → pruning cut

The 'branch collar' is a layer of tissue around the base of the branch, formed when side branches begin to age and lose vigour. This is the tree's most effective natural barrier against organisms which cause decay. Its position is more clearly seen in branches which have died back to the trunk.

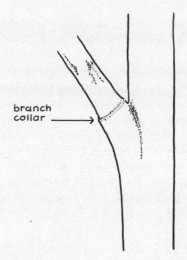

branch collar →

Always leave the branch collar intact, whether you are pruning live, dying or dead branches on hardwoods or conifers.

d Cut branches over 12mm (1/2") in three stages, as shown. If you try to saw through them with one cut, they are likely to break and pull off a strip of bark. This damages the tree.

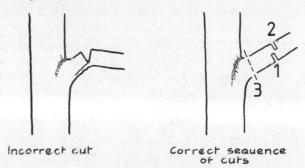

Incorrect cut   Correct sequence of cuts

Make the first cut about one third of the way through the branch from the bottom, but not so far that the saw binds. This prevents the bark from tearing at the sides. Make the second cut from the top, parallel with and a little beyond the first cut. This severs the branch, leaving a projecting stub. Trim the stub with a third cut, from the top.

Never leave a snag or stub. At best, this will only produce a mass of unsightly regrowth. More often, stubs die back, providing a foothold for infection and rot which can then more easily be transmitted to the rest of the tree.

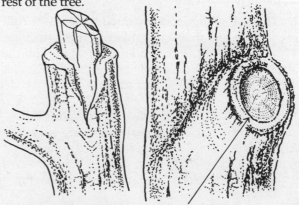

Stubs prevent proper callus formation   Healthy callus formation

e Cut heavy branches in short sections, following the procedure given above.

The weight of a branch varies according to its length and diameter, and also according to the tree species. There is also considerable variation between trees within a species and even between branches and main stem, so it is not easy to predict the weight before cutting. A section of branch 150mm (6") in diameter and 1.2m (4') long on a dense species such as oak or beech can weigh up to 20kg (50lb). The same weight is reached in a 300mm (1') diameter branch only 300mm (1') long.

Always be sure to err on the side of safety when cutting heavy branches. The descent is usually controlled by 'slinging', which involves roping the section of branch to be cut. This procedure can be dangerous, and should only be undertaken by trained and experienced people.

WOUND TREATMENT

Until fairly recently, it was recommended that all cuts and wounds in trees be treated with a wound paint which was claimed to seal the wound against fungal attack until the natural callus had formed. The value of this treatment has now been brought into question. The following information is in part from Capel (Arboricultural Association, 1987).

a If the tree is healthy, and the pruning cuts have been made cleanly and correctly, no further treatment should be needed. The tree itself forms a chemical protection boundary which prevents the spread of pathogens inward.

b Wound treatments, to be completely effective, would have to seal the wound, repel insects, be long-lasting, and have fungicidal and growth-promoting properties. The products currently available, including latex paints, bituminous products, and phytotoxic and other fungicides, fail to meet these requirements. Recent research indicates that they are also largely ineffectual against decay, and that some compounds may even promote it.

c The use of fungicidal wound sealants in fruit orchards is the main exception to these findings. Wounds on fruit trees should be treated with the appropriate sealant to prevent silverleaf disease and canker caused by the *Nectria* fungi.

Proprietary sealants may have other limited beneficial properties, as they appear to encourage healthy callus growth in the first year after pruning, and remain effective for several seasons. They are less useful, however, on over-mature trees, where rapid callus growth would be of most value.

If applying a sealant, first carefully trim any torn edges around the wound with a sharp knife, but do not 'shape' it. This practice is no longer recommended, as it involves the removal of live tissue and increases the area left open to infection. Remember to avoid cutting into the branch collar. Paint the sealant only around the edge of the wound unless the tree is of the plum or cherry family (*Prunus* spp), in which case cover the entire surface.

Pests and Diseases

Trees are home to a wide variety of other organisms, ranging from bacteria and viruses to birds and insects. Although these may affect the individual tree in terms of health and lifespan, they hardly ever pose a threat to entire woodlands, due to the natural system of checks and balances present in a woodland ecosystem. Individual trees within a woodland which die from fungal attack or other causes provide habitats which are essential for the survival of many life forms. Treatment of pests and diseases is, however, very important in planting schemes aimed primarily at wood production, as well as in the management and preservation of valuable amenity trees. The Forestry Commission publish detailed information on individual pests and diseases (see their current catalogue of publications).

PESTS

Insects

The best way of keeping insect pests under control is by providing adequate nesting and feeding habitats for insect-eating birds. Nest boxes are useful in urban areas, and may be necessary in some young woods with little diversity of structure. 'Nest Boxes' (British Trust for Ornithology), available from the RSPB, provides details on design and construction. Many insect outbreaks eventually collapse as a result of naturally occurring disease, or as parasites and predators reach effective population levels. On mature trees, insect attack is rarely deadly, although it may appear alarming and can reduce both growth rates and timber quality. Seedlings and young trees, particularly conifers, are more vulnerable.

In urban areas, certain limes are prone to develop infestations of the lime leaf aphid (*Eucallipterus tiliae*), which secretes a sticky fluid called honeydew. This can create a serious nuisance in public places (Hibberd, 1989, p137).

Birds

The only species which may cause serious damage in woodlands is the starling. Starlings roost communally, especially in winter, and they may cause the death of trees in the roost area due to the toxic effect of their droppings, although some roosts are occupied for many years with little damage. Where large numbers of trees have begun to be affected, the roosts can be dispersed by means of amplified distress-call apparatus and bird-scaring cartridges fired from shotguns or Verey pistols. See Curry, Elgy and Petty (1977) for details.

Mammals

Various mammals can cause extensive damage in established woodlands, parks and in some urban areas. For early protection against rabbits, deer and other mammals, see p94. Chemical repellents effective against deer and rabbits are discussed on p101.

a Rabbits. Although most rabbits in Britain died from myxomatosis in the 1950s, some areas were little affected by the disease, and in many others populations have again built up to high levels. Rabbits damage young trees of most species. For information on controlling rabbits in established woodlands, see Forestry Commission Leaflet 67, 'Rabbit Management in Woodlands' (Pepper, 1976).

b Squirrels. For both amenity trees and commercial tree crops, bark stripping by grey squirrels is a very serious problem, as trees are damaged at an advanced stage and control is very difficult. Squirrels strip bark from the trunks and branches of pole-stage trees, normally 10-40 years old, and can cause damage from ground level up to about 16m. The most susceptible species are sycamore and beech, with pines, oaks, ash, larch and birch also badly affected. Bark stripping seriously weakens or kills trees.

Squirrels cannot be excluded from a woodland, and even if a population is killed, others will rapidly move into the area. Food and habitat is always in short supply, and is the main natural control on the survival of young animals. In a large woodland, the only feasible method of management is to control numbers by killing immediately before and during the damage period (April-July). If control is done at other times, numbers will only build up again by the following damage period. Although some species at certain stages are more vulnerable - in particular, pole-stage beech - damage can occur unpredictably. The risk of damage is greatest when mast years followed by mild winters and early springs have led to an increase in the population.

Among the legal methods of control, cage-trapping and hopper-poisoning with Warfarin are the most efficient. Many people disagree with Warfarin baiting, however, as other mammals and birds may eat grain spilled by the squirrels; the poison can also enter the food chain once the squirrels have died. In areas such as central Wales, where both grey and red squirrels are present, live trapping should be used as it is illegal to use Warfarin in the presence of red squirrels. In small-scale plantings, providing an alternative source of food during the susceptible period (April-July) may reduce damage. For further details, see the Forestry Commission publications 'Grey Squirrel Control' (Rowe, 1983) and the 'Wildlife Rangers Handbook' (1985).

c Mice and voles. These gnaw the bark of young trees and may cause serious damage in young plantations and nurseries, although removal of grass around the trees normally acts as a control. Mice and voles are usually a problem only in certain years when populations peak. In such circumstances control may be necessary by laying poison, which should be placed in lengths of rainwater downpipe or tile drains. For details see the 'Wildlife Rangers Handbook' (Forestry Commission, 1985).

d Deer. The native red and roe deer and the introduced fallow and Sika deer can cause damage by browsing young trees and branches, stripping bark and using the stems as fraying stocks. Fencing, as described in chapter 6, is the most effective protection. It does, however, present potential problems. If deer are forced out of their natural woodland habitat, they may cause greater damage in surrounding agricultural areas and are more likely to be poached, hit by cars or killed by dogs. Careful culling of resident woodland herds, while tolerating a continued low level of damage, may be a better solution. The 'Wildlife Rangers Handbook' (Forestry Commission, 1985) comprehensively covers deer management.

Whatever the methods used for controlling deer populations, the Devon Wildlife Trust (1970, p9) suggests several measures to ensure that any damage done by an accepted herd can be kept to a minimum. These include retaining natural browse (especially bramble and hazel) where possible, and limiting weeding and clearing of shrubs and herbaceous growth to divert the deers' attention from the young trees and provide additional browse. Thickets where deer are known to shelter can also be retained. Other measures entail leaving roe deer rutting stands unplanted, and providing 'lawns', either by leaving small areas unplanted or by seeding and fertilizing stands of trees such as larch, in which there is often some growth of grass, to improve the grazing.

117

DISEASES

Tree diseases are often difficult to prevent or cure. The best or only solution to many serious diseases is to plant resistant types of trees in suitable sites.

A few of the most important diseases from a conservation point of view are described below. Many of these (e.g. beech bark disease) are seriously damaging in urban areas. Anthracnose of London plane has been included, as this tree is so widespread on urban sites. Watermark disease, poplar canker and fireblight are bacterial, whilst the others are caused by fungi. Dutch elm disease is discussed in a separate subsection, (p199).

Forest diseases and diseases of mature trees

a Honey fungus (*Armillaria mellea*) attacks the roots of a wide range of tree species and is mainly recognised by its black bootlace-like rhizomorphs. It nearly always spreads from old infected stumps of broadleaved trees in the immediate vicinity, and is most serious where conifers are planted on old broadleaved sites, and in gardens and arboreta where it can harm valuable specimens. It can also devastate hedgerows planted with susceptible species. Members of the family *Rosacaea*, which includes many fruit trees, are usually killed. Older trees of other genera can often live for long periods with the fungus, but conifers may develop root rot and become susceptible to wind-throw.

While control is usually impossible in woodlands, in gardens and arboreta you should grub up old stumps to prevent them from acting as sources of infection, and also remove and burn any infected trees with all their major roots. To prevent infection from reaching a tree, cut a trench outside the tree to the depth of the roots and outside the drip line, so that the roots are not harmed. Line the trench with 500 gauge black polythene before back-filling.

b Beech bark disease is caused by the fungus *Nectria*, which gains access through wounds opened up by the scale insect *Cryptococcus fagi*. The disease is locally severe in southern England, mainly affecting vigorous trees aged 25 years or more growing in pure stands on good soils. The drought of 1976 seemed to increase its severity, although some trees were relatively resistant and selective breeding may provide a long-term solution. Often the disease causes only temporary set-back, with recovery within 10 years, but the stems of affected trees are liable to decay internally and snap. Affected trees should be felled promptly if their timber is to be used, and newly infected trees and those which are markedly infested by the scale insect should be removed during plan-tation thinnings. On specimen trees, it is a good precaution to apply a tar-oil wash with a pressure sprayer to control the insect. Use 300ml (1/2 pint) of tar diluted in 6l (1.25 gallons) of water to cover the bole of a mature tree about 15m high. Spray between December and early February, taking care not to damage surrounding vegetation. You may have to repeat the treatment every three to five years.

c Sooty bark disease of sycamore, caused by the fungus *Cryptostroma corticale*, was first found in a London park in 1945, and since that time has spread to many parts of south and central England. The disease is dependent on hot summer temperatures. Although there is no direct method of control, within the region of occurrence it is likely to be held in check by relatively cool summers. In the area surrounding greater London, where devastating outbreaks may occur, its effects can best be limited by assuring that any sycamores planted are intermixed with other tree species.

d Phytophthora root rot is a disease which attacks the roots of sweet chestnut (where it is known as ink disease), beech, common lime, maples and horse chestnut as well as several conifers and ornamental cultivars. It is most likely to occur in trees on heavy or wet soils, such as the patches of 'poached' ground occurring where livestock gather under trees. While control is not possible, the risk of infection can be reduced by preventing compaction and wet conditions around the bases of trees, for example by building tree guards (p97).

e Watermark disease of cricket bat willow, caused by *Erwinia salicis* bacteria, leads to dieback and ruins the timber of this species. The spread of Watermark disease has been reduced by compulsory felling orders which apply to certain counties (p46), and by the planting of setts taken only from healthy trees or stool beds.

f Fireblight (*Erwinia amylovora*) is an extremely infectious bacterial disease which affects pears, apples, rowan, hawthorns, whitebeam, and other species. Its main impact is in orchards and nurseries. The treatment of infected trees is not feasible. Previous attempts to control the spread of the disease proved ineffective, and were dropped in 1987 for the area south of a line from Preston to Hull, where the disease is now widespread. To prevent infection, it is best to choose resistant species for group or mass planting, such as in landscaping schemes. Popular ornamental stock, including *Pyracantha*, are a major source of infection. In a conservation project, hawthorn hedges or other susceptible plantings should not be made near orchards.

g Poplar canker is a disease caused by the bacterium *Xanthomonas populi*. On vulnerable species or cultivars (not Lombardy poplar), it can cause severe die-back and, occasionally, death. Stems, twigs and branches may be affected by the cankerous growths, and in wet conditions, a bacterial ooze. The best method of control is to use resistant cultivars in infested areas.

h Anthracnose of London plane, caused by the fungus *Gnomonia platani*, is the only common disease of the species in Britain. The last time in which a serious outbreak occurred was in early summer 1979, when a cold winter followed by a cool spring contributed to its development (Clouston and Stansfield, 1982, p72). The fungus causes four types of blight, to buds, twigs, shoots and foliage. Although some trees can be rendered unsightly by extensive dieback or experience heavy summer leaf fall, the disease kills few trees. There are no feasible methods of control at present. Damage by road de-icing salts (see below) is sometimes confused with this anthracnose.

Dutch elm disease

The current epidemic of this disease, caused by an aggressive form of the fungal pathogen *Ophiostoma ulmi*, reached its peak in the mid-1970s. The pathogen is carried by elm bark beetles (*Scolytus* spp), which burrow into the tree, allowing the fungus to destroy the veining in the xylem layer. The disease is also carried by coppice shoots and suckers, which is the main method of elm regeneration. English elm rarely sets viable seed.

Suckers arise around living or dead trees, up to 50m from the original tree, and are very invasive. The elm hedgerows and hedgerow trees which were so prevalent in southern England were formed from coppice and sucker growth, and being linked by their root systems, were particularly susceptible to the disease. By mid-1980, an estimated 18 million English, wych and smooth-leaved elms had died or been felled, mainly in the area south of a line from Chester to the Wash and in south Wales. The disease continues to spread, not only from infected root systems, but also via the elm bark beetle, which can affect shoots and suckers two years or older.

The Forestry Commission has been monitoring the survival rate of regenerating elms since 1977, as detailed in B J W Greig (Arboriculture Research Note 13/88/PATH). The findings in this report indicate that the elm population in Britain will be subject to periodic waves of infection, as has happened on the Continent for at least the past 30 years. For the next few decades, it therefore seems likely that the elm will appear in the landscape as a small suckering tree the size of hawthorn or hazel. It is hoped that the pathogen will eventually become less aggressive, or possibly be controlled by a recently discovered virus-like disease of the fungus itself. In the meantime, any elms regenerating in areas where planting or replanting take place will at most provide useful shelter.

Arboriculture Research Note 2/88/PATH, which presents information on the results of experiments to breed resistant elms, makes useful reading for those interested in using non-native elms in amenity plantings. Some of the new clones now being tested in trial plantings in Britain have a high level of resistance to the disease. They are not immune, however, and are not yet thoroughly tested. For these reasons, use in small-scale mixed schemes only is advisable.

Damage to Mature Urban Trees

The most common disorders of urban trees derive primarily from man-made hazards. Atmospheric or soil pollution, physical damage, and the disturbance of soil or roots may all create conditions of severe stress for trees, contributing to poor health or an early demise.

Air and soil pollution

As with tree diseases (above), the best defence against air pollution is to plant resistant species. Lime, sycamore and London plane, for example, tolerate fluoride gases well, while the latter two are also resistant to sulphur dioxide.

There is little one can do about soil pollutants such as gas, which can leak from the mains into the soil, or oil or herbicide spills. The common problem of de-icing salts leaching into the soil can be corrected by an application of gypsum (calcium sulphate), which both helps remove it, and improves soil structure (Rushforth, 1987, p125).

Physical damage and disturbance

Few trees can survive serious physical damage or disturbance to either their aerial parts or roots, but these are distinct hazards to trees in built-up environments. While not all potential damaging factors can be foreseen from the outset, any that can should be considered at the planning stage to allow for adequate protection.

Techniques for discouraging vandalism have been discussed in chapter 6, but the most serious potential damaging agent to older established trees is construction work. The following information is from Hibberd (1989, pp108-111) and Clouston and Stansfield (1982, p90).

Damage to trees by construction work

Earth-moving operations such as property development, landscaping or road works can cause serious damage to trees in the following ways:

a Soil level changes. If these occur within the rooting area of the tree, either direct damage to the roots or damaging modifications in the rooting conditions can result. For example, a raised soil level within the drip line can eventually asphyxiate tree roots by seriously lowering oxygen levels. Covering the root zone with Tarmac or other impervious materials will have a similar effect.

b Soil compaction from heavy machinery. This can lead to root death. Building materials should never be stacked over the rooting zone, as otherwise dieback can occur.

c Seepage of toxic chemicals. Oil, wood preservative, paints and other chemicals can harm or kill roots if they are spilled, or seep from cracked containers, within the rooting zone.

d Trenching for services. If this is to take place near the tree, note that the minimum spread of a tree's feeder roots is likely to be 25% more than the crown diameter. Any digging within this area must be done with extreme caution. Mechanical diggers should be used only to within a few feet of the rooting zone, after which all excavation around the roots should be by hand. Any cables, etc., should be run under the roots, and the entire operation should be done in the quickest time possible to prevent drying of the roots.

e Damage above ground. Branches and stems can be badly wounded by heavy machinery, leaving them open to decay. Similar wounds can happen when fires are lit too near trees. If the lower crowns and bark are scorched, the bark may later fall away and expose the underlying tissues to pathogens.

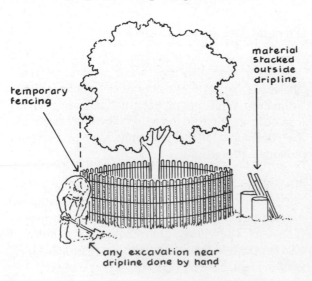

temporary fencing

material stacked outside dripline

any excavation near dripline done by hand

Guidelines to protecting trees in this situation are given in British Standard 5837, and in the booklet, 'Conservation of Trees and Shrubs in Built-up Areas' (Devon Wildlife Trust, 1969).

Felling

Although felling is necessary in certain pre- and post-planting situations (see below), the subject properly belongs to a treatment of ongoing woodland management. An in-depth discussion of felling techniques is therefore beyond the scope of this handbook, although some guidelines are given below. Felling and all related tasks (e.g. burning, stacking, etc.) are fully covered in 'Woodlands' (Brooks, 1988).

Felling of larger trees and coppice poles is also dangerous work, requiring careful study of procedures beforehand and either close supervision or, preferably, a course of practical training in the field. Only the felling of smaller trees is discussed in any detail here.

REASONS FOR FELLING

The following are circumstances in which tree felling could be considered a part of the tasks associated with tree planting and aftercare:

a Site preparation. You may need to fell some trees or shrubs in order to plant others. As mentioned on p81, however, widespread clearance is not recommended because of the disruption it can cause to existing wildlife habitats. It may be best, where appropriate, to clear areas and plant groups of trees within these clearings.

b Selective thinning. This is essentially a commercial forestry technique which is used to maximise production of a woodland 'crop'. In commercial plantations, individual trees which are poor quality in terms of timber production (e.g. poorly formed or weak) are thinned to provide more growing space for the remaining trees, with the aim of producing a uniform stand of high-quality, even-age trees. The thinnings also provide an intermediate financial return. Thinning in commercial forests is covered comprehensively by Rollinson (1988).

In a woodland-type planting, selective thinning for the purposes of conservation and amenity will be aimed mainly at diversifying or maintaining the age and size structure. For example, it is normal practice to plant 5-10% more trees than are actually needed, to allow for failures. If the failure rate is lower than expected, you may wish to remove a number of specimens to prevent overcrowding and the related problems of spindly growth and reduction of light reaching the understorey. Selective thinning may need to be carried out at intervals of 5-20 years, but this will be dependent on species, objectives, site conditions and rate of growth. Frequent, light thinning is generally better for wildlife. Other conservation measures you can take while thinning are to avoid the bird-breeding season (March-July), concentrate on crown rather than understorey thinnings, and leave prunings or brashings in piles to provide insect habitats (Smart and Andrews, 1985).

Whatever your objectives in thinning, note that timing is usually very important. Infrequent, heavy thinning, for example, carries the risk of wind-blow of the remaining trees when their shelter is suddenly removed, as their roots are not adapted to wind-sway. If broadleaves have been planted with a nurse crop of conifers, the conifers must be thinned in time to prevent them from suppressing the broadleaves. Where the intention is to keep both species in such a mixture to maturity, there is a further problem. Species commonly grow at different speeds at different ages, so thinning will need to be carried out in such a way that one species is not unduly favoured over the other.

c Control of invasive species. If rhododendron, sycamore or other invasive introduced species begin to outnumber the trees you have planted, you may need to clear them.

PRE-FELLING CONSIDERATIONS

Refer to the safety points in chapter 4, in addition to those below.

1 Think through all the aspects of the work. This includes not only felling, but preliminary clearance, stump treatment and disposal of the cut material.

2 Study the tree to decide on likely directions of fall. The weight of the crown is a major factor in determining this. Work out escape routes, and make sure they are cleared of brambles and other obstructions.

3 Check for any potentially hazardous obstacles (e.g. nearby buildings, overhead cables). Do not fell within 15m (50'), or two tree lengths, whichever is the greater, of electricity cables.

4 Be aware of present or imminent weather conditions. Never fell in heavy rain or strong wind. On steep slopes, be particularly sure of your balance and footing.

5 Put up warning signs on footpaths, etc., in the vicinity of felling.

6 Make sure that the people felling trees are working at least three tree lengths away from each other.

7 Never work alone, but ensure that no-one else enters the danger zone.

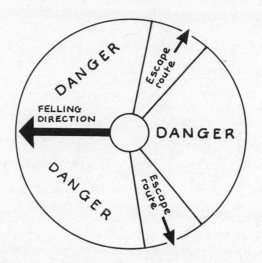

8 Unless otherwise directed, leave as low a stub as possible. This is particularly important with slender saplings and coppice shoots. If these are felled with one oblique stroke, the long, sharply pointed stub that results presents an obvious and very dangerous hazard.

9 Felling should be done in late autumn and winter (October-March). At this time the trees are less sappy and are easier to cut, handle and season than in spring or summer. Herbaceous undergrowth has died back, so visibility is good whilst wildlife disturbance is minimal. Decide on the area to be cleared in September, if this has not already been determined.

On wet, badly drained sites you may have to work in late summer or autumn to minimise soil damage. Try, however, to avoid work during spring and early summer, the height of the nesting and flowering season.

FELLING OF SMALLER TREES

Trees with a stem diameter of about 75mm (3") at the base can be felled by cutting straight through, using either a billhook or bowsaw. A helmet is optional when felling small trees, although wearing one is advisable. Even small trees hurt if they fall on you!

Note that the 'front' of the tree is the side on which it is intended to fall, which makes the 'back' the side opposite to that.

With a bowsaw

The bowsaw is the safest, most efficient and most versatile felling tool. Use it whenever possible.

1 Crouch or kneel to one side of the tree. You will be sawing through from the back.

Make the cut level or angled slightly downward in the direction of fall. Using the full length of the blade, saw with easy relaxed strokes. Use a slight rocking motion, cutting 'on the corner' as shown below, for greatest speed.

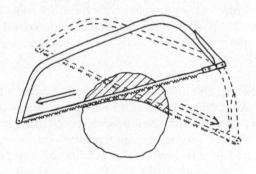

Place one hand on the end of the frame to power the stroke, and rest the other hand lightly on the back of the frame to keep it in line with the blade and ensure an equal force on push and pull strokes. This prevents the blade from twisting in the cut. When necessary, you can use the smaller size saws, in particular the triangular 530mm (21") saw, one-handed.

2 With the larger, longer-bladed saws, the blade tends to vibrate if you exert more than a very slight pressure in the direction of the cut. With these saws, minimise vibration by just keeping the saw blade in contact with the stem and by pausing for an instant at the end of each stroke.

3 If the tree starts to settle back or twist, use one hand to push it in the direction of fall. Saw faster as the tree falls to minimise the risk of the stem splitting. Keep sawing to sever the stem.

With a billhook

As a felling tool, the billhook is best restricted to use on light coppice material and multi-stemmed shrubs where a bowsaw is awkward. When felling with a billhook:

1 Stand or kneel to the side of the tree, far enough back to achieve a full swing without endangering yourself. Standing is best for a powerful stroke, but kneeling may be more comfortable or necessary to avoid obstructions. Note that unless the tree is heavily leaning, you will be cutting into the front of the tree as shown.

Use the billhook one-handed, controlling the descent of the tree with the other hand, placed well up the stem for safety.

2 Do not try to cut directly across the grain, as the tool is not designed for this. For small stems, which can be severed with one blow, use a slightly upward sweeping stroke to sever the stem.

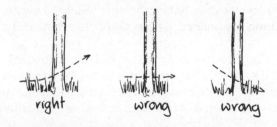

right   wrong   wrong

Avoid cutting downward, or you will drive the hook into the ground and dull or chip the edge. If the cut results in a sharply pointed stub, trim it flat immediately.

3 Cut thicker stems by notching, as shown. Progressively enlarge the notch with downward and upward strokes until you can finish off with an upward stroke. Keep out of the way of the tree as it falls.

When felling slightly larger trees up to 150mm (6") in diameter at the base, an undercut should be made at the front, about one-third of the way through, before the felling cut is made from the back.

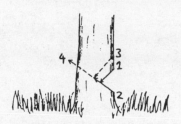

FELLING LARGER TREES

For the reasons indicated above, the treatment of heavy felling in this handbook is in brief outline form only, and should not be used as a guide to practical work. See Brooks (rev. 1988) for details on the subject.

Note the following points:

a Any buttresses at the base of the tree should be removed first, using a bowsaw, an axe, or a combination thereof. These tools will also be the main ones used for all the cuts described below.

b A felling sink offers more control over the direction of fall than a simple undercut, and this is essential on any tree over 150mm (6") in diameter at the base of the stem.

c The felling cut should be parallel to and about 50mm (2") above the back of the sink. This can be a tricky procedure, but it is important because it reduces the risk of the butt bouncing back.

d While the sink controls the direction of fall, it is almost useless without an adequate hinge, which is your source of control over the tree before and during its fall. The hinge attaches the main stem to the stump, and minimises any risk of the tree falling sideways or backwards. As a rule of thumb, it should be 20mm (¾") for every 150mm (6") in the diameter of the stem. Perhaps the most common beginners' mistake is to continue the felling cut until the tree starts to fall - by which time there is often little or no hinge remaining!

If you feel it is necessary, additional control can be gained by attaching a rope or winch cable to the tree and pulling in the direction you want the tree to fall. The length of the rope must be twice the height of the tree.

e Once the tree has been felled, it is important to sned, log up and stack the logs and brushwood in one operation, before moving on to another tree. Snedding is the removal of branches from a felled trunk; logging up, the cross-cutting of the trunk into logs. Like felling, these tasks are both safer and more enjoyable if performed at an unhurried pace.

Billhooks, snedding axes and bowsaws are the appropriate tools for these jobs. When snedding, start at the butt end and work towards the tip, always cutting away from you. Unless the trunk is very big, keep it between yourself and the branch you are snedding to minimise the risk of the tool bouncing off the stem. With bigger trees, particularly broadleaves with large crowns, it is important to make sure the stem is stabilised to prevent it from rolling towards you as you work. Once the tree has been snedded and the branches stacked, it is easier to log up the tree into whatever lengths are required by starting at the tip end. Supporting the tree so that the cuts open up as you saw also helps.

HANGING TREES

A hanging tree is one which is caught in the branches of neighbouring trees. Smaller hanging trees can be freed without mechanical aids. Put your shoulder under the stem, lift the end - keeping your back straight and using your legs to lift - and walk briskly away from the tangled end so that the tree drops. Never leave the site until you have freed all hanging trees. Brooks (rev.1988) contains instructions on dealing with larger hanging trees.

COPPICING, LAYERING AND STOOLING

This section covers coppicing techniques, as well as layering and stooling as methods of propagating coppice. For a general description of coppice establishment and management, see pp28-29.

Although oak coppice was often cut in spring to allow the bark to be peeled easily for the tanneries, most coppice is traditionally cut from October to March. This timing makes the work easier because of the absence of foliage, and also allows for a full season's growth afterwards. Coppicing can take place at any time of year, however, except in August, as the shoots would then not have time to harden off before the frosts. The information below is in part from Crowther and Evans (1986).

Coppicing procedure

Billhooks are fastest to use on young regrowth. On older coppice, saws are usually best. The 530mm (21") bowsaw with a triangular frame is particularly useful on trees with multiple stems, provided that they are not too large.

The following points are additional to the information on felling, above.

a Take a close look at the coppice before you start. Remove any hard debris (e.g. stones, tin cans) lodged between the stems. Then decide which way to fell the stems by checking the likely direction of the fall, the ease of cutting at the base, the presence of any intertwining crowns, and the space available to drop the stems.

b Remove any young growth at the base of the stool, to avoid interference when cutting.

c Remove the stems one by one. For smaller stems, use the appropriate procedures for felling smaller trees, above. Stems up to 150mm (6") in diameter will need to be undercut, and larger stems will require a felling sink. Where the stems are all about the same size, cut from the outside to the inside of the coppice stool in a spiral fashion, as shown.

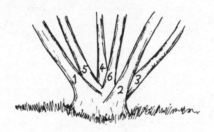

With stems of varying sizes, clear the smaller first to give access to the larger.

d Make each cut sloping upward towards the centre to shed rainwater and prevent rot. Avoid leaving any snags, or stripping the bark off the stump, as this can invite decay.

e Low cuts will maximise coppice regrowth. It may be easier and quicker to make a high cut first and then cut a second time to remove the stub.

right   wrong

Note that ash is traditionally coppiced at 300-900mm (1-3') high in some coppice woodlands. On the evidence of past practice, this method should be followed unless there are other reasons against it.

f After coppicing, brush any dirt or sawdust off the cut surfaces so that they will shed water more efficiently.

Layering procedure

Layering is a useful technique for propagating coppice if there are large gaps between stools, or the coppice regrowth is spindly. Hazel and chestnut respond well to this treatment, but other species can also be layered successfully. Always layer after the clearance work of felling is finished, so that you don't trample on the layered stems during the course of the work.

To layer, proceed as follows:

1 When coppicing a stool, leave one or two stems for layering.

2 Using a billhook or a bowsaw, cut through the stem from the top, at a downward angle away from the stem. Cut in the direction in which you wish to lay the stem, as shown.

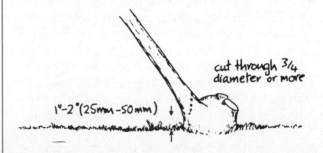

cut through 3/4 diameter or more

1"-2" (25mm-50mm)

The length of the cut is important. If you cut too far, the stem may break off as it is lowered to the ground, or die after layering; if the cut is too short, the stem will split downward into the base as you lower it. When you near the point where you want the cut to stop, gently pull the stem down and to the left to open up the mouth of the cut. Then continue cutting and pulling simultaneously until the stem can be eased down to the ground.

3 Trim the protruding stub with a small bowsaw, placing the cut as low as possible and sloping it upward toward the first cut. This will allow rain to drain away.

4 Mark out the line of the stem along the ground, using a spade or mattock and following any bends in the stem.

5 Move the stem aside and dig out a trench along the marked line. Dig it deep enough to ensure that bent or whippy stems won't spring out.

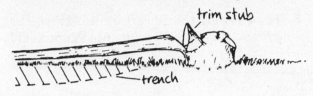

6 Position the stem along the trench and choose a spot to peg it down. This should be a point where it is in close contact with the ground.

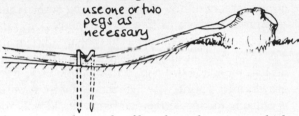

The pegs can be made of hazel or other stems which have a strong side branch emerging at an acute angle. Cut these off with a saw or billhook to form rough pegs at least 300mm (1") long, with crooks about 100mm (4") long. Trim them on a stump, cutting the points in line with the crook.

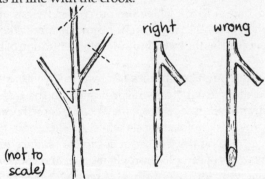

For very springy stems, use two pegs facing opposite ways. Knock them in with a lump hammer.

7 Cover the stem with earth (preferably not leaf mould) in the area where you want it to root. Cover it to a depth of 75-150mm (3-6"), and tread in firmly around the stem.

If you can't get the stem to lie along the ground, cut a notch in the upper side of the stem where it lies closest to the ground and heap earth over the notched section.

8 If the layered stem sprouts, you can either leave it untouched to grow in place, or wait 7-12 months, and then cut it off from the parent stool for transplanting.

Stooling

Stooling is an alternative method of propagating cut coppice stems. Coppice in the normal way, as above, but leave several stems untouched. Then mound earth over the stool, as shown below. In time, new shoots will grow with roots formed in the loose soil. When they are ready for transplanting, push the earth aside and sever the shoots from the stumps, making sure to keep their root systems intact.

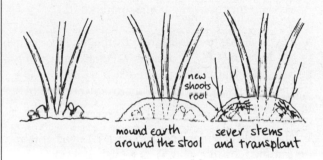

POLLARDING

Pollarding is a very similar procedure to coppicing in most respects, except that the felling will be carried out on a short trunk 1.5-3m (5-10') high. The higher the boll, the more strenuous the work.

Traditionally, pollarding has been carried out on farm, riverside and wood bank trees as a method of wood production which effectively prevents deer or livestock from browsing on the branches. If properly carried out (see below), pollarding can vastly prolong the life of the tree.

In urban areas, 'topping', a kind of pollarding, is often practised on tall woodland trees which have been planted in confined spaces. With this method, the trees are left to grow and then lopped back hard at the 3-5m (10-15') level, after which they are pollarded every few years. However, topped trees are unsightly for most of the year, have poorly anchored branches which may be dangerous if left to grow large, and often become infected due to the large wounds produced. Poplars, planes and limes survive this treatment best, but even with these species it is far better to avoid the need to pollard by thinning or reducing the crowns early on, or by planting smaller varieties or cultivars.

Traditional pollarding begins when the trees are fairly young, before major branches have grown thick and heavy. It is repeated at five to twenty year intervals, in the same way as coppicing, depending on the size of the poles required. Such trees often reach immense age and girth, and it is well worth maintaining pollard management even when the poles are no longer needed, to keep the crowns from collapsing under their own weight and to maintain the life of the tree. Introducing diversity of age and size in the pollard population of a site may also be worthwhile. In the past, when pollarding was a much more common practice, it is probable that the age range of pollards was much wider. If pollards are important on a site in terms of landscape, conservation and historical value, starting new pollards in proximity to existing ones can not only create such diversity, but will also provide replacements for any old pollards that die.

When starting new pollards or maintaining existing ones, keep the following points in mind:

a New pollards are best started by the time the stem is 100-150mm (4-6") in diameter. Pollarding can be successfully initiated with trees up to 300mm (1') diameter, but this is a difficult operation and hazardous for the inexperienced.

b The height at which a new pollard is started is often determined by the height to which livestock can reach. Allow an extra 300mm (1') above their reach, as regrowth may not be right from the top of the cut stem. Allow 1.8m (6') for fallow deer, 2.1m (7') for cattle, and 2.7-3m (9-10') for horses, assuming the tree is not fenced off.

c Late winter is the best time to pollard, as this avoids the bird-nesting season and minimises the time it takes the wounds to heal.

d The safest tool to use when pollarding is a bow saw. Use standard felling techniques (see above) when cutting a new pollard, but take extra care when judging the size and direction of the sink in order to prevent the stem from splitting. Be sure your feet, or the base of the ladder, are out of the way, since the butt end of the cut section of stem will drop abruptly when severed. When pollarding old trees with large branches, cut the branches in short sections using the cutting technique described under the section on pruning, above. It may be easiest to climb into the crown of an old pollard and saw branches off from above, but take great care when doing this.

If you will be re-pollarding large pollards which have been neglected over a long period, the following suggestions, from P. L. Mitchell (1989), may be useful. They are based on the results of a questionnaire which was circulated to regional offices of the Nature Conservancy Council and the National Trust.

a The success of re-pollarding depends on the species. Hornbeam, ash and willow are usually successful, while oak is variable and beech is markedly unsuccessful.

b Stubs left on re-pollarded trees have in some cases actually improved regrowth. At Weald Country Park, for instance, hornbeam responded much better to re-pollarding when stubs 600mm (2') long were left. In normal arboricultural practice, leaving stubs is not recommended because they serve as entry points for decay (see p115). For old neglected pollards, however, it is apparent that the younger bark on the stubs is needed for successful regrowth, as more buds may grow from it. The decay which may enter from a stub is unlikely to be a serious problem, as old pollards may survive for centuries with heart-rot.

c Cutting branches on the slant also stimulates regrowth in old pollards, by increasing the perimeter of cut bark from which some shoots arise.

d Old pollards which are burry and twiggy rather than smooth-barked may be much more likely to succeed, as the burrs indicate a concentration of buds.

e Although beech does not respond well to re-pollarding, leaving one major branch on the tree may improve its rate of regrowth. The foliage on the branch provides photosynthesis while the shoots are growing, freeing the tree from complete reliance on the reserves of carbohydrates in its stem and roots. After one year (or two to three, if regrowth is slow), the branch should be lopped.

Appendix A

Conservation and the Volunteer Worker

The British Trust for Conservation Volunteers aims to promote the use of volunteers on conservation tasks. In addition to organising work projects it provides support to over 600 affiliated groups, offering advice and help with insurance cover, tool purchase and practical technical training.

To ensure the success of any conservation task it is important that the requesting person or agency, the volunteer and the leader all understand their particular responsibilities and roles. All voluntary work should be undertaken in the spirit of the Universal Charter of Volunteer Service, drawn up by the UNESCO Coordinating Committee for International Voluntary Service. Three of its most important points are:

1 'The work to be done should be a real need in its proper context and be directly related to a broad framework of development'. In terms of conservation, this means that tasks should be undertaken as integral parts of site management plans, not as isolated exercises. Work should never be undertaken solely for the benefit of the volunteer. Necessary follow-up work after tasks should be planned beforehand to ensure that volunteer effort is not wasted.

2 'The task should be a suitable assignment for a volunteer'. Volunteers cannot successfully tackle all types of work and they should not be used where there is a risk of serious accident or injury, where a financial profit will be made from their labours, where the job is so large that their efforts will have little overall effect, where the skills required are beyond their capabilities so that a bad job results and they become dispirited, or where machines can do the same job more efficiently and for a lower cost.

3 'Voluntary service should not replace paid local labour'. It should complement such work, not supplant it. Employers should make sure in advance that the position of volunteers and paid workers is clear with respect to any relevant labour unions. Further advice may be found in 'Guidelines for the relationships between volunteers and paid non-professional workers', published by the Volunteer Centre UK, 29 Lower King's Road, Berkhamstead, Herts HP4 2AB.

Volunteers are rarely 'free labour'. Someone has to pay for transport, materials, tools, insurance, refreshments and any accommodation charges. Before each party makes a commitment to a project it should be clear who is to pay for what. While volunteers may willingly fund their own work, 'user bodies' should be prepared to contribute and should not assume that all volunteers, who are already giving their time and effort, will be able to meet other expenses out of their own pockets. Several grant-aiding bodies may help pay the cost of environmental and conservation projects, notably English Nature (formerly the Nature Conservancy Council, the World Wide Fund for Nature and the Countryside Commissions. Details may be found in 'A guide to grants by the Department of the Environment and associated bodies for which voluntary organisations may be eligible', available from The Department of the Environment, Room C15/11, 2 Marsham Street, London SW1P 3EB.

It is important that volunteer workers be covered by some sort of public liability insurance for any damage or injury they may cause to property or to the public. Cover of up to £250,000 is recommended. Volunteers should also be covered against personal accident.

The volunteer group organiser should visit the work site well before the task, to check that the project is suitable and that volunteers will not be exploited and to plan the best size of working party and the proper tools and equipment. Volunteers should be advised in advance on suitable clothing for the expected conditions. Normally they should be physically fit and come prepared for work and they should genuinely want to volunteer - those 'press-ganged' into service are likely to work poorly, may do more harm than good and may be put off a good cause for life! Young volunteers need more supervision and are best suited to less strenuous jobs where achievements are clearly visible, and it is recommended that where they are involved the task should emphasise education.

Note that the Agriculture (Avoidance of Accidents to Children) Regulations, 1958, legally restrict the riding on and driving of agricultural machines, vehicles or implements by children under 13 years.

Volunteer group organisers and 'user bodies' both should keep records of the work undertaken: the date of the project, jobs done, techniques used, number of volunteers and details of any notable events including accidents, unusual 'finds', publicity, etc. Such information makes it easier to handle problems or queries which may arise after the task. It also provides a background on the task site for future visits, supplies practical data by which the site management plan can be evaluated and allows an assessment to be made of the volunteer effort.

Appendix B
Species Tables

1 Native Trees and Shrubs

The table on the following pages includes commonly managed native species of trees and shrubs over 1.5m (5') tall, excluding climbers. Some species have been included which, though rarely planted, have considerable habitat value and should be encouraged when possible. Indications of which species are suitable for farm (e.g. shelterbelts) and urban use are included under 'Management notes'. Information is from a variety of sources, written and verbal, relying where possible on the experience of conservation land managers.

TABLE HEADINGS

Size and growth

Size = normal maximum height in Britain (+) = fast grower in good conditions, (-) = slow grower.

Tolerance

C = tolerates cutting, D = tolerates or prefers damp soil (usually with some flow of soil water), E = tolerates exposure, F = tolerates spring frosts, O = tolerates sea wind, P = tolerates smoke or air pollution, S = tolerates or prefers shade, V = grows in a wide variety of soils, I = tolerates infertile dry soil.

Preferred conditions

L = light demanding, T = frost tender (damaged by late spring frosts), W = wind firm.

Management notes

A = availability: A1 - freely in a range of sizes, A2 - in a restricted range of sizes, A3 - from some nurseries, A4 - from specialist growers only, A5 - may be in short supply; B = attractive bark; C = varieties, cultivars or related species available in columnar (fastigiate) form; E = suitable for elm replacement; F = showy flowers or fruit; f = showy autumn foliage; H = suitable for use in livestock hedges; I = invasive; P = easily propagated, c - by cuttings, l - layering, s - seeds, x - suckers or stooling; S = suitable for use in shelterbelts or amenity hedges; T = major timber use in Britain; t = limited or specialised timber use in Britain; U = suitable for urban use (e.g. in confined spaces, near buildings, along streets or in polluted conditions); W = varieties, cultivars or related species available in weeping (pendulous) form.

Comments

The abbreviations 'N', 'S', 'SE', etc., refer to general regions of Britain, but distributions cannot be indicated precisely in the limited space. See Perring and Walters (1962) for details. See Appendix C for a map showing which species should be encouraged in particular regions of Britain.

NOTES FOR TABLE

1 Do not plant poplars near buildings because of possible damage by roots.

2 Evergreen or semi-evergreen broadleaved species.

3 This species is replaced by smooth-leaved elm as the common hedgerow and woodland elm in East Anglia and East Kent, and by the Cornish elm in parts of the West. See Jobling and Mitchell (1974) for identification of elm species.

4 This species, *Pyrus pyraster*, is probably feral rather than truly wild. The wild pear, *P cordata*, is one of Britain's rarest native trees.

5 'Summer' willow, bearing flowers during or after coming into leaf.

6 'Spring' willow, bearing flowers before the leaves appear. An important early spring food source for bees and other pollinating insects.

Common name	Scientific name	Growth	Tolerance	Preferred conditions	Management notes	Comments
CONIFERS						
Juniper	(*Jun. communis*)	6m (20') (-)	O	Chalk, limestone, brown earths, acid or dry soils	(C, Pcs, U) Bird/ insect food (fruit), nest cover, deer browse	Mainly SE, N Eng. & Scot. birch & pine woods. Poor regen-eration. Berries flavour gin.
Pine, Scots	(*Pinus sylvestris*)	24m (80')	EFIV	(LW) Light/sandy soil or acid peat if drained, low rain; tolerant	(A1, B, Ps, S, T, U) Best conifer for wildlife	Useful nurse. Often regenerates nat-urally where protected from grazing. Susceptible to exposure from seawind.
Yew	(*Taxus baccata*)	14m (45') (-)	EPSV	Mainly chalk, limestone but tolerates all but very acid soil	(C, PCs, S, U, W) Bird food (fruit), nest sites, deer browse	Good windbreak or clipped hedge, but poisonous to livestock. Plant small. Dense shade
BROADLEAVES						
Alder, common	(*Alnus glutinosa*)	22m (73') (+)	CDEPSV	Hardy. Any damp soil (best if flushed) except very acid	(A1, E, I, Ps, S, t, U) Bird food (seed), nests, insect habitat	Often coppiced. Stands flooding, helps stabilise banks. Fixes nitrogen, improves soil - so good in reclamation schemes. Voles eat bark. Good nurse for other species.
Alder buckthorn	(*Frangula alnus*)	6m (20')	CD	Damp peats to acid sands in lowland fens and woods	(Ps, t) Bird and small mammal food (fruit)	Brimstone butterfly food. Once widely coppiced for fuse charcoal.
Ash	(*Fraxinus excelsior*)	28m (90') (+)	CDEOPSV	(LWT) Best in deep calcareous loams	(A1, E, Ps, T, U, W) Bird & small mammal food (seeds)	Profitable but difficult as timber tree. Good coppice. Avoid in gardens and cultivated areas because of surface rooting and freely naturally regenerating. Good deadwood.
Aspen	(*Populus tremula*)	24m (80') (+)	DEOPS	(L) Hardy. Heavy clay, damp fertile soils	(A3, I, Pcx, S, t, U, W) Good gen. wildlife value, deer browse.	Pioneer or nurse for upland shelterbelts but timber seldom good in Britain. Bushy on poor soil. Suckers freely[1]
Beech	(*Fagus sylvatica*)	28m (90')	CEPS	(TW) Any soil except peat, heavy clay	(A15, C, E, f, H, Ps, S, T, U, W) Bird and small mammal food (seeds)	Good for underplanting. Needs nurse on exposed sites. Bark disease and grey squirrel damage in some areas. Good park tree.
Birch, hairy	(*Betula pubescens*)	18m (60') (+)	CDEPV	Tolerant but especially on poorly drained peat and heath soils	(A1, Ps) Invertebrate habitat, bird food (seeds)	Good nurse, best in groups. Major fen, heath felled-wood invader but sometimes hard to es-tablish on sites which have not carried trees.

130

Common name	Scientific name	Growth	Tolerance	Preferred conditions	Management notes	Comments
Birch, silver	(*Betula pendula*)	18m (60') (+)	CDEFIPV	(LW) Prefers light soils in drier parts of country but very tolerant	(A1, B, C, f, I, Ps, S,t,U, W) As for hairy birch	As for hairy birch.
Blackthorn	(*Prunus spinosa*)	3m (10') (+)	EOPV	Calcareous to neutral soil	(I, H, Plsx, S) Insect food, esp. butterflies	Good for hedges, but suckers invasively. Important scrub coloniser.
Box[2]	(*Buxus sempervirens*)	5.5m (18')	O	Chalk, limestone or neutral soil	(F, Pcs, S, t)) Bird nest cover.	Local native but widely planted in south. Cover for game.
Broom	(*Sarothamnus scoparius*)	2m (6')	E	(L) Neutral to acid sandy	(F, Ps, S) Insects, esp. butterflies	Useful nurse for conifers and to bind unstable slopes and improve poor soil.
Buckthorn, purging	(*Rhamnus cathartica*)	4.5m (15')	D	Calcareous, mainly damp but also drier sites	(A4, Pcls) Butterfly food plant	
Buckthorn, sea	(*Hippophae rhamnoides*)	6m (20')	DEIO	Poor sandy soil near coast and deep soil over chalk	(I, Psx, S) Winter bird food (berries)	Good seaside hedge mixed with blackthorn but often very invasive.
Cherry, bird	(*Prunus avium*)	14m (45')	P	OK on clay; best on shallow soil over chalk, neutral to acid well-drained loams	(E, F, Plsx, U, W) Insects. Bird food (fruit)	Mainly N., in field margins and open woods. Good mixer when planted in thin woodlands.
Cherry, wild	(*Prunus padum*)	15m (50') (+)	PV	Fertile woodland soils, esp. on chalk; also clay, deep acid soils. Tolerant	(A1, C, E, F, f, Plsx, S, t, U, W) Bird food (fruit)	Mainly S.Tolerates some shade, suitable for shelterbelt margins or mixed with oak or beech.
Crab apple	(*Malus sylvestris*)	6m (20')	PV	Any soil, incl. calcareous	(C, F, Psx, W) Insects. Birds. Small mammal food (fruit)	Throughout, but less common in C, N. Scot. Edible fruit (jelly).
Dogwood	(*Cornus sanguinea*)	3m (10')	CS	Calcareous or neutral soils, lowland woods	(A1, I, Pclsx) Bird nest cover	Mainly Eng., W. Wales but also S. Scot. Invasive on downlands.
Elder	(*Sambucus nigra*)	6m (20')	CEO	Lowland woods, scrub, disturbed phosphatic calcareous to neutral loams	(C, F, I, Pcs) Insects (flowers), bird food (fruit), early nests	Invasive in hedges. Edible berries and flowers (jam, wine).
Elm, common	(*Ulmus procera*)	33m (110')	CEFOPV	(L) Any ordinary soil, esp. fertile free-draining deep loams	(A3, C, f, Px, S, t) Bird nest cover. Insects, esp. b/flies	Mainly midlands and S., in hedgerows. Much reduced by Dutch elm disease. Branches liable to fall without warning[3].
Elm, wych	(*Ulmus glabra*)	30m (100') (+)	COPS	(W) As for comm. elm	(A3, C, Ps, S, t, U,W) As for common elm	Thrives in woods, hilly country and near water, esp. N. and W. valleys. Slightly less disease -prone than comm elm. Non-suckering.

Common name	Scientific name	Growth	Tolerance	Preferred conditions	Management notes	Comments
Gorse	(*Ulex europaeus*)	2.5m (8') (-)	EIO	(L) Dry sandy, neutral or acid soils, lowland scrub	(A3, F, I, Ps) Insects, bird nesting cover. Burns readily.	Stands extreme wind, sea spray. Useful fodder. *U. galii* & *U. minor* similar but dwarf and limited to W.
Guelder-rose	(*Virbunum opulus*)	4.5m (15')	CDE	Lowland woods, hedges on neutral to calcareous damp fertile clay and loam	(F, f, Pcs) Insects (flowers) Bird and mouse food (fruit)	Mainly Eng.
Hawthorn, common	(*Crataegus monogyna*)	9m (30')	CDEOPV	Very tolerant, all but very wet or acid soils	(A1, C, F, H, I, Ps, S U, W) Flowers attract insects. Bird and mammal food (seeds) bird nest cover	Hardy, thorny. Important hedge shrub, scrub pioneer. Good natural regeneration.
Hawthorn, Midland	(*Crat. oxyacanthoides*)	9m (30')	CDPSV	As native, mainly in woods on clays and heavy loams	As for common hawthorn	Native in SE, C. Eng. In hedges, often indicates relict woodland. Hybrids with common hawthorn frequent.
Hazel	(*Corylus avellana*)	6m (20')	CSV	Tolerant, especially calcareous to slightly acid loams and clays, in woods	(A1, t, F, Plsx, S) Bird & mammal food (nuts) and insect habitat	Mainly lowlands, but also upland oak woods. Important trad. coppice species (wattles etc.) Edible nut.
Holly[2]	(*Ilex aquifolium*)	15m (50') (-)	CDEOPSV	Dry soil, deep soil over chalk	(A1, F, H, Pcs, S, U, W) Bird food (fruit), nests; deer browse	Woodland sub-canopy tree, useful in hedges and shelterbelts. Holly blue butterfly food plant. Plant May or Sept only if bare rooted.
Hornbeam	(*Carpinus betulus*)	20m (70') (-)	CEFPSV	Tolerant but best on silt, gravel over heavy subsoil	(A2, C, E, f, Ps, S, t, U) Bird food (fruit)	Mainly SE lowland mixed woods, often coppiced.
Lime, common	(*Tilia x europaea*)	40m (135')	P	(W) Fertile soils, clay	(t, U, W) Insects (flowers), bird food, nests	Doubtfully native hybrid widely planted. Creates honeydew (drip). Often lopped or pollarded in towns.
Lime, large-leaved	(*Tilia platyphyllos*)	30m (100')	P	(W) Fertile soils, clay	(E, Psx, S, t, U, W) As for comm. lime	Rare, local native. Good for parks. Creates honeydew.
Lime, small-leaved	(*Tilia cordata*)	18m (60')	CPS	(W) Fertile soils, clay	(A2, E, Psx, S, t, U, W) As for comm. lime	Native in Eng. & Wales. Important constituent of mixed woodlands. Creates honeydew.
Maple, field	(*Acer campestre*)	10m (36')	CPSV	Any soil, esp. calcareous clays and loams. Very hardy	(A2, C, f, Ps, S, U, W) Flowers for insects. Mammal food (seeds)	Common coppiced tree in Eng. Best autumn colour on heavy soil.
Oak, pedunculate	(*Quercus robur*)	30m (100') (-)	COV	(LTW) Best on well-aerated deep fertile loams, but very tolerant	(A25, E, Ps, T, U) Very good gen wildlife value. Avoid shallow, poorly drained or peaty soils, exposure, frost hollows.	Important for timber; trad. for coppice, tanbark. Scrubby on sandy soils.

Common name	Scientific name	Growth	Tolerance	Preferred conditions	Management notes	Comments
Oak, sessile	(Quercus petraea)	30m (100') (-)	COV	(LTW) As for pedunculate oak, but tolerates poorer, more acid soils and more shade and frost	(A2, C, Ps, T) As for pedunculate oak	As for pedunculate oak. Less subject to insect, mildew attack and keeps better form as forest tree.
Pear, wild	(Pyrus pyraster)	9m (30')	DV	(L) Wood margins, hedges, parks; shelter	(F, Psx, W) Avoid v. acid soils	Doubtfully native, mainly S., as isolated trees & thickets of suckers. Edible fruit [4].
Poplar, black	(Populus nigra)	30m (100')	D	River and stream flood-plains rather than woods	(Px) Good gen. wildlife value	Native relict, E. Anglia & Midlands, now mainly displaced by quick-growing hybrids.
Poplar, grey	(Populus canescens)	30m (100') (+)	CDOPSV	Tolerant but best on light loam	(A5, I, Px, S, t) Good gen. wildlife value	Hybrid of white poplar & aspen. Very free suckering, good for windbreaks[1].
Poplar, white	(Populus alba)	20m (65') (+)	DPOV	Damp or dry, on clay or over sand, gravel or chalk	(C, Px, S)	Doubtfully native. Good for coastal windbreaks. Drops branches [1].
Privet[2]	(Ligustrum vulgare)	3m (10')	V	Tolerant, esp. calcareous loams and clays in lowland wood and scrub	(I, Pcs, S) Some insects. Bird food (fruit)	Native mainly S. Semi-evergreen. Good game cover but can spread to form thick tangles.
Rose, dog	(Rosa canina)	3m (10')	CEOV	Lowland hedges, woodland fringe on calcareous to neutral clays, loams	(F, Pcsx) Birds (fruit) Insects (flowers)	Root stocks for rose cultivars, hips for jam.
Rowan	(Sorbus aucuparia)	9m (30')	DEOPV	(L) Esp. lighter soils, sandy, peat, well-drained acid loams	(A1, C, F, Ps, S, U) Bird & insect food (fruit). Avoid lime	Useful for streets, grass verges. Edible berries (jam). Tolerates exposed sites. Susceptible to browsing.
Service tree, wild	(Sorbus torminalis)	22m (70')	CS	Heavy soils in lowland woods	(E, Psx, U) Insects (flowers) Bird food (fruit)	Local but widespread in S & Midlands. Indicates ancient woodland on native sites. Edible fruit (jam).
Spindle	(Euonymus europaeus)	7.5m (25')	C	Calcareous to neutral loams, in lowland woods	(F, f, Ps, U) Flowers attract insects. Bird food (fruit)	Mainly in S. Attractive shrub. Alternate host for bean aphis (aphis fabae).
Wayfaring tree	(Viburnum lantana)	6m (20')	CI	Lowland wood, scrub and hedges on calcareous loam	(F, f, I, Pcs) Insects (flowers) Birds (fruit)	Mainly SE. Invasive on deserted downland pasture.
Whitebeam	(Sorbus aria)	12m (40')	CPS	Chalk or limestone	(A2, C, F, Ps, S, U) Bird & insect (fruit)	Native mainly S but widely planted.
Willow, bay[5]	(Salix pentandra)	12m (40') (+)	CDOP	Fertile loam, fen peat, clay, deep acid soils	(A4, I, Pc) Moth and butterfly food, bird nesting, roe and fallow deer fraying stocks	Stands flooding, helps stabilise banks. Coppice useful for wattles.
Willow, crack[5]	(Salix fragilis)	25m (80') (+)	CDOP	Fertile loam, deep acid soils, river banks	(A4, I, Pc, S) As above	As above. Older trees often shed limbs.

Common name	Scientific name	Growth	Tolerance	Preferred conditions	Management notes	Comments
Willow, goat[6]	(*Salix caprea*)	10m (30') (+)	CDOPV	As for bay willow, and dry soil over sand or gravel	(A2, I, Pc, S, W) As for bay willow	As for bay willow. Competes, so limit shelter use to water-logged peat or exposed coastal sites.
Willow, grey[6]	(*Salix cinerea*)	10m (30') (+)	CDOP	Wet sites, esp. rather acid in lowland woods	(A3, I, Pc) As for bay willow	As for bay willow. Major fen carr species.
Willow, osier[6]	(*Salix viminalis*)	6m (20') (+)	CDOP	Fertile loam or peat, deep acid soils	(Pc, S) As for bay willow	As for bay willow. Cultivars grown for baskets & wattles.
Willow, white[5]	(*Salix alba*)	25m (80')	CDEOP	As for bay willow	(Pc, S) As for bay willow	As for bay willow. Many cultivars, incl. cricket bat willow. Often pollarded.

2 Native Species to Plant, by Zone

Map with location of numbered zones

The information in the following table and map is taken from Soutar and Peterken (1989). The eleven numbered zones in the map indicate areas where different native species are recommended for planting in afforestation or amenity schemes. The boundaries shown are not precise, but reflect instead the broad pattern of natural distribution. They most closely follow the presumed natural distributions of Scots pine, bird cherry, small-leaved lime, hornbeam and beech. The accompanying table links the particular species to the numbered zones.

In all cases, additional information on the conditions (e.g. soil types) in specific locations within the zones must be considered before choosing a species. (See Table 1, above, for information on preferred conditions for each species.)

The table shows particular zones where the use of native stock derived from local sources is preferred (marked by 'L'). The seed used to grow these trees should be collected from semi-natural stands a maximum of 10 miles away from the planting site. Although it may not always be feasible, the ideal to aim for is to restrict all amenity planting of native species to trees of local provenance.

NATIVE SPECIES TO BE ENCOURAGED WITHIN THE NUMBERED ZONES

Large and medium-sized trees	1	2	3	4	5	6	7	8	9	10	11
Alder, common	*	*	*	*	*	*	*	*	*	*	L
Ash	*	*	*	*	*	*	*	*	*	*	L
Aspen	*	*	*	*	*	*	*	*	*	*	L
Beech						*	*	*			
Birch, hairy	*	*	*	*	*	*	*	*	*	*	L
Birch, silver	*	*	*	*	*	*	*	*	*	*	L
Cherry, bird	*	*	*	*		L					L
Cherry, wild		*	*	*	*	*	*	*	*	*	L
Crab apple			*	*	*	*	*	*	*	*	L
Hornbeam						*	*				
Lime, large-leaved				L	L		L				
Lime, small-leaved				L	L	L	L	L	L		
Maple, field				L	*	*	*	*	*	*	
Oak, pedunculate		*	*	*	*	*	*	*	*	*	L
Oak, sessile		*	*	*	L	L	L	L	L	*	L
Pine, Scots		L									
Poplar, black					L	L	L	L	L		
Rowan	*	*	*	*	*	*	*	*	*	*	L
Service tree					L	L	L	L	L	L	
Whitebeam		L		L			L	L			L
Whitebeam, Irish											L
Willow, crack		*	*	*	*	*	*	*	*	*	
Willow, goat	*	*	*	*	*	*	*	*	*	*	L
Willow, white			*	*	*	*	*	*	*	*	L
Yew				L			L	L			L

Small trees and shrubs	1	2	3	4	5	6	7	8	9	10	11
Alder buckthorn				*	*	*	*	*	*	*	L
Blackthorn	*	*	*	*	*	*	*	*	*	*	L
Box							*	*			
Broom	*	*	*	*	*	*	*	*	*	*	L
Buckthorn, purging				*	*	*	*	*	*		
Dogwood				L	*	*	*	*	*	*	
Elder		*	*	*	*	*	*	*	*	*	L
Gorse	*	*	*	*	*	*	*	*	*	*	L
Guelder-rose	*	*	*	*	*	*	*	*	*	*	L
Hawthorn, common	*	*	*	*	*	*	*	*	*	*	L
" " Midland					L	L	L	L			
Hazel	*	*	*	*	*	*	*	*	*	*	
Holly	*	*	*	*	*	*	*	*	*	*	L
Juniper	L	L	L	L			L	L			L
Rose, dog	*	*	*	*	*	*	*	*	*	*	
Rose, field				*	*	*	*	*	*	*	
Spindle				*	*	*	*	*	*	*	L
Wayfaring tree					*		*	*	*		
Willow, bay			*	*							L
Willow, grey	*	*	*	*	*	*	*	*	*	*	L
Willow, osier	*	*	*	*	*	*	*	*	*	*	

3 Urban Broadleaves for Particular Locations

The following table (Hibberd, 1989, pp66-67) gives a method of choosing broadleaved trees for different urban locations (e.g. urban fringe, city centre). This involves considering a group of related trees with desirable attributes, and then choosing from this group the species and cultivars best suited to specific locations. Thus, a small cultivar of *Betula pendula* will tolerate a range of soils, present an attractive appearance and have wildlife value like its native parent, but be the right size for a restricted space.

The examples given below will be particularly useful if you need to select species or cultivars for a wide range of urban situations.

Species with wildlife, timber production or shelter value, suitable for urban fringe woodlands, large parks and roadsides	Trees suitable for surburban developments, small parks and streets	Small decorative cultivars and exotics suitable for city centre developments and office blocks
Alders - *Alnus cordata* *Alnus glutinosa*	*Alnus glutinosa* 'Aurea'	*Alnus incana* 'Pendula' or 'Imperialis'
Ash *Fraxinus excelsior*	*Fraxinus excelsior* 'Pendula' *Fraxinus ornus*	*Fraxinus oxycarpa* 'Raywood'
Beech *Fagus sylvatica*	*Fagus sylvatica* 'Dawyck'	*Fagus sylvatica* 'Aurea pendula'
Birches *Betula pendula*	*Betula pendula* 'Dalecarlica' *Betula jacquemontii*	*Betula pendula* 'Youngii'
Cherries *Prunus avium*	*Prunus avium* 'Plena' *Prunus subhirtella*	A huge range of Japanese flowering cherries is available
'Chestnuts' *Castanea sativa*	*Aesculus indica*	*Aesculus parviflora*
Hazel *Corylus avellana* *Corylus colurna*	*Corylus maxima* 'Purpurea'	*Corylus avellana* 'Contorta'
Maples and Planes *Acer campestre* *Acer pseudoplatanus*	*Acer platanoides* 'Drummondii' or 'Schwedleri'	*Acer capillipes* *Acer palmatum* 'Dissectum'
Oak *Quercus petraea* *Quercus robur*	*Quercus rubra* 'Aurea'	None recommended
Rowan and Whitebeam *Sorbus aucuparia*	*Sorbus hupehensis* *Sorbus aria*	*Sorbus aucuparia* 'Beissneri' *Sorbus sargentii* *Sorbus aria* 'Pendula'
Thorns *Crataegus monogyna*	*Crataegus x prunifolia*	*Crataegus oxyacantha* 'Paul's Scarlet'
Willows *Salix alba*	*Salix alba* 'Vitellina'	*Salix caprea* 'Kilmarnock' *Salix daphnoides*

Appendix C

Grants

In addition to the grant schemes for planting or restocking sponsored by the Forestry Commission and other bodies that administer government grants, there are many smaller schemes which are directly or indirectly concerned with tree planting or aftercare. A number of these, although by no means all, are listed below. For a broad overview of the financial assistance available for tree projects, see the booklet, 'Grants and Other Financial Assistance for Trees' (Lorrain-Smith, 1989), available from the Calderdale Metropolitan Borough Council Leisure Services Department, Wellesley Park, Halifax, West Yorkshire HX2 OAY.

Note that most organisations have a strict rule that a project will be disqualified from grant eligibility if work on it begins before an offer of grant has been made.

FORESTRY COMMISSION

Woodland Grant Scheme

The Woodland Grant Scheme, introduced in April 1988, succeeded both the Forestry Grant Scheme and the Broadleaved Woodland Grant Scheme, which were closed to new applications on 15 March 1988. The Woodland Grant Scheme offers substantially increased grants for new planting and restocking. There is also a supplement of £200 per hectare for planting on existing arable or improved grassland where a Farm Woodland Scheme annual payment (see below) is not being claimed.

Applications may be made by the owner(s) of the land or by a tenant, provided that all the parties concerned are joined in the application.

Grants are available for individual areas of 0.25 hectare and over. It is not acceptable for individual areas of less than 0.25 hectare to be aggregated, except where, with the Forestry Commission's agreement, restocking is to be undertaken by planting very small groups of trees with the object of creating or infilling an uneven-aged wood.

The objectives of the Woodland Grant Scheme are as follows:

a to encourage timber production

b to provide jobs in and increase the economic potential of rural areas with declining agricultural employ-

ment and few alternative sources of economic activity

c to provide an alternative to agricultural production and thereby assist in the reduction of agricultural surpluses

d to enhance the landscape, to create new wildlife habitats and to provide for recreation and sporting uses in the longer term

e to encourage the conservation and regeneration of existing forests and woodlands.

The scheme is intended to encompass a wide range of management objectives and thus encourage multiple purpose woodland management. In order to comply with statutory requirements, the production of utilisable timber must be one of the objectives, although it will not necessarily be the principal objective. The latter could, for example, be to create a woodland which makes a positive contribution to the landscape and which is designed to create a diversity of wildlife habitats.

The scheme applies to the establishment of conifer, broadleaved and mixed woodland whether by means of planting or by natural regeneration. Planting of broadleaves on suitable sites is encouraged by attracting a higher rate of grant, and this rate of grant also applies to native pinewoods in specified areas of Scotland (see below).

There are various provisions which applicants must observe relating to the broadleaved component of existing woods, ancient woodland sites, native pinewood sites, ancient monuments and other matters. Planting consisting mainly of one species of conifer must incorporate other conifers or broadleaves, preferably through the retention of existing trees.

Grants are paid at the appropriate rate in proportion to the area occupied by conifers and broadleaves respectively. Rates of grant are subject to review. The 1989/90 rates for planting, restocking and natural regeneration are shown below.

| Area approved planting or re-generation (ha)* | Rate of Grant | |
	Conifers (£ per ha)	Broadleaves (£ per ha)
0.25-0.9	1005	1575
1.0-2.9	880	1375
3.0-9.9	795	1175
10 +	615	975

* 1 ha = 2.47 acres.

The grant band is determined by the total of the areas approved for planting or regeneration in each separate block or wood within the 5-year plan. The grants are paid in instalments. Existing natural regeneration under 20 years of age or neglected woodlands under 20 years of age which have not previously been grant aided may qualify for partial grant.

The maximum tree spacings normally acceptable are 2.1m for conifers and 3m for broadleaves. Provided that there is a sensible reason for wider tree spacings, such spacings will be grant-aided *pro rata*.

Applicants will be required to work in accordance with a five-year Plan of Operations approved by the Forestry Commission.

Further details and application forms are available from the local Forestry Commission Conservancy Office (see p145).

New Native Pinewood Grants

Under the Woodland Grant Scheme the higher (broadleaved) rate of grant is available - subject to certain conditions - to those who wish to establish new native pinewoods of natural character outside existing native pinewoods. The rules and guidelines below are additional to those required under the standard conditions of the Woodland Grant Scheme, which have been stated above. Applications can be accepted under the Farm Woodland Scheme (see below) if all conditions are satisfied.

Areas within the Scottish Highlands are eligible for the New Native Pinewood Grant if they are within a former natural distribution of Scots pine-dominated pine-birch forest, and have appropriate site characteristics. This distribution is strictly delineated, but other areas north of the Forth-Clyde valleys which meet the site criteria may be eligible, if applicants can bring forth suitable evidence that these areas were pine-dominated. The final decision in such cases will lie with the Forestry Commission.

The general objective of the Scheme is to establish new pinewoods which emulate the native pinewood eco-system. As existing remnants of native pinewood cover a wide range of habitats with considerable internal diversity of species, composition and distribution, the scheme covers an equally wide range of specific proposals.

Operational guidelines for the new pinewoods cover fencing, ground preparation, draining, pine plant supply, tree species other than pine, spacing, fertilization and other factors. The booklet 'Native Pinewoods Grants and Guidelines' (Forestry Commission, 1989), which includes information on establishing new native pinewoods, also contains guidelines for the management of existing ones. For further information, contact the local Forestry Commission Conservancy Office as above.

MINISTRY OF AGRICULTURE, FISHERIES AND FOOD

Farm Woodland Scheme

This scheme, run jointly by the Agriculture Departments (see below) and the Forestry Commission, is designed to encourage the establishment of new woodlands on farms. It came into operation on 1 October 1988, initially for a three-year experimental period.

During that period, the overall planting target and limit is 36,000 hectares. The scheme is primarily aimed at arable land and grassland improved within the last 10 years, to help ensure that the savings in agricultural support costs are achieved, and to avoid the planting of marginal land and other areas of possible conservation value.

The aims of the scheme are:

a to divert land from agricultural production and assist the reduction of agricultural surpluses

b to enhance the landscape, create new wildlife habitats, encourage recreational use, including sport, and expand tourist interest

c to contribute to supporting farm income and rural employment

d to encourage greater interest in timber production from farms and, in the longer term, to contribute to the nation's timber requirements.

The minimum area of planting per holding is 3 hectares (1 hectare in Northern Ireland, where holdings are smaller), with a maximum of 40 hectares. Each block of woodland must be a minimum of 1 hectare to ensure that real reductions in surplus production are achieved.

Farmers who plant trees on land previously in agricultural production are eligible for planting grants from the Forestry Commission, which are paid in three instalments. Annual payments will be made for 20-40 years, depending on the choice of species. For predominately oak and beech plantings, the payments will be made for 40 years; for other broadleaves and mixed woodland containing more than 50% broadleaves by area, 30 years; for other woodland, 20 years; and for traditional coppice, 10 years. Annual payment rates are shown in the following table .

Less Favoured Areas	Severely Disadvantaged	Disadvantaged	Elsewhere
	(£/ha*)	(£/ha)	(£/ha)
Arable land & improved grassland which has been cultivated and reseeded within last 10 years	100	150	190
Unimproved grassland (incl. rough grazing)	30	30	-

* 1 ha = 2.47 acres.

Information on and applications for this scheme and those which follow are available from divisional offices of the appropriate department, or from headquarters of the Ministry of Agriculture, Fisheries and Food (England); Department of Agriculture and Fisheries for Scotland (Scotland); Welsh Office Agriculture Department (Wales); or Department of Agriculture for Northern Ireland (Northern Ireland).

Farm and Conservation Grant Scheme

This scheme has recently replaced the Agricultural Improvement Scheme, but the encouragement of improvements to farms is still the aim of the available grants. Environmental and Countryside Grants may be available for the planting of shelterbelts, hedges (including hedgelaying) and hedgerow trees. The enclosure of grazed woodland (at least 75% broadleaved) to exclude stock is also allowed.

In Less Favoured Areas the grant for all these works is 50%. Elsewhere it is 40%, except for shelterbelts containing less than 50% broadleaves, where the rate is 15%. The grants are payable at those percentages of allowable expenditure from £750 up to a ceiling which depends on the farm's labour requirement. The maximum allowable is £74,000.

Other agricultural grants

Although not specifically related to tree planting or aftercare, the following schemes may provide funding for tree planting.

a *Set-Aside Scheme*. The aim of this scheme is to reduce surplus agricultural production of particular arable crops. Farmers receive compensation payment for taking at least 20% of the base year relevant crops out of production. Alternative land uses may be chosen from several options, including new tree planting in suitable locations. To participate in this option, the land must have been approved by the Forestry Commission for planting under the terms of the Woodland Grant Scheme, unless the area is less than 0.25 hectares, is under short rotation coppice manage-

ment or is planted with fruit trees. Planting grants are also the same as for those under the Woodland Grant Scheme.

b *Farm Diversification Scheme*. This scheme aims to assist farmers in developing non-agricultural profit-making activities on their farms. Grants exist for capital investment, feasibility studies and initial marketing costs. The planting of groups of trees as an element of landscaping around farm buildings may be included, although planting for timber production is not.

c *Environmentally Sensitive Areas (ESA) Scheme*. This scheme, introduced in 1986, aims to protect and conserve ESAs by providing grant funding to farmers living and working in them. The ten designated ESAs are all farming areas chosen for their outstanding ecological or landscape importance. Special payments may be available under particular ESA schemes to improve the conservation value of existing farm woodlands, which may include planting.

COUNTRYSIDE COMMISSION

The Countryside Commission offers Landscape Conservation Grants to two groups: local authorities, public bodies and voluntary organisations; and farmers and landowners. Local authorities (usually county councils or metropolitan borough councils) administer these grants.

Landscape Conservation Grants are available for planting trees and small woods, as well as managing small woods or existing trees and conserving other important landscape features. The aim of the grants is to benefit the landscape and thus contribute to public enjoyment of the countryside. Projects must be in the countryside, in England or Wales.

Grants may be available for planting trees, generally broadleaves, on areas under 0.25 hectare. Species must be chosen according to site and soil conditions, landscape, agricultural needs, and benefits to wildlife conservation. The planting of shrubby understoreys in copses may be eligible for funding, as may costs involved in fencing, guards and shelters, stakes and ties, and mulches. Grants may also be available for pollarding riparian willows and alders, replanting or maintaining significant landmark trees such as those in avenues, and tree surgery.

The maximum grant aid is 50% of the acceptable costs, although all grants are discretionary.

The Countryside Commission also vets applications to have very fine landscapes designated for the purpose of avoiding Inheritance Tax. This service affects not only woodland, but parkland with trees and pasture-woodland.

Contact the Countryside Commission for further details about any of the above schemes (p143). Applications should be made to the planning department of your county council or, if the site of the project is not within a county, of your borough council.

English Nature (formerly NCC)

English Nature offers a variety of grant schemes, normally up to a maximum of 50%. Listed below are the schemes in which tree planting may play a significant part.

a Conservation Project Grants. Where sites are of high conservation value, grants for up to 50% of the cost of new projects may be available. Such projects may include the creation, maintenance and development of wildlife habitats, such as woodlands. Projects must cost at least £200 to be eligible, and grant aid may be available to cover up to 50% of acceptable costs.

b Schools Grant Scheme. Under this scheme, funding is available for the creation and management of conservation areas for the purpose of encouraging the study of nature within the school curriculum. Examples of habitats which could be created include hedgerows and shrub plantings, copses and shelterbelts. Grants can be made in a range from £50-500.

Further information is available from the national office of the English Nature Grants Section (p143). Anyone interested in applying for a grant may find it useful to discuss project details in advance with the Scheme Co-ordinator or their contact at an English Nature local office. Applications should be made to the English Nature Grants Section, Peterborough.

TRUSTS AND CHARITIES

The Tree Council

The Tree Council has very limited funds available to help well-planned tree and woodland projects designed for the amenity of the public. Schemes must normally be promoted by private individuals or voluntary organisations, although parish councils and schools may be eligible. Either tree planting or the restoration of neglected woodland are eligible for grant aid, as long as the sites are on land which is accessible to the general public. Planting in towns and village centres is given preference.

Adequate provision for tree maintenance must be arranged before the funds can be granted. The grants are relevant not only to the labour of planting and other work, but also to the costs of the trees, stakes and ties, fencing and guards. The rate of grant is up to 50% of the total tree planting costs, which must amount to at least £100. Note that application should have been made to other sources of support before applying to The Tree Council.

The last dates of application are 31 July for autumn planting, and 31 December for spring planting. Applications should be made to The Tree Council (p145).

The Prince of Wales Committee

The Prince of Wales Committee Grant Scheme is aimed at supporting and promoting voluntary environmental work in Wales. Grants, which may be awarded to volunteers and voluntary groups, can be made for tree planting and landscaping schemes, among other possibilities. The amount of grant ranges from £50-4000, but other possible sources of funding should have been explored before application.

Applications should be made to the Prince of Wales Committee, Fourth Floor, Empire House, Mount Stuart Square, Cardiff CF1 6DN.

ENVIRONMENTAL AWARDS

Shell Better Britain Campaign

Under this scheme, projects are eligible for grant aid if they result in tangible improvement of the local environment, involve a high proportion of the local community and are beneficial for the wider community, and are carefully planned. Although the campaign's focus is not tree planting per se, a substantial percentage of projects in 1988 involved trees. Grants up to £500 are awarded.

Further information is available from Shell Better Britain Campaign, Red House, Hill Lane, Great Barr, Birmingham B43 6LZ; or, for Scotland, from Balallan House, 24 Allan Park, Stirling FK8 2QG.

Ford European Conservation Awards

The Ford European Conservation Award is an annual competitive awards scheme which includes four categories: natural environment, young people's projects, heritage, and conservation engineering. Eligible projects include tree planting in towns, the creation of woodlands in the countryside and conservation projects by those under 18. Entries are invited from individuals, community groups and organisations involved in conservation projects which address a real conservation need. Prizes for category winners are £2500; for the national winner, £5000; and for the overall European winner, an additional $10,000.

Contact the Conservation Foundation, 1 Kensington Gore, London SW7 2AR for further information.

Trust House Forte Community Chest

Anyone with a specific proposal for conserving the local environment anywhere in Britain may enter. In past years, grants have been awarded for tree planting. Grants ranging from £100-1000 are awarded each month.

Contact the Conservation Foundation for further information (address as above).

LOCAL AUTHORITIES

Many county councils and other local authorities can give various types of help with tree planting. This may include grants, free trees, or direct help with planting and maintenance. Such aid is distinct from the Countryside Commission scheme for local authorities and other bodies (see above). The tree officers employed by most local authorities can also provide advice, not only on their own schemes but also on the other grant schemes listed in this appendix.

Appendix D

Relevant Organisations

Conservation and Amenity

Biological Records Centre
Monks Wood Experimental Station, Abbots Ripton, Cambridgeshire PE17 2LS © 04873 381

Botanical Society of the British Isles
c/o Department of Botany, Natural History Museum, Cromwell Road, London SW7 5BD

British Association of Nature Conservationists
122 Derwent Road, Thatchum, Newbury, Berks RG13 4UP © 0635 60478

British Ecological Society
Burlington House, Piccadilly, London W1V 0LQ © 071 434 2641

British Herpetological Society
c/o London Zoo, Regents Park, London NW1 4RY

British Trust for Conservation Volunteers
Head Office: 36 St Mary's Street, Wallingford, Oxon OX10 0EU © 0491 39766

Divisional Offices:
-*North:* Training Centre, Balby Road, Doncaster, S Yorks DN4 0RH © 0302 859522
-*West:* BTCV Conservation Centre, Firsby Road, Quinton, Birmingham, W Midlands B32 2QT © 021 426 5588
-*South East:* BTCV, Southwater Country Park, Cripplegate Lane, Southwater, W Sussex RH13 7UN © 0232 645169
-*Northern Ireland:* The Pavillion, Cherryvale Playing Fields, Ravenhill Road, Belfast BT6 0BZ © 0232 645169

British Trust for Ornithology
Beech Grove, Station Road, Tring, Hertfordshire , HP23 5NR © 044 282 3461

Civic Trust
17 Carlton House Terrace, London SW1Y 5AW © 071 930 0914

Common Ground
45 Shelton Street, London WC2H 9HJ © 071 379 3109

Community Service Volunteers
237 Pentonville Road, London N1 9NJ © 071 278 6601

Conservation Society
12a Guildford Street, Chertsey, Surrey JT16 9BQ © 09328 60975

Council for British Archaeology
112 Kennington Road, London SE11 6RE © 071 582 0494

Council for National Parks
45 Shelton Street, London WC2H 9HJ © 071 240 3603/4

Council for the Protection of Rural England
Warwick House, 25 Buckingham Palace Road, London SW1W 0PP © 071 976 6433

Council for the Protection of Rural Wales
31 High Street, Welshpool, Powys SY21 7JP © 0938 2525

Country Landowners' Association
16 Belgrave Square, London SW1X 8PQ © 071 235 0511

Countryside Commission (*England and Wales*)
Headquarters: John Dower House, Crescent Place, Cheltenham, Glos GL50 3RA © 0242 521381

Countryside Commission for Scotland (until April 1992)
Battleby, Redgorton, Perth PH1 3EW

Countryside Council for Wales Plas Penrhos, Penrhos Road, Bangor, Gwynedd LL57 2LQ © 0248 355141© 0738 27921

Department of Agriculture (*Northern Ireland*)
Hydebank, 4 Hospital Road, Belfast BT8 8JP © 0232 647161

Department of the Environment Countryside and Wildlife Branch (*Northern Ireland*)
Calvert House, 23 Castle Place, Belfast BT1 1FY © 0232 230560

English Nature (formerly Nature Conservancy Council)
Northminster House, Peterborough PE1 1UA © 0733 40345

The Environment Council
80 York Way, London N1 9AG © 071 278 4736

Farming and Wildlife Trust Ltd
National Agriculture Centre, Stoneleigh,
Kenilworth, Warwickshire CV8 2RX
✆ 0203 696699

Farming and Wildlife Trust Ltd *(Northern Ireland)*
Hydebank, 4 Hospital Road, Belfast BT8 8JP
✆ 0232 647161

Field Studies Council
Central Services, Preston Montford, Montford
Bridge, Shrewsbury SY4 1HW ✆ 0743 850674

Friends of the Earth
26-28 Underwood Street, London N1 7JQ
✆ 071 490 1555

The Game Conservancy
Burgate Manor, Fordingbridge, Hampshire
SP6 1EF ✆ 0425 52381

Institute of Terrestrial Ecology
Monks Wood Experimental Station, Abbots Ripton,
Huntingdon, Cambridgeshire PE17 2LS
✆ 04873 381

Landscape Institute
12 Carlton House Terrace, London SW1Y 5AH
✆ 071 839 4044

Mammal Society of the British Isles
Harvest House, 62 London Road, Reading,
Berkshire ✆ 0734 861345

National Farmers' Union
Agriculture House, Knightsbridge, London
SW1X 7NJ ✆ 071 235 5077

National Farmers' Union of Scotland
17 Grosvenor Crescent, Edinburgh EH12 5EN
✆ 031 337 4333

The National Trust
36 Queen Anne's Gate, London SW1H 0AS
✆ 071 222 9251

National Trust for Northern Ireland
Rowallane House, Saintfield, County Down
BT24 7LH ✆ 0238 510721

National Trust for Scotland
5 Charlotte Square, Edinburgh EH2 4D
✆ 031 225 5922

Nature Conservancy Council *(Scotland) - until April 1992)*
12 Hope Terrace, Edinburgh EH9 2AS
✆ 031 447 4784

The Open Spaces Society
25a Bell Street, Henley-on-Thames, Oxon RG9 2BA
✆ 0491 573535

Ordnance Survey
Romsey Road, Maybush, Southampton SO9 4DH
✆ 0703 792635

The Ramblers' Association
1/5 Wandsworth Road, London SW8 2LJ
✆ 071 582 6878

Royal Society for Nature Conservation
The Green, Nettleham, Lincoln LN2 2NR
✆ 0522 752 326

Royal Society for the Protection of Birds
The Lodge, Sandy, Beds SG12 2DL ✆ 0767 80551
RSPB Northern Ireland: Belvior Forest Park, Belfast
BT8 4QT ✆ 0232 692547

Rural Development Commission
141 Castle Street, Salisbury, Wiltshire SP1 3TP
✆ 0722 336255
and
11 Cowley Street, London SW1P 3NA
✆ 071 276 6969

Scottish Civil Trust
24 George Square, Glasgow G2 1EF
✆ 041 221 1466

Scottish Conservation Projects Trust
Balallan House, 24 Allan Park, Stirling FK8 2QG
✆ 0786 79697

Scottish Landowners' Federation
18 Abercromby Place, Edinburgh EH3 6TY
✆ 031 556 4466

Scottish Wildlife Trust
25 Johnston Terrace, Edinburgh EH1 2NH
✆ 031 226 4602

Town and Country Planning Association
17 Carlton House Terrace, London SW1Y 5AS
✆ 071 930 8903

Ulster Wildlife Trust
Barnetts Cottage, Barnett Demesne, Malone Road,
Belfast BT9 5PD ✆ 0232 612235

World Wide Fund for Nature UK
Panda House, Weyside Park, Godalming, Surrey
GU7 1XR ✆ 0483 426444

Trees and Woodlands

Agricultural Training Board
Summit House, Glebe Way, West Wickham, Kent
BR4 0RF © 081 777 9003

Arboricultural Association
Ampfield House, Ampfield, Romsey, Hants
SO51 9PA © 0794 68717

Association of Professional Foresters
Brokerswood House, Brokerswood, near Westbury,
Wilts BA13 4EH © 0373 822238

British Timber Merchants' Association *(England and Wales)*
Ridgeway House, 6 Ridgeway Road, Long Ashton,
Bristol BS18 9EU © 0272 394022

Centre for Urban Ecology
Birmingham Settlement, 318 Summer Lane,
Birmingham B19 3RL © 021 359 7462

Department of Agriculture for Northern Ireland: Forest Service
Dundonald House, Upper Newtonards Road,
Belfast BT4 3SB

Forestry Commission
Headquarters: 231 Corstorphine Road, Edinburgh
EH12 7AT © 031 334 0303
Forest Research Station (and Arboricultural Advisory and Information Service): Alice Holt Lodge,
Wrecclesham, Farnham, Surrey GU10 4LH
© 0420 22255
Northern Research Station: Roslin, Midlothian
EH25 9SY © 031 445 2176

Conservancy Offices:
-North England: 1A Grosvenor Terrace, York
YO3 7BD © 0904 620221
-East England: Great Eastern House, Tenison Road,
Cambridge CB1 2DU © 0223 314546
-West England: 2nd Floor, Avon Fields House,
Somerdale, Keynsham, Bristol BS18 2BD
© 0272 869481
-North Scotland: 21 Church Street, Inverness IV1 1EL
© 0463 232811
-South Scotland: Greystone Park, 55/57 Moffat
Road, Dumfries DG1 1NP © 0387 69171
-Mid Scotland: Portcullis House, 21 India Street,
Glasgow G2 4PL © 041 248 3931
-Wales: Victoria House, Victoria Terrace,
Aberystwyth, Dyfed SY23 2DQ © 0970 612367
-Forestry Commission Publications: Forest Research
Station, Alice Holt Lodge (see above) or Blair Adam
Store, Clentry by Kelty, Fife KY4 0JQ
© 0383 830311

Forestry Safety Council
231 Corstorphine Road, Edinburgh EH12 7AT

Forestry Training Council
231 Corstorphine Road, Edinburgh EH12 7AT

The Forestry Trust for Conservation and Education
The Old Estate Office, Englefield Road, Theale,
Reading, Berkshire RG7 5D2

Groundwork Foundation
Bennetts Court, 6 Bennetts Hill, Birmingham
B2 5ST © 021 236 8565

Horticultural Therapy
Goulds Ground, Vallis Way, Frome, Somerset
BA11 3DW © 0373 64782

Horticultural Trades Association
19 High Street, Theale, Reading, Berkshire
RG7 5AH © 0734 303132

Institute of Chartered Foresters
22 Walker Street, Edinburgh EH3 7HR
© 031 225 2705

Men of the Trees
Sandy Lane, Crawley Down, West Sussex RH1 4HS
© 0342 712536

National Small Woods Association
Red House, Environmental Centre, Hill Lane, Great
Barr, West Midlands B43 6LZ © 021 358 0461

Royal Forestry Society of England, Wales and Northern Ireland
102 High Street, Tring, Hertfordshire HP23 4AH
© 044 282 2028

Royal Scottish Forestry Society
10 Atholl Crescent, Edinburgh EH3 8HA
© 031 229 8851

The Tree Council
35 Belgrave Square, London SW1X 8QN
© 071 235 8854

Timber Growers UK
Admel House, 24 High Street, Wimbledon Village,
London SW19 5DX © 081 944 6340

Woodland Trust
Autumn Park, Dysart Road, Grantham, Lincs
NG31 6LL © 0476 74297

Appendix E

Specialist Suppliers

The following is a brief list of suppliers and manufacturers of some items mentioned in the text. Tree nurseries are included at the end. It is not a complete list, and these firms are not recommended in preference to any others.

General forestry equipment

Conservation Practice Ltd, Tools and Trading The Training Centre, Balby Road, Doncaster DN4 0RH ✆ 0302 859522

- *hand tools, wheelbarrows, protective clothing, sundries*

Chieftain Forge Ltd Burnside Road, Bathgate, West Lothian EH48 4PU ✆ 0506 52354

- *machinery and hand tools, tree ties, guards and shelters*

Honey Brothers Ltd New Pond Road, Peasmarsh, Guildford, Surrey GU3 1JR ✆ 0483 61362

- *tree surgery and tree climbing equipment, chainsaws, protective clothing, tree ties and shelters, anti-transpirants, sundries*

Husqvarna UK Ltd Oldends Lane, Stonehouse, Glos GL10 3SY ✆ 045382 2382

- *hand tools, chainsaws and other machinery, protective clothing*

Stanton Hope Ltd 11 Seax Court, Southfields, Laindon, Basildon, Essex SS15 6LY ✆ 0268 419141

- *fencing and forestry hand tools, chainsaws, protective clothing, tree guards, ties and shelters, traps, chemicals, granular herbicide applicators, sundries*

Planting and maintenance tools for the disabled

Wilkinson Sword Ltd Sword House, Totteridge Road, High Wycombe, Bucks HP13 6EJ ✆ 0494 33300

- *long-handled digging tools, 'Grabber' hoes and rakes, pruning tools*

Wolf Tools Ltd Alton Road, Ross-on-Wye, Herefordshire HR9 5NE ✆ 0989 767 600

- *Auxiliary grips for ordinary tools, double hoes, long-handled tools*

Chemical repellants

'Aaprotect' - available from Stanton Hope Ltd (see above) and from ICI Plant Protection, Woolmead House West, Bear Lane, Farnham, Surrey GU9 7UB ✆ 0252 724525

'Dendrocol 17' - available from Berkshire Factors Ltd, Dale House, London Road, Sunningdale, Ascot, Berks SL5 0ER ✆ 0990 24101

Red dye for liquid herbicides

Hortichem Ltd, 14 Edison Road, Churchfields Industrial Estate, Salisbury, Wiltshire SP2 7NU ✆ 0722 20133

Planting products

Acorn Planting Products Ltd Little Money Road, Loddon, Norwich NR14 6JD ✆ 0508 28763

- *tree guards, shelters, mulching mats*

Corruplast Ltd Correx House, Madleaze Industrial Estate, Bristol Road, Glos GL1 5SG ✆ 0452 301893

- *tree shelters*

Economic Forestry Group plc Forestry House, Great Haseley, Oxfordshire OX9 7PG ✆ 08446 571

- *tree ties, guards, shelters, loose mulches*

English Woodlands Ltd Burrow Nurseries, Cross in Hand, Heathfield, East Sussex TN21 0UG ✆ 04352 2992

- *tree ties, guards, shelters, loose mulches*

H S Jackson and Son (Fencing) Ltd Stowting Common, Nr Ashford, Kent TN25 6BN ✆ 023 375 393

- *tree ties, guards, shelters, loose mulches*

J Toms Ltd 5 Wheeler Street, Headcorn, Ashford, Kent TN27 9SH ✆ 0622 891111

- *tree ties, guards, shelters, mulching mats*

Tretec Ltd The White House, Scorrier, Redruth, Cornwall TR16 5AT ✆ 0209 821186

- *'Bull Toobs'*

Tree Guards (Wire Netting) Bristol Somersby Orchard, Greyfield, High Littleton, Bristol BS18 5YQ ✆ 0761 70489

- *tree guards and shelters*

Tubex Ltd No 1, Tannery House, Tannery Lane, Send, Woking, Surrey GU23 7HB ✆ 0483 225434

- tree ties, guards and shelters,

Polyhouses and polyhouse equipment and supplies

Bailey Polythene Ltd PO Box 64, Knowle, Solihull, West Midlands B93 9NZ ✆ 05645 4259

- repair patches, joining tape for polythene covers

Clovis Lande Associates Ltd 104 Branbridges Road, East Peckham, Tonbridge, Kent TN12 5HH ✆ 0622 872581

- prefabricated polyhouses, benching, replacement polythene covers

Fordingbridge Ltd Arundel Road, Fontwell, Arundel, West Sussex BN18 0SD ✆ 0243 554455

- polyhouses, benching, replacement polythene covers, various types of plastic film

Planter Systems Ltd Unit F1, Coedcae Lane Industrial Estate, Llantrisant, Mid-Glamorgan CF7 9EW

- paperpots JPP

Polygrow Unit 1, Bacton Wood Mill, Spa Common, North Walsham, Norfolk ✆ 0692 403665

- small garden polyhouses

Ronaash Ltd Kersquarter, Kelso, Roxburghshire TD5 8HH ✆ 0573 25757

- Rootrainers

TREE NURSERIES

Aberdeen Tree Nurseries Ltd (EFG) Tillicorthie, Udney, Ellon, Aberdeenshire AB4 0SD ✆ 06513 0839

Banff and Buchan Nurseries Ltd Baley Farm, Portsoy, Banff AB4 2YQ ✆ 0261 43291

BTCV Enterprises (Trees and Wildflowers) Plashett Wood, Rose Hill, Isfield, Uckfield, E Sussex TN22 5QU ✆ 0825 750244 (profits from the sale of trees go to BTCV)

C. Arnot and Son (Nurseries) Ltd Rosebank Nurseries, Muir of Lownie, Forfar, Angus, Tayside DD8 2LJ ✆ 0307 62139

Castle Howard Nursery The Estate Office, Castle Howard, Yorks YO6 7DA ✆ 0653 84333

Christies (Fochabers) Ltd The Nurseries, Fochabers, Morayshire IV32 7PF ✆ 0343 820362

Firecrest Forestry Nursery Hall Road, Little Bealings, Woodbridge, Suffolk IP13 6LU ✆ 0473 625937

Glassonby Forest Nurseries Glassonby, Penrith, Cumbria CA10 1DT ✆ 07683 382

Higher Heath Nurseries The Meadows, Higher Heath, Whitchurch, Shropshire SY13 2JA ✆ 0948 841156

Hilliers Nurseries Ampfield House, Ampfield, Romsey, Hampshire SO5 9PA

Kingfield Tree Nursery Church Close, Church Street, Winsham, Chard, Somerset TA20 4JD ✆ 0460 30697

Lynders Forest Nursery Hilltop, Upton Bishop, near Ross-on-Wye, Herefordshire HR9 7UQ ✆ 098 985 212

North Surrey Nursery Group Stafford Lake Nursery, Stafford Lake, Knaphill, Woking, Surrey GU21 2SJ ✆ 04867 6367

Oakover Nurseries Ltd Calehill Stables, The Leacon, Charing, Kent TN27 0ET ✆ 023371 3016

Trees Company The Gardeners Cottage, Arden House Estate, Arden, by Ballock, Dunbartonshire, Scotland ✆ 0389 85611

Trees Please Nursery Low Urpeth Farm, Birtley, Chester-le-Street, County Durham ✆ 091 410 3233

W. Crowder and Sons Thimbleby Nurseries, Horncastle, Lincolnshire LN9 54Z ✆ 06582 6363

Woodland Improvement (Nurseries) Ltd Newent Lane, Huntley, near Gloucester, Glos GL19 3EY ✆ 0452 830344

Appendix F

Bibliography

Tree planting and aftercare, as well as tree nurseries, woodlands and other subjects related to trees, are covered by a wide range of published source material. The list below includes works to which reference has been made in the text, as well as other useful sources.

Note that the Arboriculture Research Notes which have been used as textual references are not listed individually below, but may be obtained from the Forestry Commission Publications Section at Alice Holt Lodge (see Appendix D for address).

Agate, E J (1986) *Fencing* British Trust for Conservation Volunteers

Agricultural Development and Advisory Service/ Forestry Commission (1986)
Practical Work in Farm Woods Ministry of Agriculture, Fisheries and Food. Series of 8 leaflets

Agricultural Development and Advisory Service (1983) *Which Tree?: A farmers' guide to tree selection* Ministry of Agriculture, Fisheries and Food

Aldhous, JR (1972) *Nursery Practice* HMSO Forestry Commission. Bulletin 43

Aldous, T (ed) 1979 *Trees and Buildings: Complement or Conflict?* RIBA Publications and The Tree Council

Bean, WJ (1970) *Trees and Shrubs Hardy in the British Isles* 3 vols. Butler and Tanner

Beddall, SL (1950) *Hedges for Farm and Garden* Faber & Faber

Beckett, K and Beckett, G (1979)
Planting Native Trees and Shrubs Jarrold Colour Publications

Blatchford, ON (ed) (1978)
Forestry Practice HMSO Forestry Commission Bulletin 14

Blyth, J, Evans, J, Mutch, W E S and Sidwell, C (1987) *Farm Woodland Management* Farming Press Ltd

Brooks, A (revised 1983)
Hedging British Trust for Conservation Volunteers

Brooks, A (revised 1988)
Woodlands British Trust for Conservation Volunteers

Bunce, R G H (1982) *Trees and Their Habitats* Forestry Commission

Bunce, R G H and Jeffers, J N R (1977)
Native Pinewoods of Scotland Institute of Terrestrial Ecology

Caborn, J M (1965) *Shelterbelts and Windbreaks* Faber

Capel, JA (1987) *A Guide to Tree Pruning* Arboricultural Association

Clouston, B (1977) *Landscape Design with Plants* Heinemann

Clouston, B and Stansfield, K (eds) (1981)
Trees in Towns: Maintenance and Management Architectural Press

Crowe, S (1979) *The Landscape of Forests and Woods* HMSO Forestry Commission Booklet 44

Crowther, R E and Evans, J (1984)
Coppice HMSO Forestry Commission Leaflet 83

Curry, F A, Elgy, D and Petty, SJ (1977)
Starling Roost Dispersal from Woodlands HMSO Forestry Commission Leaflet 69

Davies, RJ (1987) *Trees and Weeds: Weed Control for Successful Tree Establishment* HMSO Forestry Commission Handbook 2

Department of the Environment (1978)
Trees and Forestry HMSO
Joint Circular 36/78
from the Department of the
Environment and 64/78
from the Welsh Office

Devon Wildlife Trust (1969)
*Conservation of Trees and
Shrubs in Built-up Areas*

Devon Wildlife Trust (1970)
*Wildlife Conservation and
Woodland Management*

Devon Wildlife Trust (1977)
*Creating a Woodland Nature
Reserve*

Edlin, HL (1970)   *Trees, Woods and Man*
Collins

Edlin, HL (1975)   *Collins Guide to Tree Planting
and Cultivation* Collins

Edlin, HL (revised 1985)
Broadleaves HMSO Forestry
Commission Booklet 20

Evans, J (1984)   *Silviculture of Broadleaved
Woodland* HMSO Forestry
Commission Bulletin 62

Fairbrother, N (1974)   *The Nature of Landscape
Design* Architectural Press

Forestry Commission *Catalogue of Publications*
Published annually by the
Forestry Commission.
Includes details of all
publications available from
the Arboricultural Advisory
and Information Service, the
Forestry Commission and
the Forestry Safety Council.
Most titles which are
included in the catalogue
and referred to in this
bibliography are listed here
by author.

Forestry Commission (1982)
*OECD Scheme for the Control
of Forest Reproductive Material
Moving in International Trade*
Forestry Commission

Forestry Commission (1986)
*Guidelines for the Management
of Broadleaved Woodland*
Forestry Commission

Forestry Commission (1987a)
Control of Tree Felling
Forestry Commission

Forestry Commission (1987b)
*Forest Reproductive Material
Regulations 1977 - An
Explanatory Booklet* Forestry
Commission

Forestry Commission (1989)
*Environmental Leaflets
(Forests* and: *Water,
Archaeology, Landscape
and Conservation)*
Forestry Commission

Forestry Commission (1990)
*Code of Practice for the Use of
Pesticides in Forestry* HMSO

Forestry Safety Council
Forest Industry Safety Guides
Forestry Safety Council

Fuller, R J and Warren, M S (1990a)
*Coppiced Woodlands: Their
Management for Wildlife*
NCC

Fuller, R J and Warren, M S (1990b)
*Woodland Rides and Glades:
Their Management for Wildlife*
NCC

Game Conservancy   *Woodlands for Pheasants*
Game Conservancy
Booklet 15

Gemmel, R P (1977)   *Colonisation of Industrial
Wasteland* Arnold

Gordon, E G and Rowe, D C F (1982)
*Seed Manual for Ornamental
Trees and Shrubs* HMSO
Forestry Commission
Bulletin 59

Grayson, A J (ed) (1989)
*The 1987 Storm: Impacts and
Responses* HMSO
Forestry Commission
Bulletin 87

Greig, J W and Strouts, R G (1983)
Honey Fungus HMSO
Arboricultural Leaflet 2

Griffin, N and Watkins, C (1988)
'The control of tree felling:
recent developments in
statute and case law'
Quarterly Journal of Forestry
82:1:1988 pp26-32

Hibberd, B G (ed) (1988)
Farm Woodland Practice
HMSO Forestry
Commission Handbook 3

Hibberd, B G (ed) (1989)
Urban Forestry Practice
HMSO Forestry
Commission Handbook 5

Hillier, H G (1977) *Hillier's Manual of Trees and Shrubs* David and Charles

Insley, H (1988) *Farm Woodland Planning* HMSO Forestry Commission Bulletin 80

James, N D G (1972) *The Arboriculturalist's Companion* Blackwell

Kent County Council (1986)
Trees from Seed: A school's guide to tree seed collection, propagation, planting and aftercare

Landscape Institute (1990)
Trees and Shrubs for Landscape Planting RIBA Publications

Liebscher, K (revised 1984)
Tree Nurseries BTCV

Low, A J (1986) *Use of Broadleaved Species in Upland Forests* HMSO Forestry Commission Leaflet 88

McCullen and Webb (1982)
A Manual on Urban Trees An Foras Forbatha

Miles, R (1967) *Forestry in the English Landscape* Faber

Ministry of Agriculture, Fisheries and Food (MAFF) (1977) *Shelter Belts for Farmland* MAFF-Leaflet 15

MAFF (1990) *Code of Practice for Safe Use of Pesticides on Farms and Holdings* MAFF

MAFF (1990) *Pesticides 1990* HMSO

Mitchell, A F A (1974) *Field Guide to the Trees of Britain and Northern Europe* Collins

Mitchell, A F A and Jobling, J (1984)
Decorative Trees for Country, Town and Garden HMSO Forestry Commission

Mitchell, P L (1989) 'Repollarding large neglected pollards: a review of current practice and results' *Arboricultural Journal* 1989, Vol 13 pp125-142

Mummery, C and Tabor, R (1978)
Essex Woodlands in Trust Essex Naturalists' Trust

Mummery, C, Tabor, R and Homewood, N (1976)
A Guide to the Techniques of Coppice Management R Tabor and Essex Naturalists' Trust

Nature Conservancy Council (1985)
Why Plant Native Broadleaf Trees? NCC

Neal, E (1982) *Badgers in Woodlands* HMSO Forestry Commission Forest Record 103

Nicholson-Lord, D (1987)
The Greening of the Cities Routledge & Kegan Paul

Pepper, H W (1978) *Chemical Repellants* HMSO Forestry Commission Leaflet 73

Pepper, H W, Rowe, J J and Tee, L A (1985)
Individual Tree Protection Arboricultural Leaflet 10

Pepper, H W and Tee, L A (1986)
Forest Fencing HMSO
Forestry Commission
Leaflet 87

Peterken, G F (1972) *Conservation Coppicing:
A Preliminary Report*
NCC, Monks Wood
Experimental Station

Peterken, G F (1974) 'A method for assessing
woodland flora for
conservation using indicator
species' *Biological
Conservation* 6:4:'74 pp239-45

Peterken, G F (1977a) 'General management
principles for nature
conservation in British
woodlands' *Forestry*
L:1:1977 pp27-48

Peterken, G F (1977b) 'Habitat conservation
priorities in British and
European woodlands'
Biological Conservation
11:1977 pp223-36

Peterken, G F (1981) *Woodland Conservation and
Management*
Chapman and Hall

Rackham, O (1976) *Trees and Woodlands in the
British Landscape* Dent

Rackham, O (1986) *The History of the Countryside*
Dent

Readers Digest (1981) *Trees and Shrubs of Britain*
Readers Digest

Reed, M (1983) *The Making of Britain:
The Georgian Triumph
1700-1830*
Routledge & Kegan Paul

Rollinson, T J D (1988) *Thinning Control* HMSO
Forestry Commission
Field Book 2

Rose, F and Hardin, P T
*Pasture-Woodlands in Lowland
Britain and their importance for
the Conservation of the
Epiphytes and Invertebrates
Associated with Old Trees*
NCC and Institute of
Terrestrial Ecology

Rowe, J J (1973) *Grey Squirrel Control* HMSO
Forestry Commission
Leaflet 56

Rowe, J J (1976) *Badger Gates* HMSO
Forestry Commission
Leaflet 68

Rushforth, K (1987) *Hillier Book of Tree Planting
and Management*
David and Charles

Sheat, W G (1957) *Propagation of Trees, Shrubs
and Conifers*
MacMillan

Shigo, A L (1990) *Tree Pruning: A World-wide
Photoguide*
Shigo and Trees, Associates
(available from S & D Tree
Care Services)

Shigo, A L, Vollbrecht, K and Hvass, N (1987)
*Tree Biology and Tree Care: A
Photo Guide*
Honey Brothers Ltd
(Guildford, Surrey)

Sinden, N (1989) *In a Nutshell*
Common Ground

Smart, N and Andrews, J (1985)
*Birds and Broadleaves
Handbook* RSPB

Soutar, R and Peterken, G (1989)
'Native Trees and Shrubs for
Wildlife '*Tree News* 9:
1989, pp14-15

Springthorpe, G D and Myhill, N G (eds) (1985)
Wildlife Rangers Handbook
Forestry Commission

Steven, H M and Carlisle, A (1959)
*The Native Pinewoods of
Scotland* Oliver and Boyd

Stubbs, A E (1972) *Wildlife Conservation and
Dead Wood*
Devon Wildlife Trust

Task Force Trees (1988)
Task Force Trees Action Pack
Countryside Commission

Warren, A and Goldsmith F B (1974)
Conservation in Practice
John Wiley

Williamson, D R and Lane, P B (1989)
The Use of Herbicides in the Forest
Forestry Commission Field Book 8

Wilson, K W (1981)   *Removal of Tree Stumps*
HMSO Arboricultural Leaflet 7

Woodell, S R J (ed) (1985)
The English Landscape: Past, Present and Future
Oxford University Press

Woodland Trust (1986)
Community Woodland Resource Pack
Woodland Trust

RELEVANT PERIODICALS

Arboricultural Journal

The Dendrologist

Forestry

Forestry and British Timber

Grower

Growth Point

Horticulture Week

Landscape Design

Quarterly Journal of Forestry

Scottish Forestry

Timber Grower

Tree News

Urban Forest

Appendix G

Glossary

Afforestation The planting of trees on previously unwooded land.

Anaerobism Often a condition of heavy clay soils which have been compacted to the point where no free oxygen is available, leading to bacterial decay and root death. Also a condition of wet stagnant soils.

Ameliorant Chemicals or organic matter which are applied to soils, with the intention of improving soil properties and correcting nutrient deficiencies.

Ancient woodland Woodland that has existed continuously on the site since at least 1600 AD.

Artificial woodland Woodland which is not semi-natural, e.g. a new plantation.

Ball-rooted tree Tree transplanted with the soil around its roots intact.

Bare-rooted tree Tree lifted from nursery soil and transported to the planting site with the roots bare of soil.

Bark Outer protective tissue of a woody stem.

Bast Thin layer of tissue between the bark and the cambium, which carries leaf-sap downwards to the roots.

Beating up Also known as 'filling up'. Replacing failures after tree planting.

Bole The stem or trunk of a tree.

Bolling The permanent trunk of a pollard.

Brash Small branches trimmed from the sides and top of a main stem. Also known as lop and top and as slash. (v) To cut away the side branches of conifers to about 6' (2m) to improve access or for fire protection.

Branch bark ridge A layer of compacted xylem tissue and wrinkled bark that forms a ridge in the upper crotch of a branch, and serves as a natural protection boundary that resists decay.

Branch collar A collar of tissue that forms around the base of a tree's branches in some species, usually as the tree ages. With the branch bark ridge, one of the tree's main protection boundaries against decay.

Bryophytes Mosses and liverworts.

Buttress Reinforcing projection near the base of the tree. Also known as a spur.

Callusing The growth of new tissue across a wound (e.g. from pruning), which derives from living cells at the edge and can protect the tree from bacterial and fungal decay.

Cambium A layer of cellular tissue beneath the bark of a tree, in which the growth of bark and wood takes place.

Canker On a branch or stem, a dead area which has been caused by bacterial or fungal attack.

Canopy The uppermost layer of woodland structure. Usually from 25'-100' (8m-30m) above ground. Contains the standard, emergent and understorey trees.

Chitted seed Seed in which the radicle, or that part of the embryo which develops into the primary root, has just emerged.

Clone A tree or strain of trees propagated vegetatively from a single individual.

Coppice Broadleaved wood which is cut over at regular intervals to produce a number of shoots from each stool. Also known as copse. (v) To cut the shoots from a stool so that more will regrow.

Coppice with standards A two-storey wood in which some trees (standards) are grown among the coppice (underwood).

Coupe A coppice plot cut on a regular basis or a clear-felled area in a plantation. Also known as a panel.

Covert A small wood, usually in the midst of farmland, managed primarily for game.

Crown The spreading branches and foliage of a tree.

Crown lifting Removal of the lower branches of a tree, leaving the upper crown untouched.

Crown reduction Pruning back the crown to its main branches whilst maintaining its overall symmetry of shape. Also known as drop-crotching.

Crown thinning Pruning to lessen the bulk of branches in the crown.

Cultivar A cultivated variety, or sub-division, of a species, consisting of plants which differ in some form from what is regarded as the norm for that species. Can also be applied to members of a hybrid group.

Cutting A small section of young shoot or root used to propagate a new plant.

Danger zone The area within two tree lengths, in any direction, of a tree being felled.

Drip line The ground below the outermost branches of a tree's crown, where most of its feeding roots are concentrated.

Ecology The study of how living things relate to each other and to their environment. Also used loosely to describe the interrelationship itself, e.g. 'the ecology of the site'.

Emergent tree A tree, the crown of which overtops the standards in the woodland canopy.

Epiphyte A plant growing on another without being parasitic.

Feathered tree A small tree furnished with lateral shoots to near ground level. A term most commonly used in connection with nursery planting stock.

Felling cut A cut made from the back of the stem which fells the tree. Also known as a back cut.

Field layer That part of the woodland structure containing herbaceous plants and undershrubs. Usually several inches to several feet (about 100mm to a couple of metres) above ground level.

Flush An area of ground receiving nutrient-rich runoff. (v) The first spurt of growth after winter dormancy when the buds break.

Forest A tract of land, not necessarily wooded, controlled by the Crown - originally for large game - and administered to special rules. An area in which such rules once applied. Now also a term commonly used to denote a large woodland tract.

Formative pruning The pruning of a young plant to achieve a desired shape.

Greenhouse effect A phenomenon of the biosphere, whereby certain gases (e.g. CO_2) absorb incident energy reflected from the earth's surface, trapping it and thus leading to a rise in temperature. The naturally occurring greenhouse effect is necessary for the equilibrium of life on earth as it is currently known, but higher emissions of greenhouse gases into the atmosphere from artificial sources may accelerate global warming to a degree where that equilibrium is endangered.

Ground layer That part of the woodland structure, up to several inches (about 100mm) above ground, which contains bryophytes and the seedlings of plants of the higher layers.

Habitat The normal abode of a plant or animal. The recognisable area or environment in which an organism normally lives.

Hardwood Any broadleaved (deciduous) tree, irrespective of the actual hardness of its wood.

Heartwood The inner wood of larger branches and trunks which no longer carries sap.

Hele-in Temporarily 'storing' transplants or planting stock in a trench backfilled with earth while waiting for transplanting or planting conditions to improve.

High forest Woodland dominated by full-grown trees suitable for timber.

Hinge A portion of stem which is left uncut during felling to help control the timing and direction of fall. Also known as a hold.

Honeydew Sticky substance produced by aphids, which can cause nuisance when it drips from an infested tree onto anything below.

Kerf The cut made by a saw.

Layer A side shoot which roots to form a new but connected plant where it touches the ground. (v) To bend over and peg down a shoot so that it will take root.

Leader The main top shoot of a tree.

Mulching The application of a suitable material (e.g. chopped bark, polythene sheeting) to the surface of the soil around a tree to conserve moisture, stabilise soil temperature and suppress weed growth.

Natural target pruning Pruning in such a way that the branch bark ridge and branch collar remain intact, to prevent decay from entering, and to encourage the tree to form healthy callus growth quickly.

Node A swelling on a shoot which marks the position of a resting bud.

Orthodox seed Tree seed which responds well to the preconditions (e.g. moisture reduction) necessary for long-term cold storage.

pH A measure of acidity and alkalinity on a scale from 0 to 14.0. pH 7 is neutral, less than 7 is acid and more than 7 is alkaline. In soils a pH of 4.5 and below is regarded as extremely acid, pH 6.6-7.3 is neutral and over 9 is very strongly alkaline.

Park Originally, land enclosed for the keeping of semi-wild animals. Later, a rural or urban area enclosed for amenity.

Pasture-woodland Woodland in which grazing or browsing has been the dominant influence.

Photosynthesis The process in which the energy from sunlight is used by green plants and tree foliage to build up complex substances from carbon dioxide and water.

Phytotoxic A substance harmful to plant tissue and plant growth.

Plantation An area of woodland where most of the trees have been planted for timber.

Pole stage The stage in which the young tree resembles a pole - between the thicket stage and maturity.

Pollard A tree which is cut at 6'-12' (2-4m) above ground level, then allowed to grow again to produce a crop of branches. (v) To cut the branches from such a tree so that they will regrow.

Primary woodland Woodland that has had a continuous cover of native trees throughout its history.

Provenance The place of origin of a tree stock, which remains the same no matter where later generations of the tree are raised.

Pruning Cutting branches from a standing tree. Done to manage the crown shape of amenity trees, remove diseased branches or produce knot-free wood in timber trees.

Recalcitrant seed Tree seed which cannot have its moisture content reduced below a certain high level, making it unsuitable for long-term cold storage.

Recent woodland Woodland which has grown up since the year 1600 AD.

Ring-barking Damage to a tree in which bark has been removed from the entire circumference of the stem.

Root collar The bottom of the stem, usually at ground layer.

Root scorch Damage to the roots through direct contact with an inorganic fertilizer.

Root – shoot ratio The ratio of root growth to the branches and other aerial part of a plant.

Rotation Length of time between successive final fellings of a plantation (e.g. excluding thinnings) or cuttings of a coppice plot.

Sapwood Wood which carries sap. In a young stem, this may be all of the wood; in a larger, older tree or branch, it may be the outermost layer.

Scarifying/Screefing Scraping away the surface vegetation prior to planting, to prevent weed competition.

Scrub In ecology, an area dominated by shrubs, possibly as a stage in succession to high forest. In forestry, an area of unproductive woodland.

Secondary woodland Woodland growing on a site that has been cleared at some point in time.

Seedling Used to refer to a plant raised from seed (rather than from vegetative propagation) while it remains in its original seedbed. After planting elsewhere it is known as a transplant.

Semi-natural woodland On ancient sites, woods made up mainly of native species growing where their presence is apparently natural and which have not obviously been planted. On recent sites, all stands that have originated mainly by natural regeneration.

Setts Woody shoots of species (e.g. willow) which root easily when inserted into the soil.

Shrub layer That part of the woodland structure, from about 6'-15' (2-4.5m) above ground containing shrubs and young growth of canopy trees.

Singling Cutting out all but one to three stems on a coppice stool so that it will grow into a timber tree. Singled stems are known as 'stores' to distinguish them from 'maiden' trees.

Sink A wedge-shaped cut made in the front of a tree to control direction of fall when felling. Also known as a bird's-mouth.

Softwood The timber of any coniferous tree, irrespective of the actual hardness of the wood.

Stag-headed Trees with dead branches which protrude from the top of a live crown. Usually the result of old age, although may also occur because of injury. Also very commonly caused by agricultural drainage lowering the water table, and occasionally caused by a raised water table, e.g. as a result of new pond construction.

Standard A tree suitable for timber. A transplanted tree with 6' (1.8m) or more clear stem. In woodland structure, a tree forming the dominant layer of the canopy.

Stem The living trunk of a shrub or tree.

Stool The stump or cut base of a shrub or tree from which new shoots grow.

Stooling A method of propagating coppice in which regrowth from stools is earthed over to root and later cut away for transplanting.

Structure The pattern of woodland habitat elements such as the height and density of crowns, position and size of glades and shape and orientation of margins.

Succession The process by which one community of plants gives way to another in a series from coloniser to climax.

Sucker A young tree arising from the roots of an older tree.

Thicket stage Stage after planting and before the pole stage when young trees have grown up enough to form a dense thicket.

Thinning Removal of selected trees from a crop to give the remainder more growing space. A tree so removed.

Timber Tree trunk suitable for making beams (i.e. with minimum dimensions of 4.5m/12' length, 70mm/3" top diameter) or sawing into planks; a tree with such a trunk; the use made of such a trunk.

Transpiration The process by which a plant loses the major part of the water it absorbs, to allow further absorption by the roots. Transpiration takes place through the stomata (a type of valve) in the leaves.

Transplant Small tree less than 1.2m in height, which has been moved from one nursery bed to another to improve the development of the root system.

Undercut Cut made in the front of a tree to reduce the chance of splitting when felling. In the nursery, an undercut tree is one which has had its roots severed to improve development without transplanting.

Understorey tree A tree, the crown of which is below that of the dominant trees in the canopy.

Underwood Wood, whether growing or cut, of coppice poles, young suckers or (less often) pollard poles.

Viable seed Seed which is capable of germinating.

Whip A transplant under about 3' (1m) high. Also a weak spindly stem in a plantation.

Wood The part of the stem, inside the cambium, which supports the tree, carries water to the crown and stores reserves of food over the winter. Also poles and branches of smaller diameter than timber.

Xylem The woody vascular tissue of a plant which conducts water and mineral salts in the stems, roots and leaves, and supports the softer tissues.

Index